Strand Book Store $10.00
Watson/The Book of Ian Wats
Publisher Price $19.00   12/01/10 - H
FICT-HORROR

9 789911 576637

D1782597

THE BOOK OF
IAN WATSON

THE BOOK OF

MARK V. ZIESING
WILLIMANTIC, CONNECTICUT

THE BOOK OF IAN WATSON
published by
Mark V. Ziesing
P.O. Box 806
Willimantic, CT 06226

Copyright © 1985 by Ian Watson

Cover and interior illustrations by Joe Shea

Cover logo by Matt Berger

Cover photo by Judy Watson

All rights reserved. No part of this book may be reproduced
without written permission.

FIRST EDITION

Signed Edition ISBN 0-9612970-4-2
Trade Edition ISBN 0-9612970-3-4
LC No. 85-050240

Preface

Welcome to *The Book of Ian Watson*, a kind of autobiography woven of fiction and non-fiction.

Here are some of the main strands of my life as a writer and person: strands African, strands Japanese; strands science-fictional, strands political. And linguistic. And satirical. And a few other things, besides.

Here we take a journey down into the mine of the imagination. Here we chase flying saucers and fail to catch them, but we arrive on some alien worlds, nonetheless. Meanwhile, back home, the Earth too becomes quite strange at times. Here we try to trap death; and meet an Egyptian Pharaoh who believes he has triumphed, but is undone by a kiss. Here we discover the real reason why Winston Smith worked so hard in the Ministry of Truth rewriting newspapers; and find an American President going through a change of life. Here we encounter Sufis and whales, demon librarians and gamblers. We visit a Shinto shrine and dine at an Irish restaurant in Paris.

I have tied these assorted strands together in what I hope you'll find to be a continuous, invigorating, entertaining pattern—but we always hope that about books, don't we?

Here is my book. Me. And your book too.

Welcome. Soyez le bienvenu. Irassyaimase.

Acknowledgements

'The Flags of Africa' and 'Imaginary Cricket' first appeared in *London Magazine;* 'Shrines and Ratholes', 'Towards an Alien Linguistics', 'Hype, Hype, Hoorah!', 'April in Paris' and 'Some Cultural Notes, and Pest Control' first appeared in *Vector;* 'Roof Garden Under Saturn' first appeared in *New Worlds;* 'The False Braille Catalogue' and 'The Big Buy' first appeared in *Ad Astra;* The Crudities of SF', 'UFOs, Science, and the Inexplicable', 'Down the Mine' and 'Up the Poll' first appeared in *Arena;* 'Who can Believe in the Hero(ine)?' and 'Some Sufist Insights into the Nature of Inexplicable Events' first appeared in SFWA *Bulletin;* 'Showdown on Showdown' first appeared in *Isaac Asimov's Science Fiction Magazine;* 'Dome of Whispers' first appeared in *Imagine;* 'A Cage for Death' first appeared in *Omni.*

Table of Contents

The Flags of Africa	1
Shrines and Ratholes (Part I)	17
Imaginary Cricket	21
Roof Garden Under Saturn	31
Towards an Alien Linguistics	43
The False Braille Catalogue	62
The Love Song of Johnny Alienson	78
The Crudities of Science Fiction	91
The Big Buy	99
Who Can Believe in the Hero(ine)?	106
Showdown on Showdown	113
UFOs, Science, and the Inexplicable	135
Horrorscope	144
Some Sufist Insights into the Nature of Inexplicable Events	157
Dome of Whispers	162
Down the Mine	179
A Cage for Death	187
Up the Pole	203
Shrines and Ratholes (Part II)	212
The President's Not for Turning	216
Hype Hype Hoorah!	233
The Real Winston	241
April in Paris	259
Some Cultural Notes and Pest Control	269
The Culling	278
The Pharaoh and the Mademoiselle	295

AFRICAN

IAN WATSON

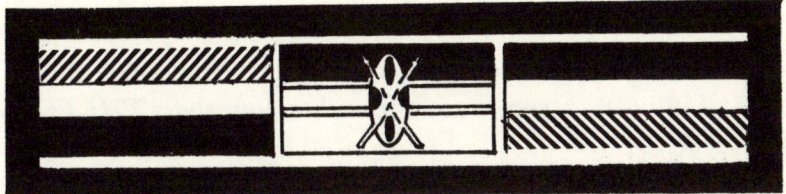

"Always something new out of Africa," said the Roman, Pliny. I lived in East Africa for two years. And what was new in fiction? The French *nouveau roman*. How Alain Robbe-Grillet, author of *La Jalousie*, would have loved to read the reports in *The Standard*, published in Dar es Salaam, of a peculiar misconceived murder trial up-country where fact and fiction were weirdly intermingled . . .

The Flags of Africa

Under the hurricane lamp the policeman was turning the teacher's effects over. The crowd had unfastened the teacher's shirt and trousers greedily, ready hands had drawn them off, later they dressed him in a dirty white gown. The policeman removed the keys from the teacher's pocket and went straightway to search his house. What did he hope to find there?

Holding the hurricane lamp up high the African watched his prisoner through the bars of the door. The American was still sitting in much the same position with his back against the wall and his eyes half-shut and his hands clasped in his lap.
'Do you want anything?'
'It feels so cold in here.'
'It's a hot night, you're lucky.'

The hurricane lamp belonged on the table between the portrait of Julius K. Nyerere and the multicolour chart *THE FLAGS OF AFRICA*.

THE FLAGS OF AFRICA was the most important thing in the room.

What was Mauritania's flag?
YELLOW CRESCENT & YELLOW STAR on GREEN.
Senegal?
HORIZONTALS: GREEN,
YELLOW,
& RED
with a GREEN STAR in the CENTRE of the YELLOW HORIZONTAL.
Ivory Coast?
VERTICALS: ORANGE, WHITE, & GREEN.
Upper Volta?
HORIZONTALS: BLACK,
WHITE,
& RED.

Congo (Kinshasa)?
A BAND OF RED lined with ORANGE BANDS
cutting DIAGONALLY across a BLUE BACKGROUND
from BOTTOM LEFT to TOP RIGHT
with an ORANGE STAR in the TOP LEFT CORNER.

'To develop powers of observation and memory,' wrote Assistant Inspector De Souza in the *Tanzania Police Journal*, 'it is essential to set yourself tests more stringent than Rudyard Kipling ever devised for Kim. . . .

An act of pure cognition in an arbitrary medium.

Why shouldn't Ivory Coast be BLACK and WHITE and RED, and Upper Volta ORANGE and WHITE and GREEN?

Lose a flag and you lose it in the rainbow, in the visible spectrum . . .

Togo?
HORIZONTALS: GREEN,
YELLOW,
GREEN,
YELLOW,
GREEN
with a LARGE RED SQUARE containing a WHITE STAR in the TOP LEFT extending down as far as the BASE of the CENTRE (GREEN) HORIZONTAL.

The two pictures on the teacher's walls were a chaos of colours with no design, no horizontals, verticals, diagonals or stars. Maybe a madman painted them. One was full of blots of dull greens and browns with a single splash of orange at the top and it was like a flag in that respect, with its orange disc, but it had none of the integrity of a flag. It was a flag reflected in a rainy puddle. The other was a seasick swirl of greens and yellows and blues. It reminded him a little of the Central African Republic, though the colours were much more confused.

Affectionately the policeman spread the exercise books out on the table in the light of the hurricane lamp.

Niger?
HORIZONTALS: GREEN,

WHITE,
& ORANGE
with an ORANGE DISC in the very CENTRE.

Picking up the exercise books one by one, the policeman leafed through them, noting that the writing looked regular, thoughtful and neat, in some parts, but in other parts it looked frantic and misshapen as if the words had been tossed down on to the page where they broke and splashed and hung askew. A man's handwriting was like a man's voice. A man's friends recognized the same voice whether he whispered, or sang out loud.

Two of the exercise books had lost their covers, two came from a stationery company in Chicago, the remaining three carried the name of the local Indian printing works. So he put them in this order provisionally, first the two that had lost their covers, then the two from Chicago, last the three from the Indian printers.

The difference between Sudan and Gabon?
Sudan had
    HORIZONTALS: BLUE,
                        YELLOW
                        & GREEN.
Gabon had
    HORIZONTALS: GREEN,
                        YELLOW,
                        & BLUE.
What had Rwanda got that Guinea hadn't got?
Rwanda and Guinea both had
    VERTICALS: RED, YELLOW, & GREEN.
But Rwanda also had
  a BIG BLACK LETTER 'R' in the CENTRE.
What was the difference between Senegal and Mali?
Senegal and Mali both had

IAN WATSON

VERTICALS: GREEN, YELLOW, & RED.
But Senegal had
a GREEN STAR in the CENTRE.
While Mali had
a BLACK MATCHSTICK MAN.

As he sat there, winged beetles dashed themselves through the bars on the windows at the roaring lamp, pattering down on to the exercise books, their wings crisped by the pillar of heat rising from the lamp chimney, their legs kicking in the air. Frantically they rotated on their polished shells and for long moments lay still in exhaustion. His sense of the flaglike neatness of the evidence was offended by the brittle caramel bodies littering it.

How many countries had stars?
Tunisia Morocco Algeria Mauritania Senegal Liberia Congo (Kinshasa) Cameroun Togo United-Arab-Republic Central-African-Republic Ghana Libya Somalia.
These stars were WHITE and BLACK and GREEN and YELLOW and RED, like the stars in the night sky. Tunisia and Algeria boasted of the RED STAR. Somalia Libya Liberia and Togo, strangely for African nations, bore WHITE STARS.

The policeman opened a packet of *Ten Cent* cigarettes, lit one from the lamp chimney, sucked smoke in. Abruptly he brushed the books clean of beetles with a sweep of his hand.
Over the bush, beyond the hills where the crime had taken place, a full yellow moon was rising. For a while longer he watched a line of fire creeping down one of the hillsides. He expelled smoke from his lungs in satisfaction into the night where the land also smoked in the moonlight. . . .

Inside the cell: anaesthesia, of the flesh against the cold

cement; of the feelings, towards a dead woman who happened to have been his wife. . . .

'It's a matter of life and death,' the teacher was shouting. 'My wife is lying there right now. She's hurt. She thinks I'm bringing help. Every second you delay me you're hurting her. What do you think happened? You don't think I . . . no that's crazy. You must be crazy. You know me, I'm the teacher, I teach your sons and daughters. You don't seriously think I . . . but I can see you do. You mustn't. That's wrong, awful wrong. You understand what I'm saying? Listen I wasn't running away. Why should I do that! I was cycling for help. I hadn't time to stop when you shouted. She may be dying in pain and fear all alone while we stand here arguing. You know I can't run away even if I wanted to. Won't you give me an answer? Haven't you got an answer? Look at me, you all know who I am, I'm your teacher. Would the Government have put me in charge of your sons and daughters if there was the slightest shade of suspicion, any doubt at all? Have your children ever said anything was wrong? Don't be afraid to say. You must speak out or hand me back my bicycle.'

'We all saw him running away, racing off on his bicycle, bumping along the road like a drunk or madman. He fought like a madman too, see how my shirt's torn. He didn't say a word to us. He just fought. When we had him helpless, then he started to plead. But before that not a word of explanation!'

'He was up there on the very top of the hill on that rock platform above the boulders. It was like a play that the mission children put on. She was dressed like one of the saints in white, he was the Devil tempting her. He stretched out his hand and showed her the whole world. A child could have understood. She fell as if she expected there would be soft pillows below not stones. . . .

'He ran down the hillside with great leaps like an animal. I'm astonished he didn't break his ankle. Leap, leap, leap, from one boulder to the next. Like the most agile antelope. I wouldn't have dared those leaps in my young days. When he reached the bottom she was trying to stand up, hanging on by one of the boulders. He threw her down again and knelt astride her. He strangled her. I saw his two hands pressing her down while she struggled, then knotted round the neck. That's when he picked up his bicycle, after he strangled her.'

'I was hoeing my fields when I saw her falling. She fell over and over like a great white bird.'

'But he didn't strangle her. They were struggling and he picked up a small white stone and struck her on the side of the head with it over and over again till she lost her senses, and each time he took his hand away the stone was redder with blood than before. The stone was white like his hand then slowly it turned red.'

The policeman listened to them politely, sitting on the saddle of his bicycle, resting one foot on the ground for support.

When the sun touched the horizon, a bulging orange yolk, he had lowered the flag outside the police station, lamenting how sun-bleached and weather-stained it was. He locked the flag away in his cupboard and when he came outside again, the orange yolk had sunk without splitting, leaving a white wispy cloud behind like an albuminous cord still attached to it.

Up on the hilltop, on that rocky platform, the sun was still engaged in setting, was only now bulging out like the yolk that would flood the world.

Congo (Kinshasa)?
   A BAND OF RED lined with ORANGE BANDS
     cutting DIAGONALLY across a BLUE BACKGROUND

from BOTTOM LEFT to TOP RIGHT
with an ORANGE STAR in the top LEFT CORNER.

Quite natural that the farmer in his field, the witch skulking beneath a baobab tree, and the young catechist walking along the road reported seeing different events. How many citizens could say for sure whether the green triangle or the blue triangle was next to the flagstaff, on the flag he had just taken down? Yet they stood up for it and cheered it and saluted it.

He listened patiently with one foot resting on the ground. He didn't get off his bicycle. Even when the American teacher shouted and struggled—the crowd kept a tight hold on him—he stayed seated. Important not to become personally involved in a sweaty struggle, important to control the situation in the way a traffic policeman controls cars, and that wasn't by putting his shoulder to them and shoving.

Gabon?
HORIZONTALS: GREEN,
YELLOW,
& BLUE.

To what extent could he trust the evidence of eyes that would swear the black diagonal (bordered with yellow) on their own national flag ran from top left to bottom right? (The shame of seeing the flag flown upside-down outside the Regional Commissioner's Headquarters!) Lawyers tested the truthfulness of the witness by word of mouth, without ever testing his eyes. They should use *THE FLAGS OF AFRICA:*
an optical chart for illiterates.

'We were bringing him to you to arrest him.'
'He was fleeing as if a devil . . .'

'But we know how to deal with devils, don't we old woman! We catch them and lock them up!' The catechist spoke with venom.

The witch, wrapped up in her black buibui, stared through him. Her hands and feet looked like a model of their own bare veins and tendons. But if her arms and legs seemed skeletal in proportion to the voluminous buibui, she was balancing a heavy branch on her head.

Personally he didn't believe in spirits infesting the air. A flag was the air made visible and there was nothing sinister in it, only stars and bands of colour, birds and a black sun.

But was it the same air as the witch breathed through her beak?

From the hilltop, the witch wasn't visible, standing motionless in the shade of an elephantine baobab with a branch on her head. The tree towered over her with its crown of stiff white arms, a petrified squid. One of its fallen pods lay at her feet like a baby's bald head with a few downy hairs. Fat black ants ran into a crack to fetch the sherbet clinging round the seeds.

A powder-blue and grey bird landed in the grit a few feet from her and rushed to right and left snatching up ants, each rush leading it closer to her.

She saw the woman in white appear behind the man on the hilltop. The man pointed at something far away with a casual gesture, and the woman stepped forward to see it. As she stepped forward . . .

The bird raced along another tangent, and entered the shade cast by the branch on her head. The witch suddenly spat into the sand just in front of the bird, startling it into the air . . .

The man stumbled towards the rock's edge and regained his balance only by stepping behind the woman, hiding her from the witch's gaze for a moment. Nevertheless the white dress was already billowing up around white kicking legs . . .

'How did you get here so quick with that tree on your head? Maybe you changed yourself into a crow and flew here with it in your beak?'

The witch spat at the catechist's feet and he hopped back quickly to avoid her spittle.

In her own mind maybe she did something, thought the policeman, but only in her own mind.

Chad?
   VERTICALS: BLUE, YELLOW, & RED.
Gambia?
   HORIZONTALS: RED,
                   BLUE,
                   & GREEN
but the part of the BLUE HORIZONTAL was crossed by WHITE VERTICALS.

The farmer stepped back from his hoeing, wiped his face with the back of his hand, and saw stars as he poked the sweat from his eyes with his knuckles. Soon the field would be ready, the little rains would fall, seedlings would sprout in their beds, tall green tobacco would wave.

A huge white bird swooped down among the boulders.

Then he noticed the man racing crazily down the slope, and the bird turned into a white-frocked woman pulling herself laboriously upright with both hands, her face a small red blob of effort in the distance.

She fell billowing among the rocks, a white flag of surrender.

'Don't let her die all alone I beg you! If she dies all alone I'll hold you responsible, I'll always remember.'

But how much do you remember? Can you describe this nation's flag from memory?

On the way up, she stopped to get her breath back beside an ants' nest. It would be the most horrid death to be eaten alive by ants. Yet it was a punishment in Africa. The prisoner was covered with honey and staked out upon an antheap.

Her hands and ankles were bound tightly to the four stakes, her spine was arched above the heap like a bow, her belly to the sun. The blood ran to her head, the sun blinded her. She shut her eyes, but how long dare she keep them shut? The temptation to see the ants moving on to her body—as if seeing was controlling or anticipating—was so strong. But when the ants moved across her face her eyes would blink shut again instinctively. How long would her eyelids protect her eyes? How long would her eyelids continue to exist? She expelled the air from her lungs fiercely, snorting it out of her nostrils as if she'd just surfaced after swimming underwater for a long stretch—blowing like a sealion. But the ants boiled over her from the depths of their heap, their deep secret chambers and galleries where slaves toiled and herds of aphids dumbly grazed waiting for milking time, and where the pulsing heaps of eggs were packed. They boiled out, nipping the honey. She could bear this nipping fire on her body, but not her face. No not the face. The eyes. She thrashed her head from side to side in an effort to crush the ants, clenched her mouth tight to protect the tongue she will scream with later. She blinked her eyelids desperately and rolled her eyes. She opened her lips and sucked in ants to crush them. But how could she drink the boiling sea? The ants were no longer individuals that could be caught and crushed between her teeth or blown off her chin on to her chest, they were a surging black sea, a spreading fire, a roasting alive. They clothed her nudity in an acid suit. Her legs were spread wide apart by the stakes to let them feed on her sex.

Fiercely she contracted her child-bearing muscles. Her whole body a flux of raw muscle. Surely she would die of exhaustion. She could hold her breath for two minutes while she swam underwater. Could she hold her breath while the ants ate her? When you are mad do you still feel the pain? Pain has to be faced. It's a condition of being in this century. Everyone has to face the likelihood that one day she will be strapped on a table and a man in a rubber apron will come to her with instruments for twisting and screwing and burning, that one day she will bear a baby with her legs strapped together. One day it will happen, your life ends in a chaos of pain and mutilation and madness. And what happens to your psyche then, if the patterns of the mind are pain and terror at the end?

The pebble she had dropped on the mouth of their nest was already moving, lifting, tilting.

He was gazing out across the bush when she reached the summit. A fresh breeze brushed the top of the hill.

Before them the wild bush stretched out indefinitely studded with termite mounds, grey swollen baobabs and tall wooden cacti with dull green branches. Other hills like the one they stood on looked like the cores of tiny old volcanoes on a flat lunar surface where the gravity was not too strong. The sinking swollen sun silhouetted a few tiny wide-branched trees on distant ridges. Parts of the bush, where the lines of fire had passed, were charred ghostlands with clumps of black straw floating on a dust ocean.

The wild northern Masai with long knotted hair, bouncing earbangles, loping gait, and yellow calabashes full of blood and milk, were racing silently through the bush, their thoughts on death and cattle. It was the only high point of defence. They surged up the hill, leaping from boulder to boulder with great agility, ululating like a wind and casting long shiny spears that sparkled against the stones. . . .

Ghost spears and ghost raiders riding through the air, riding the breeze from the north across the burnt bush, where in the heat of the day they had taken the form of whirling dust devils. . . .

'What a wonderful setting for the murder!' she exclaimed. 'But I wish there weren't so many ants.'

A little way from the flat ochre stone her head rested on, lay a dark maroon handkerchief bunched into the shape of a fist.
Like a crumpled flag, the policeman thought.

He settled down to read the exercise books by the light of the hurricane lamp, chose one from the Indian Printers.
Opening it, he saw the title!

The Fall of Woman, or The Great African Murder Story.

JAPANESE

IAN WATSON

Although Africa made me aware of the Third World, and of politics, it was Japan which dosed me with future shock and made me become a science fiction writer. Thirteen years after leaving Japan, the French magazine *Actuel* asked me and other writers to answer the following two questions. Which place has been magical in your life? And which was the worst rathole you visited? Here is my answer to the first question . . .

Shrines and Ratholes (part 1)

Just outside Kyoto is a remarkable and magical shrine: the Fushimi Inari Taisha Shrine, set upon Mount Inari in Fushimi Ward.

Well now, *many* Japanese shrines are remarkable places (not least the Shrine of Gratitude for Penis, at Tagata near Nagoya—which is full of enormous polished wooden phalluses!). And in a sense all Shinto shrines are magical. For in Japan two entirely different religions coexist (just as so much else which is apparently contradictory coexists there merrily). One is Shinto, an earth-religion, with its shrines. The other is Buddhism, a religion of the psyche, with its temples. The first is bodily, superstitious, mythic, 'primitive'. The second is abstract, transcendental; and people switch from one to the other, as need be. It's rather as though Europeans were Christians on Sunday, Wednesday and Friday, and paid offerings to the Devil, of the old religion, on the other days.

This Inari shrine at Fushimi is dedicated to the gods of human prosperity; so at the Industrial Festival held there every April the Hall of Worship is full of offerings of industrial products: TV sets, video games, whatever... But the really mind-blowing thing isn't the shrine buildings, nice as they are. Nor the sideshows and stalls selling barbecued sparrows, china foxes, masks with phallic noses and TV monster masks. It's the 10,000 *torii* gateways, painted bright vermilion, packed shoulder to shoulder in a stone corridor that leads up the mountain and then around the top in a 4-kilometre-long circuit—through trees with a host of white paper bows tied to them for good fortune, like flocks of butterflies.

Climbing this mountain up the red stone corridor, with the sun shafting through, was a totally numinous experience for me. It was like being a corpuscle flowing through my own bloodstream externalised: a sensory event of far more impact than the calm elegance and aesthetic trance of the Buddhist Golden Pavilion in Kyoto itself; and during the 3 days of the New Year prosperity festival nearly two million people visit Fushimi, and this red corridor is dense with human corpuscles.

But I don't like large crowds. But I don't much care for earth-religions, which remind me of national soil and Nazism. But I have never actually set any story in Fushimi... So why is this place so numinous, and luminous, for me?

It's because, while living in Japan, I found myself as a writer; and for me the shrine at Fushimi is a quintessence of Japan.

Japan switched me on to writing science fiction, the métier in which I found myself. I began writing SF as a psychological survival mechanism, for there in Japan (at the end of the Sixties) were all the seductions and all the terrors of the 21st century;

Tokyo where I lived was the science fiction city.

But more importantly, in a deeper sense—I see now—Japan has a genius for making contradictions coexist (as Shinto and Buddhism coexist)—not least the contradiction between traditional past and futuristic present, between the calligrapher and the cyberneticist. Such places as the Inari shrine forced me to perceive analogies, to yoke together contradictions in a paradoxical knot—while at the same time deranging my senses through sheer visual impact.

Didn't the New Year festival, with a 'toothpaste tube' of people squeezing up Mount Inari through the bloodstream corridor, resemble rush-hour on the Tokyo underground? Didn't people accept the crush of life in megalopolis because the pursuit of economic growth had a quasi-religious flavour? Didn't the Japanese accept the transformation of their land from a place of calm, beauty and nature, into a materialistic science fiction fantasy, precisely because there were deep traditional spiritual forces at work in this? Wasn't the psychedelic art of the advertisers not simply a borrowing from the West, but a reincarnation of the garish fairground colours of Shinto?

In the first three books which I then set out to write, there were two features in common, as regards structure and flavour. Each book contained three very diverse, but intersecting plotlines. And each book (or at least two of them—Japan itself features in the other one) juxtaposed the ancient or traditional (Amazonian Indians, the Incas) with something hypermodern (alien visitors, a trip to Mars).

The fusion of contradictions! And the reincarnation of ancient traditions in a futuristic setting!

I'd say that Japan rewired my brain to think this way—and rewired my emotions too, since to comprehend a place like the Inari Shrine cannot simply be a cerebral experience but must also be a sensuous and bodily one: a realization that this corridor of red gates is indeed a living bloodstream, belonging to an alien culture, true, but also at the same time for a while it was my own.

So perhaps I can say that Japan helped me to become an alien, by giving me a blood transfusion.

Let's try my hand at a sort of *haiku:*

A Fushimi
Le sang montant
Vers les étoiles.

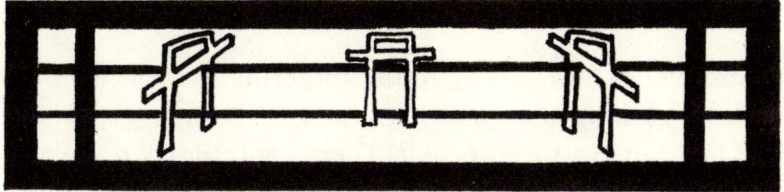

My first book was published in Japan, in a series of simple English readers aimed at high school and university students. We had flown our large, eccentric tabby cat out to Tokyo; and a Japanese modern classic is Natsume Soseki's *I am a Cat*, **in which a feline resident of the same ward of Tokyo as ours—Bunkyo Ward—observes the impact of modernisation upon Meiji Era Japan. My own** *Japan: A Cat's Eye View* **relates a British cat's insights into Japanese society in the late 1960s—and the little book has steadily sold thousands of copies ever since. Hence the fact that I had a publisher in the early, gestatory days described below . . .**

Imaginary Cricket

We play imaginary cricket along the platform of the bullet-train station at Odawara, huge, empty and high. She bowls an imaginary ball, I hit with an imaginary bat. It's been a puzzling day and we want to puzzle somebody. The station is a high steel and glass causeway through the town and the red neon symbol of Marubutsu Department Store reflects in the glass, seems to brand the hill behind with a mystic emblem. One of the superexpresses appears far away at the end of the track, sending its sound waves ahead of it, zing-*zing,* zing-*zing,* rhythmic, climaxing in a booming whistle. The train speeds through the central tracks at a hundred miles an hour, lightning flickering from its overhead contacts, sucking our minds towards it. A high speed train empties itself visually of people. There's only the train-skeleton, no human beings in it.

Can anyone see us from the train? Or is the platform a smooth white unit, stripped of even us? It's been a puzzling day and we want to puzzle somebody. We arrived at the station on a bus whose conductress sang out all the way, at every stop and start and turn, 'Awry . . . awry . . . .' It's the English phrase 'all right' turned into Japanese, seems intended as a tranquillizer; but it reminds us that far from being all right, something is awry in our sense of the word, something is all wrong . . . but we're not sure what, can't pin it down. We've seen a tattered international village, a reconstructed castle, a lioness with a tumour, views of Fuji. We've been round the 'Golden Course'—a sequence of boiling sulphur springs, valleys, a lake. We've travelled by mountain-railway, cable-car, boat and bus. And we can't say why on earth anyone should want to go round the Golden Course, yet we can't say either what is wrong with the whole scene. Suspicions of something vastly wrong, a confidence trick (which reminds me of a science fiction story where the first spacemen discover that the moon is a huge facade with no far side—only scaffolding)—but you could note a million details and miss the synthesis; the day remains a great enigma.

It's difficult to correlate your impressions in Japan. The whole tendency of Japanese culture is against correlation—and foreigners find it easy to lose themselves in details: ikebana, Zen, sumie, haiku. . . .

Is Japan complex, or simple? It's in our nature to try to fit the jigsaw puzzle together; and this is impossible in Japan. Each experience insists on being separate. How to connect them? The Japanese don't see it this way. We believe that what the world needs is generalists. We try to explain our sense of wrongness about this day on the Golden Course by reference to ecology, the life of the commuter, Shintoism. It's our way of seeing. But we can't buy a length of bamboo by indicating a bamboo brush and saying we only want the handle, not the head. A brush is a brush. Each item is a separate discrete unit. So the crowd-surge of a Shinto festival has got nothing to do with the subway-surge at rush-hour or with the activities of the Japan Travel Bureau, we're told. Functions are separate; there's no synthesis. And Japan is always a mirror-image of yourself. It's your own politeness, your own aggression, your own sense of beauty, or of ugliness, that are projected back at you. Japan remains ambiguous. So we play imaginary cricket. What is the sound of one hand clapping? An imaginary cricket ball striking an imaginary cricket bat.

This year X Department Store sent its employees for their summer treat to the top of Mt Fuji. The employees brought back a couple of thousand cans of fresh air from the summit, which the store handed out to the public as an advertising gimmick. 'Today's oxygen is sponsored by X Department Store.' Because if somebody doesn't sponsor it, there won't be any? Air is no longer an aspect of Nature (what is Nature? I've forgotten), it's an economic casualty.

We live in a small house on a hillside looking towards central Tokyo. We can see Tokyo Tower, a few feet higher than the Eiffel Tower, and the Kasumigaseki Building—Japan's first skyscraper, and hero of a recent movie, since the building of such a skyscraper in this earthquake zone is either an act of heroism or of economic *hubris*—and in either event has the makings of tragedy. Already the Kasumigaseki Building has been followed by a taller World Trade Centre, and an even taller hotel is on the drawing boards. Economic pressures have revised the building codes to transform Tokyo into a skyscraper city, and Breughel's Tower of Babel is rising in grey concrete on all sides. I watched a TV programme about what will happen after the next great Kanto Earthquake. A blown-up map of part of Tokyo with magnetized toy cars on the streets. One man pushed the toy cars into tailbacks and pile-ups blocking all the roads; but while he was addressing the camera a second man methodically unblocked all the roads and parked the cars in neat lines. Noticing this, the first man wrecked the cars again. But the other man's hands were already wandering across the board nervously restoring order.

People say what a quiet area this is, where we live, and it is quiet compared with most of Tokyo; but certain noises are pandemic—sirens, loudspeakers, helicopters, piledrivers, traffic. Quiet no longer exists in any absolute sense, only degrees of noise.

But we're lucky to have a separate house to live in and empty air to look through, though it frequently smells of gas or glue, occasionally of lead or diarrhoea—for housing pressures are so bad that estate agents are combing the city for funerals and temples are selling their graveyards for high-rise apartment blocks.

The cheapest-looking cáfe may have an electrically-operated door, colour TV, taped music, intercom to the kitchen—for this is a consumer culture. But the matter of food supplies for these narrow crowded islands is fraught with comedy... and tragedy. The latest Russo-Japanese crab conference was comic enough in its way. The Russians maintained that the succulent King Crab crawls upon the Soviet continental shelf, a sedentary denizen of it. The Japanese insisted that the King Crab leaps long distances using the technique of an Olympic pole vaulter and that when it finally sinks back to the continental shelf, it does so ever so slowly, reluctantly, flapping to and fro like a Japanese paper fan (and therefore, Japanese fishermen, come and get me!). On the tragedy side, over a hundred citizens of the town of Minamata, who ate shellfish that had ingested organic mercury waste, died in agony, and hundreds more went insane, over a period of several years, before anyone could trace the source of the 'Minamata Disease'—or before anyone *chose* to trace it . . . since industry and the economy are more consequential than nature or life, and it's more important there should be a surplus of consumer goods in the shops than for these consumer goods to be safe or desirable. We had chicken for lunch today, with a 10 per cent likelihood that the chicken had been suffering from leukemia, and while nobody knows (or chooses to know) whether eating leukemia chicken is harmful to humans or not, it isn't a nice thought while you're feeding, is it? (Between the Manufacturer and the Consumer Falls the Shadow.)

Then in the summer we take a bus down to the Kanda area where the booksellers are, as well as Ho Chi Minh University as its students call it now, and eat raw fish on rice prepared by Mr Saga who won last year's Kanda competition for Those Who Tolerate Heat by wearing eighty articles of dress (including a hot water bottle and a metal box of hot volcanic tufa) at midday when it was over 90°—standing beside an open fire drinking hot sáke. We eat *uni,* sea-urchin, which—by a sort of synaesthesia—tastes exactly like the sea *smells* at low tide on the rocks. We eat the pink oily underbelly of the tuna. A sushi-bar is a noisy place because that's the scene, but it isn't crude; the younger sushi-maker borrows our empty packet of Hi-Lite and folds a ballerina with thin silver legs and a hooped skirt. So it's good eating in Japan too. A little bit of leukemia won't do any harm, will it?

However, the newspapers announce mysterious diseases that exist nowhere else in the world, unheard-of diseases involving brain damage to children, paralysis, fits—and what can cause them but something you eat or something you smell, something that has been sprayed at you by the benevolent providence of a helicopter, some poison that has been poured into the drains, or air? If the cedar trees in Shinjuku Gyoen Garden have to be fed with chemicals to stop them shrivelling from air pollution, what kind of plasma bottle does the ordinary citizen need strapped to his arm? If the cherry trees in Ueno Park lose all their leaves *before* the autumn colour season, what leaves do our lungs lose a season too soon, or alternatively what foliage grows in our lungs that never should be there? (1,200 teachers have recently had growths removed from their vocal chords.)

There's a secret invisible war going on, and it isn't the student troubles, it's the war of man against the earth. Some cities collaborate with the landscape they are set in; but Japanese cities exist by an ongoing act of brutal rape against the environment; and this secret war has its casualty lists like any other war—the forty-odd people killed every day on inadequate roads (and certain *over*-adequate roads, which the Japanese driver is unprepared for), the hundreds of people at Minamata who ate poisoned shellfish, the victims of other mystery diseases. While I write this, the wispy clouds high above are mildly radioactive with fallout from China, but the local economic miracle delivers lethal fallout every day.

There's a new affluence and new leisure. Yet how to use it? Going on holiday is just as bad as commuting to the office, with holiday trains packed to 300 per cent their normal capacity, exactly the same ultimate load as rush-hour on the subways. You escape from the dirty city to find the sea off the holiday beaches registering colon bacillus counts up to 1,600 times the maximum safe level: the sea is dilute urine. Travel posters show quiet lakes and mountains, yet the reality is a crowded rubbish-strewn neon-nerved endurance course. So Nature exists—but how do you get to it?

*

We take a train to Cape Inubo, about seventy miles out of Tokyo, to stay in a Japanese inn by the sea. There is a whitewashed lighthouse, a rocky beach with boulders by Hans Arp, a seascape, ozone. It's out of season and it's quiet. We don't know quite what to do with all the fresh air. We feel we ought to bottle it—or can it, like the employees of X Department Store.

The maid decides to make our visit into a quiz, by posing a string of alternatives when there aren't any alternatives at all—since a Japanese inn is founded on the family regimentation principle, and there is one meal to be eaten, at one time, and the *futons* are laid out at one time, and everyone has their bath at one time (in case they forget, a maid runs round the corridors chanting *Basu! Basu!*), and everyone cleans their teeth at one time, after their *basu,* and everyone has breakfast at one time, and has one thing for breakfast. Still she asks us 'Do you want Japanese food or Western food for dinner?' when there isn't any Western food. 'What sort of Japanese food do you want?' when there is one choice. 'When will you eat it?' when it will be put on the table willy-nilly. And here is the sixty-four dollar question, will you eat your Japanese dinner with chopsticks, or a spoon? She isn't being helpful, we soon shed that illusion, she is playing a childish interrogation game. There's an invisible mat and if we step off it we have drowned.

The life-style of the Japanese inn, with its domestic regimentation of the guests, its set rituals of relaxation, its priority of style over comfort, its complicated aesthetically-oriented meals, springs ultimately (as does the art of tray-landscapes, or calligraphy) from a Poverty Culture wherein each separate detail, each item in life, is of unique discrete significance, where each object and each category has a distinct aesthetic appeal and singularity. But Japan has made an almost instant transition from Poverty Culture to Affluent Society, from Aesthetics to Economics; and this has been possible because the traditional passion, bred of poverty, for proliferation of objects and functions, *becomes* the modern passion for as many separate consumer goods as possible. Keeping-up-with-the-Tanakas achieves a kind of traditional sanction which the Japanese Madison Avenue skillfully exploits—and which hopelessly blurs the traditional-Japan/modern-Japan contrast into a mist of ambiguities.

When we return from Cape Inubo, the train is more crowded. A grizzled farmer with a scrofulous head and shiny new suit ushers his son into the carriage, a dull-looking 18-year-old wearing a fresh black student's uniform, his feet squashed into dainty ballet-like black shoes; and bawls at the other farmers who follow him: 'Get out of here! This is the first class! You're down there!' The train gets so crowded that there's soon no distinction between first and second class, but the father still growls at other people who resemble him. He's taking his son to one of the examination hells, to try to get into university. On the platform of Ryogoku Station in the outskirts of Tokyo, a peasant woman stands, small and thin, with her huge gangling idiot son strapped to her back like a baby—but he's 16 years old at least and maybe weighs 11 stone. The boy's dangling hand scratches his ankle idly as he hangs on her back. He looks quite capable of walking. If she put him down. Traditional pieties . . .

Tokyo is a disaster area. Japan is a disaster area. Not in the seismological sense (though it is also that), but in the science fiction sense, the sense which Ballard uses when he describes Eniwetok or other 'terminal landscapes'; it is an apocalyptic area, has all the toys and poisons of the twenty-first century. And its disasters are accompanied by fantasies as a disease is offset by delirium: the dream-fairylands of the department stores, the fantasies of a Zen-Shintoist Madison Avenue. Trucks race through the streets with cubes of rain-forest on their backs, ferns and palms whipping to and fro on their way to a coffee bar that may be a Regency ballroom with chandeliers, stained glass windows, and Wedgewood coffee services, or an opera house, or an aquarium . . .

The wooden platform juts out from the inn above the River Kamo that flows through the centre of Kyoto and the maid pours beer for my Japanese publisher and myself, as we get drunk in the darkness, listen to the mumble of traffic in the city and the giggles of couples on the grassy bank below. The maid also giggles, with panic, as a fat moth flutters round her head, and the publisher teases her in the polyglot mixture of English and Japanese he likes to use to maids and shop assistants and waiters, to baffle them: he has this Japanese yearning for the foreign that is also a very special form of homesickness for Japan.

We're finishing off our supper with *tarako*—'cod's child': cod roe and rice in a hot soup with seaweed. But we're still drinking. Beer with everything.

'What about the Golden Pavilion?' he asks me, and I tell him I think Kinkakuji—the Golden Pavilion Temple that Mishima wrote his novel about—is aesthetically perfect and for that reason I couldn't see it, there was nothing for my eyes to grasp.

Aesthetic perfection of this kind approaches invisibility and, indeed I suppose it's better to achieve a beyond-mind trance state before one of these Buddhist structures than to analyse it. But I couldn't say that the Golden Pavilion excited me. What did excite me, I tell him, was not 'official Kyoto' at all, but the huge Inari Shrine at Fushimi just outside of Kyoto. Isn't that the spirit of the economic miracle? Isn't it a Shinto spirit?

'How do you mean?'

Well, when those hundreds of thousands of people surge uphill together at the Shinto Festival—and when they surge through the streets carrying a float, and when hundreds of people crush into a single room during a naked festival to struggle for a talisman, isn't that analogous to the surge of economic progress and the crush of living conditions in the new economic cities? And don't you think people accept these conditions because what they're doing at the factory or the office has a quasi-religious flavour? Inari is a genuinely numinous cult that is also an economic guardian (with miniature shrines protecting the prosperity of every department store and factory)—and is also a funfair for the ordinary man.

Isn't it this unique blend of religion, economics and entertainment that fuels the economic miracle? Isn't it this that creates continuity with the past? Thus the Japanese people can accept this wholesale transformation of their land, that used to be synonomous with calm and beauty and nature, into a science fiction fantasy: because there's still so much tradition in the new Japan of fantasy and disaster . . .

Don't you agree?—Shinto and the subway . . .

'But they are different things.'

'Yes, but they're the same thing too.'

He grins and pours us some more beer and shakes his head.

'I'm not a proper Osaka business man. I'm not interested in business, I'm interested in beauty.'

So we drink some more, and the maid giggles, and the couples giggle below our platform, and we listen to the river and we watch the stars above the city. A jigsaw puzzle scattered across the sky.

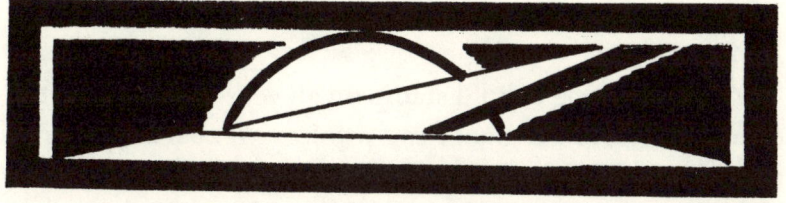

Here's the first story that I sold...

Roof Garden Under Saturn

Shortly afterwards, another commotion occurred. A booming hysterical voice rose up from the street.

"Are we living on one of Saturn's moons I ask you?" it cried mightily—yet petulantly too: the magnified voice of a flea. "And no one has told us!"

Suzuki opened one of the gates in the high metal fence surrounding the Roof Garden. He stood by the parapet wall, gazing down into the street. Anxiously. And regretting his sudden impulse. For anxiety was the worst answer to life.

Ten floors below, traffic had ground to a halt, and the crowd of pedestrians was growing denser and denser. The focus of attention was a thin scarecrow figure clinging to one of the utility poles thirty feet or so above the pavement. He was balancing on a steel rung. Yet these steel rungs only began eight or ten feet above the ground. Either he had made an incredible, superhuman leap (the hop of a flea, in fact, performed by a human!) —or else some comrade had humped him up on his shoulders. But only a policeman with a bloody nose leaned against the base of the pole.

"Come after me and I'll stamp on all your faces so help me," cried the voice of the giant flea—a voice as far out of proportion as his leap must have been. "I've got something to say to everybody. Hear me! You're wondering how I have such a mighty voice eh? Mightier than any of you police with your metal trumpets . . ."

A policeman on the edge of the crowd was indeed babbling vainly into a megaphone about air and oxygen and danger. He made as much noise as the scarecrow on the pole; yet couldn't drown that fierce flea voice, for the crowd wasn't listening to him—they were captivated and hypnotised by the scarecrow above their heads . . .

" . . . but how did I get my powerful plastic throat?" the flea was crying. "Once I was just a humble teacher, minding my own business, trying to instill the *Analects of Confucius* into the young. Till the day when I succumbed! No longer, then, could the teacher address his class of young minds in the clear ringing natural tones of authority. He must croak, he must whisper Truth. Shall we cut out these growths on my vocal chords by surgery?—growths that are the very flowers of poison and the only flowers we can ever hope to know? Why not just cut the whole throat out? Who wants a throat of flesh and blood? We can create a plastic throat, it seems, with a plastic loudspeaker. Then why not plastic men? They would not need air or food or light or water! I am speaking ironically, you understand. Look around you. What do you see in this street? Oxygen meters, smog meters, decibel meters. All telling you in no uncertain terms that this is Saturn's moon, and not the Earth! What arrangements are we making to evacuate Saturn and go home, I ask you?"

What sort of teacher was it who incited to riot instead of teaching the ceremonies of appreciation? Suzuki shook his head sadly, for the *Analects of Confucius* taught obedience and not rebellion . . .

"Do you see the thin houses?" the teacher cried, "barely three feet wide they are, yet three stories high. The residents walk sideways all day long like crabs. It's life in the thin edge of the wedge these days I tell you! We're the printed circuit people! When was it we Commuters became parts of a Computer? When the Earth became Saturn's moon and nobody realized! Can't you see? Can't you see? There's Saturn in the sky above your heads! We're on the Moon of Saturn. Let's leave and go home to Earth. I beg you. To fresh flowers and cherry blossom . . . "

The crowd gazed up at the glowing globe of Saturn hanging above the rooftop, and groaned.

And sighed.

Kim the Korean, who had helped the thin man up the pole on sheer impulse, had dived into the Store before the trouble started.

The air was hot and turgid with people inside the building. Yet it was rich with oxygen compared with the air outside, for the management of the Store enriched the stale air, as a bribe to the Consumers.

In the Karel Appel Exhibition, which Kim wandered round in bewilderment, he felt overcome with nervousness. He reckoned it was the paintings that distressed him, but wasn't sure. Overcome by a compulsion to *touch,* he found that it wasn't the paintings themselves he wanted to touch, but the section of wall beneath each painting. As he stood in front of each, he trailed his hand along the wall, as if testing the authenticity of the painting by this novel means. When he came to a huge canvas, he bent double, scrutinising the texture of the paint while compulsively he felt the wall beneath, pressing his fingers into it fiercely . . .

In this poisoned world, insane opulence was the rule. The City itself resembled a funfair built on a rubbish heap—and when he left the exhibition and forced his way into the Furniture Department, the furniture on display looked like the lootings from some palace on another world. There were gold-plated coathanger stands, marble statues of nymphs, porcelain castles with drawbridges, turrets and battlements. There was tapestry, there was a coach and horses made of coloured glass. Yet people regarded these lunatic luxuries with but a mild interest, as something unexceptional. What *was* guarded by armed policemen, however, as uniquely precious, was a show of designs for television monsters. From the walls glared and sneered children's notions of mechanical-animal-vegetable horrors—heads sunk in shoulders like the anthropophagi, porcupine men, metal men, creatures of suckers and tentacles, livid vegetables. In a topsecurity glass tank a popular star wearing a rubber monster suit paced back and forth, threatening the kiddies with stylised karate blows, while lights flashed on and off and sirens howled.

While proud excited tots prowled the rows of monsters, seeing the faces of the future, their mothers battled with walls of ice that surrounded a Car which Must be Won. Buried in the ice were dozens of ignition keys. The housewives held the palms of their hands pressed to the ice in sheer devotion like Jews at the Wailing Wall, melting the ice with their blood-heat. Some wives had established little tunnels in the ice, and their hands looked ghostly in gloves of ice like inverted X-ray pictures of hands. Some wives keened in pain, yet kept their hands where they were by will-power.

Then Kim saw the Store for what it was: a vast plot, a subterfuge. The Store was a new one—yet straightway as full of people as any other Store. Could it be said to *create* the people that filled it and played its games? Could it be said that those were the latest doll designs standing in queues on the escalators?

*

Kim took an escalator up to the Roof, and had his suspicions confirmed.

Huge red-and-white-check balloons trailed advertising streamers hundreds of feet into the pale smog, marking one of the main nodes of megalopolis. The grey haze hung lifeless yet feverishly hot . . . as hot as a greenhouse.

The Sun was not visible; but Saturn was—the great globe hanging ominously above the Store, glowing with bands of light, its rings tilted at an angle to the roof . . .

Monstrous pink plastic flamingoes were attached to the grey walls. Below the huge birds stood a whole cohort of tin buglers four feet high with tin pennants fixed to their bugles, waiting to blow a flourish on the hour. A monorail ran round the roof's perimeter: six pink pumpkin chariots carrying wondering passengers around.

There was a full-size fairground roundabout with horses to ride, up and down, round and round, to wurlitzer music; and a woman chestnut-roaster with a rococo chestnut stall and a mechanical monkey who wound the handle that churned the chestnuts. The woman was a human being, even if the monkey was mechanical. There were humans in pumpkins, but the buglers were made of tin.

Love in an iron lung . . . or a plastic bag: sitting on a rustic bench in this foul fairyland, two young lovers, the boy breathing into a plastic bag, working the bag in and out by hand like the anaesthetist his rubber lung: recircling his own foul breath which tasted purer than the tainted gas of Saturn's moon to him; his girl dizzy, head between her knees, drowning in love and gas. The boy broke off pumping the plastic bag, to snatch a kiss or a word. Accepting the vicissitudes of love under Saturn.

Though Kim did not.

For Kim stared, scandalised, at the asphixiated lovers in their metal fairyland . . .

Kim joined the sluggish crowd that oozed like a coil of toothpaste towards the Roof Garden Route and around it, gaping in wonder at the dwarf trees and fish tanks inside their oxygen tents...

Suzuki who had returned from the parapet, after seeing many people faint in the crowd, and finally the fall of their flea God of the moment from the utility pole, distrusted these people—for what did they really care in their hearts about these wonderful fishes and trees? Oh to be sure they were taught the ceremonies of appreciation. Yet Suzuki was well aware of the real reason why they flocked in their hundreds and thousands up to the roof, under Saturn. It was the spectacle of so much free oxygen, so much sheer fresh air, lavished upon these pedigree fishes and trees (that fade and tarnish far more swiftly than the human machine will ever fade and tarnish) that was the real wonder of the roof...

Today of all days, on the eve of the Fish Festival (his very own), Suzuki felt almost painfully sensitive to the well-being of the fish... and, to a lesser degree, of the trees. Ah but the fish... bloated and knotted by mutation and selective breeding into wondrously mottled finned globes which rivalled, no surpassed the fantasies of the finest glass-blower. He cast a disapproving glance over the crowd, and observed Kim staring sullenly at a particularly beautiful dwarf maple flourishing in its transparent hood of fresh air...

An insistent insect-like buzzing caught Suzuki's attention. The buzzing sound gradually asserted itself above the noise of traffic in the street, the hurdy-gurdy music of the roundabout, and the chant of adverts over the Store's loudspeakers concealed in the bugler's bugles. The noise drifted closer, on the grey air.

A curiously antique-looking biplane (that surely ought to have been in a science museum and not in the perilously opaque skyways of the City) was flying towards the Store, dodging between the tethers of the balloons.

The biplane circled the huge illuminated globe of Saturn which straddled the roof, its grey steel supports barely visible (creating a grand illusion) . . . and while it circled Saturn, the biplane pumped out a cloud of bright pink smoke.

This pink smoke settled slowly through the thick grey air towards the Roof Garden, while the crowd on the roof stamped their feet nervously and shoved their neighbours impolitely . . . for it had begun to look as though the real planet Saturn's caul of methane gas was dripping down on to the roof—a sight and a supposition that stirred currents of agitation in the spectators . . .

Suzuki wasn't concerned for his own sake. With the true Zen sensibility, it became—as it were—possible to breathe yet not to breathe . . . He was more concerned about the safety of the oxygen tents. His whole life was involved in them. Beauty could only exist on such a small scale in the modern world. The Culture of Poverty (when small things were valued because of the people's poverty) had given way to a Culture of Affluence in which, once more, small things were admired by the discerning, since the big things were compatible with human life no longer. These oxygen tents with their fish and to a lesser degree their trees represented his aesthetics, his religion, his social situation. This kind of feudal loyalty made him an excellent watchman, for he would never steal a breath of air from his beloved fish and would make sure no one else did. The watchmen watched each other like hawks, and watched the crowd like dragons.

The pink mist had by now descended upon the Roof Garden, tinting the air a delicate shade of cherry-blossom . . .

Kim felt a subtle horror creep over him. The uneasy shuffling of the crowd in this pink polluted fairyland and their laboured panting for breath made them seem like a herd of man-sized lizards on some Saturnian moon. When the pink mist cleared, they would see him as he was, a Man, and . . . The reptile pack closed round him, grunting and pawing.

He thought . . .

The explorer seized the strange idol of the Lizard People and escaped through the throng of worshippers bearing it aloft. The Tree Of Life in its tent of poisonous oxygen (paradoxical image of their religion) was his talisman and their taboo. They shrank back fearfully . . .

Kim shoved people aside rudely, embraced the plastic container with the dwarf maple in it, and wrenched it free from the air pipe. It was heavy. Much heavier than he had thought. Yet the oxygen gushing from the pipe invigorated him. He succeeded in lifting the unwieldy box and swung round . . .

Quite soon the crowd was moving on its caterpillar course again wondering at the fish and trees, squeezed by people still inside the Store who had seen nothing of the pink mist and were only too anxious to view the beauties of the roof and begin the ceremony of appreciation.

Suzuki glimpsed himself briefly, vaingloriously, as a samurai of old, clutching on antique sword still wet with blood against a background of the rising sun, rising behind a snow-capped cone . . . although in reality it had only been a chemical spray that had frozen the vandal in his tracks blinding him, not a slash of steel . . . and some of this anguish of misplaced tradition must have passed over Suzuki's normally impassive features, for another watchman, who was not his friend, took it upon himself to remark on it . . .

"We are only servants, after all, Suzuki-san. He was a man too."

"Bah," snorted Suzuki, his vision rent in half. "He was rubbish . . . to do that."

Suzuki let his thoughts dwell upon the next day's Fish Festival, to calm them . . .

Once more he would take to the City's waterways in a painted lacquered barge for the voyage upstream from Tea-Water Station. He would wear protective clothing, of course, since the waterways were somewhat full of human waste and detergents, of mercury and cadmium and other chemicals. He would breathe air from a scuba-duba back-pack since no creature but hideous rats could breathe the air of the waterways (and these breaths he anticipated with due pleasure, though not in the spirit of self-indulgence). He and his partners of the Fish Ceremony would dip symbolic oars into the streams, sometimes deep in concrete culverts, sometimes in underground tunnels dimly lit by service lamps. The high point of the journey through the poisoned waterways of the City would undoubtedly be when they passed, for a whole half-mile, beneath the massive concrete arches of the overhead expressway all freshly painted a dazzling vermilion—as massive and noble a line of sacred gateways to a shrine as Suzuki could conceive . . .

LINGUISTIC

Other languages, other perceptions . . . ?

Towards an Alien Linguistics

I have called my talk, "Towards an Alien Linguistics". But do we wish to hear about aliens who are very similar to us, and relatively easy to understand? Hardly! Yet on the other hand, do we want to hear about amazing and strange aliens, who are almost incomprehensible? Here, one runs the risk of being simply bizarre; of concocting monsters of languages and societies, for the sake of monstrosity. In either case, we do not necessarily arrive at a general theory—at an alien linguistics, but only at a literature of imaginary languages. So I want to speak about the general idea of alien languages, rather than about particular invented examples. I want to outline a few ideas for a theory of language, embracing alien languages and inspired by thinking about them—what their nature might be; how we might possibly understand them.

And immediately a problem arises. For apparently this has nothing to do with Linguistics.

The American linguist Bloomfield said that "the only useful generalizations about language are inductive generalizations".

In other words, we should base our theories upon data from actual languages. We should discover, not invent. Otherwise, we might succeed in being amusing or provocative, but from a strictly linguistic viewpoint we should be talking nonsense.

Yet I feel that this is to restrict oneself unhelpfully—in rather the same way as Wittgenstein restricted philosophy, when he refused to take account of any solutions that the sciences might propose to problems of the nature of language and knowledge. In effect, Wittgenstein fenced off a certain area, and said, "This is Philosophy; the rest isn't. The rest isn't part of the Philosophical *Game*. Psychology and Biology cannot provide *philosophical* answers". I would not wish to impose a similar restriction on Linguistics. I prefer the definition that Linguistics is not so much just about human languages, as about *the place of human language in the universe*. This retains a pragmatic, human base—while leaving the wider questions open.

The Alien is unknown. Alien Languages, obviously, are unknown. But how much do we know about human language, for that matter? The fact that we use it all the time does not mean that we know all about it. We only know about human languages in their present state. We have no real knowledge where our languages came from, or how. Nor do we have the least idea where they are going to, or why. So even human languages, in the distant past and the far future, are quiet alien to us.

It is hard to imagine that evolution on this planet is going to stop with present-day Man—unless we destroy the planet, that is. Language, too, is plainly an evolutionary phenomenon. It has been very different in the past. It has only grown to its present state through a series of radical changes in form. The growth of a rich system of transformation rules—those rules which relate the prolific structures of surface speech to a more limited number of abstract deep structures—must be one example. Without transformations, grammar would have to be extremely complex in order to express the amount of information that we normally handle today. Transformations enable us to manipulate a rich variety of concepts economically. But Speech did not spring from our foreheads—like Athene, goddess of wisdom, from the head of Zeus—fully armed with transformations. The linguist McNeill, writing about "The Creation of Language", points out that primitive speech must therefore have taken many years to learn. Yet nowadays we possess what Chomsky has described as an innate plan for acquiring language: an inborn scheme which assures that we will master speech in a remarkably short time. This is part of our genetic code, now. But it could not have been so in quite the same way for primitive man—or the stages in early life when he was receptive to language, when he was primed to learn, would have passed away before he had time to learn enough. So language - change and genetic - change must go hand in hand. It is hard to imagine that genetic change will cease. It is equally hard to imagine that language will cease to evolve and undergo radical changes. Its form, and even the genetic plan for acquiring it, must alter.

Assuming, then, that evolution carries on into the far future, building on the base of present-day Man, then we even contain the Alien within ourselves, in a very real sense: Future Man, with a language as different from ours in quality and concept, as ours today is from the speech of those first primitive men inhabiting the borderland between Nature and Culture. But we do not think very much about the dynamics of language over an evolutionary time-span—and to what state of mind they may be leading. So I think it is valuable to talk in terms of an Alien Linguistics, for it forces us, not only to think about Aliens, but to think about this Future Man, whom we do not yet know either. Science fiction, with its population of aliens from other star-systems, and also its aliens in human guise—its mutants, telepaths, etc.—establishes a vocabulary of metaphorical beings, ranging from the downright crude to the relatively sophisticated, for questioning the unknown universe and the unknown future.

Note, by the way, that in mentioning the grammar of primitive man, I made some perfectly acceptable linguistic statements. But the fact is, we do not *know* whether they are true. We have no proof that primitive speech was this—or that. Simple and telegraphic—or ponderous and complicated. All languages today show approximately the same degree of complexity and sophistication. There are no primitive languages today. Languages spoken by so-called "primitive peoples" in South America or New Guinea are, in reality, just as sophisticated as European languages—or as Chinese, or Arabic, or Eskimo. Historical records go back too short a time to show any drift towards more primitive structures. I was merely being deductive in talking about primitive speech. But it is obviously useful and desirable to know the origins of what we are talking about. Not is it meaningless to speculate about those origins. So we should not pay too much attention to Bloomfield's rule.

Alien Linguistics, then, is an idea about the relationship between language and the universe. But is it a *universal* idea? Are there any universal ideas? Must we conclude, after Lem's *Solaris*, that we cannot actually understand the alien should we encounter it; that wherever we may go we will only experience human experiences? Is the alien, by definition, unknowable; and is it therefore a waste of breath even to mention the idea of Alien Linguistics?

Let us explore this problem of universal ideas a little further, and ask ourselves what the relationship is between Language and Reality—and whether Language does represent Reality in any meaningful sense. The American Benjamin Whorf, in contrasting European languages with American Indian languages, came to the conclusion that different languages condition radically different worldviews; different realities. Whorf's studies of Hopi, Nootka, Shawnee, and the American Indian view of the universe read at times like models for an alien linguistics; and indeed a good example of Whorf-based aliens occurs in Delany's *Babel-17* with its description of the culture of Çiribia, entirely based on heat and temperature changes. Delany's moral is that "compatibility factors for communication are incredibly low". This is Whorf writ large on the galaxy.

However, since Whorf's time, Chomsky has shown that there is in all human beings an innate plan for acquiring *any* human language—and therefore that all human languages must be formally related on some deep structural level. Also, Charles Osgood, applying his technique for measuring meaning (known as the "Semantic Differential") to speakers of languages as remote from each other as English, Navajo, and Japanese, has demonstrated the existence of what he calls a "common market in meaning", based on the biological systems of emotional and purposive behaviour which all humans share.

Whether aliens will necessarily develop systems sufficiently similar for us to comprehend them, is a point to which I will return later. Meanwhile, so far as Man is concerned, the Whorf argument has to be abandoned.

Apart from this linguistic objection to the existence of universals in language, there is an important philosophical or logical objection to the idea that the underlying structure of languages and human thought may be related to the underlying structure of the universe. This objection has been voiced by several philosophers since Wittgenstein, but in essence the objection springs from various remarks Wittgenstein made in his *Tractatus.* In Wittgenstein's view, there is a fundamental logical reason why we cannot disinter Reality archeologically from behind the language that represents it. Wittgenstein wrote: "The picture cannot represent its form of representation; it shows it forth" (2.172); "No proposition can make a statement about itself, because a propositional sign cannot be contained in itself" (3.332); "That which mirrors itself in language, language cannot represent. That which expresses itself in language, we cannot express by language" (4.121). Thus, if the structure of reality is indeed mirrored in language, this in fact *prevents* language from articulating the structure of reality. In which case, to quote the logician Quine, "we do better simply to say the sentence and so speak not about language but about the world". One can either speak about language, or about the world; but not about both at once, using language. The purpose of language *is* language; there is no underlying significance. Thus it would be pointless to hunt for some universal significance which underlies, and links, the set of possible alien languages. It would be inarticulable; opaque; ungraspable.

Systems, whether it be the mathematical system or the linguistic system, apparently cannot be properly self-descriptive; cannot know themselves, authenticate themselves. They can only manifest behaviour. Wittgenstein tells us this as regards language. The Austrian logician Kurt Gödel told us this forcibly in 1931 for mathematics when he published a remarkable proof that the truth of arithmetic cannot be proved within arithmetic. The ethnologist Gregory Bateson, applying concepts from cybernetics to the problem of the nature of consciousness and the unconscious, tells us that "if, as we must believe, the total mind is an integrated network . . . and if the content of consciousness is only a sampling of different parts and localities of this network; then, inevitably, the conscious view of the network as a whole is a monstrous denial of the integration of that whole". We are conscious only at the expense of being largely *un*conscious. Consciousness is a boundary cutting through the complete circuits of total mind. Above, visible for inspection, are the arcs of circuits. Of these we are "conscious". Below, invisible, is the rest of the Mind, closed off from our inspection. Consciousness thus only exists by virtue of Unconsciousness; the total system cannot be conscious. Perhaps we might even make a comparison between the Conscious and Unconscious Mind on the one hand, and Chomsky's Surface Structures of Speech, and Deep Structures, on the other hand. Deep Structures underlie all our surface manifestations of Language. But introspection will never recover them. We cannot consciously think by means of them. And even the level of Deep Structures is some way removed from the level of Thought itself. Between the world and our expression of it are thus a series of interfaces, apparently impenetrable to consciousness. Our language is an activity; not a proof of anything.

Thus we would seem to be cut off from consciousness of Reality *by virtue* of the language which alone enables us to organise our thoughts and think about Reality. This may seem paradoxical. But really it is not so surprising. For Culture could only emerge from Nature by an act of cutting off—by alienation. This was the only way that consciousness and speech could dawn —in the act of negation. As Octavio Paz puts it in his book on Lévi-Strauss: "It was the first 'No' which set man against nature".

The origin of language in negation is discussed by Gregory Bateson, too. A simple affirmative statement about the world can only come about after the evolution of a simple negative, derived from animal displays of threat. The simple negative makes a degree of separateness of Thing from Name possible. Piaget points out that negation is possible because of the mechanisms of neural inhibition—for example, the withdrawing of one's hand after one has stretched it only a certain distance towards an object. Also, we must build mental maps of the world we are born into, by means of contrast, comparison and the separation of elements; so that the syntax of negation is already latent, too, in the plan we are born with for acquiring internal conceptual maps of the environment. It is not, be it noted, a world of "raw" data that we are born into. We have a search programme for establishing patterns in our environment already given genetically —evolved through the pressures and constraints of our environment. As do kittens. As do birds. The environment dictates the permissible plans of itself that we can learn.

Another feature which may enforce the separation of Name from Thing, and the growth of Language, is the fact that we humans receive most of our sensory information in one mode, Sight, but articulate it in another mode, Sound. The biologist C. H. Waddington speculates that species which both process and articulate information in the same sensory mode might fail to achieve this separation; their world of conventionalized symbolic forms would for them have an absolute character of Moral Authenticity about it. Species-authority would sanction the order of the world, to as great an extent as it sanctioned social order. The world would have to be as it is. Since the dolphins and toothed whales are both highly intelligent and communicate about the world in the same mode as they perceive it, Sound, this may be one of the reasons why investigators like John Lilly have had such difficulty in proving that these creatures have a genuine language. Conceivably it may turn out that language is a blind alley if it does not operate in a different mode from the basic sensory input—because it cannot grow sufficiently abstract; cannot detach itself from the world far enough to be able to reflect on it. Alternatively, dolphins and cachalots may well have an authentic language—flexible, open-ended and sophisticated; and our difficulties in even knowing whether they have or not, after years of research (with all due respect to Robert Merle's imaginative novel *The Day of the Dolphin*!) would be a fairly poor prognosis for any encounters with aliens. A third possibility is that dolphins are in a state of immense *preparedness* for true language—and remain stuck in that stage, locked in an ethical union of Name and Object, unable to abstract, deprived of the arbitrariness of the linguistic sign (in Saussure's jargon) which makes abstraction possible. And perhaps this is a vital characteristic of any true language: the movement away from Representation to Arbitrariness, which is at the same time the separation off of Culture from Nature.

It should also be remembered that dolphins and whales did not evolve wholly in the sea, but returned to the sea, perhaps 125 million years ago, after a life on land where sight obviously played a much more important role than it does for whales today.

At any rate, whatever the answer to the dolphin and whale dilemma, we can at least say confidently that alien languages *may* divide up into same-sensory languages and different-sensory languages. And furthermore, that we may well find it much harder to come to grips with the same-sensory languages. Alternatively, alien languages do not divide up in this way; and proper languages are obliged to be different-sensory.

Octavio Paz remarks that while Language signifies the distance between Man and Things, at the same time it signifies the will to erase this distance. Elsewhere he says that Nature is not a substance nor a thing, but a message. Nature is a message which Nature both sends and receives; and Man is a moment in this message. These two remarks strike me as particularly interesting. For language, by this view, is no longer merely something that happens to exist in the world, and whose purpose is no more than this. Language, on the contrary, is something which has emerged from nature in order to return to the point of origin and illuminate nature. As Paz says, "Nature is structure, and structure sends forth meanings; therefore, it is not possible to silence the question about meaning". Well, what is it possible to say scientifically about this idea that language is a functional part of the dynamic of nature? That it is a means whereby nature progressively illuminates and articulates itself?

Without deifying Nature, let us ask what it is in Nature that impels it to send a message to itself.

Here we come back to the problem of self-descriptive systems, which we have touched on in connection with arithmetic, and consciousness. We surely meet this problem too, when we consider the universe as a total system. It exists—but what sustains it? Why should it be as it is? What authenticates it? Is it possible to explain why and how a universe exists, within the limitations of this same universe? Can the universe legislate for itself, authenticate itself, describe itself—without our being forced to step outside it?

We are now compelled, as physicists are now being compelled —without mysticism or superstition—to introduce the fact of consciousness as a scientific necessity into our description of the universe.

A decade ago, the physicist R. H. Dicke pointed out that the right order of ideas mightn't be: Here is the Universe, so what must Man be? but rather: Here is Man, so what must the Universe be? He based his reversal of the traditional way of looking at things on the argument that a Universe is quite literally *meaningless* in the absence of any awareness of that Universe. But awareness requires life—which requires the presence of elements heavier than hydrogen. These can only be produced by thermonuclear cookery inside suns over a time-span of several billion years. This length of time is only available in a universe the size of ours. Why, therefore, is the Universe as large as it is? Only thus, can there be life in it! So Dicke (and Carter) arrive at the idea of a "biological selection of physical constraints". There appears to be a numerical relationship between the estimated total number of particles in the universe, the radius of the universe at its maximum point of expansion, the size of an elementary particle, the ratio between electrical and gravitational forces, and several other so-called "big numbers". This relationship indicates a universe where total size, particle size, number of particles, strength of gravity etc., are all linked to one another structurally—such that a per cent difference either way in one of the constants would produce an uninhabitable cosmos. Why are these values as they are, in the first place? How are they chosen? They cannot be influenced or determined by any previous cycle of the universe—if we accept, as seems probable, that our universe will ultimately collapse into a Black Hole and undergo probabilistic scattering so that no laws or constants are preserved. Rather, according to John Wheeler's remarkable suggestion, we must admit that in some strange way the universe is brought into being by the participation of those who participate in it.

Already, Quantum Physics compels us to accept the concept of the Participator as a fundamental physical principle rather than just a difficulty in the way of making very small measurements. Perhaps, suggests Wheeler, this is only the tiny tip of a great iceberg. I quote. "Does the universe also derive its meaning from 'participation'? Are we destined to return to the great concept of Leibnitz, of 'pre-established harmony', before we can make the next great advance?" The Universe is not legislated from outside. It is not a statistical average of other possible universes. It is unique—cut off radically by the physics of gravitational collapse from any other possible universes. Therefore, to be what it is, it must bring itself into being. It must legislate for itself; it must describe itself. To quote John Wheeler again, "Are we, in the words of Thomas Mann, 'actually bringing about what seems to be happening?' Are we destined to return to the deep conception of Parmenides, precursor of Socrates and Plato, that 'what is ... is identical with the thought that recognises it'?"

Perhaps we are. In which case, this cosmological idea is of vital importance to our concept of our own, and any alien, languages

—since language is one of the prime means by which Nature transmits a message to itself. And what must this message be about? It can only be about the definition of Nature: which, being defined, is enabled to exist. So, will the various intelligences throughout the universe necessarily be compatible on some deep level? Will they all necessarily have the same general project for consciousness? Will the structures of their languages relate to one another, in some universal, general grammar, because it is the selfsame Nature that all are part of a message from, and to? Alternatively, can all the languages of the universe be regarded as representing different stages in the transmission of Nature's self-defining message? Could there be a dynamic within languages, over an evolutionary time-span, whereby language, having divided off from Nature, returns to its point of origin to illuminate it? Can we expect a progressive revelation of the nature of language *within language*—a growing reflexiveness that mirrors the reflexiveness of the cosmos as a whole? This may be a necessary evolutionary tendency within languages; so that we might expect the languages of more advanced intelligences to be progressively less "subconscious" and "opaque".

Well, this may be the case. However, talk of "necessity" in the context of evolution tends to make people nervous. But here is an even grosser example of Necessity. How can the initial value data of our cosmos, which later will make life possible, conceivably be determined by something which only arises billions of years later—namely life? For this is what we suggest, by invoking a "participatory" universe. Now, I think this problem disappears if we reconsider Time itself. Perhaps we are mistaken to think of the Universe as developing from some time in the past—where it all "started"—towards some time in the future, where it all "stops". For one thing, we might be quite unable to locate a specific start or end-point—using Time as the measure. In his book *Black Holes: the End of the Universe,* John

Taylor of London University suggests that time may be proportional to activity; thus time will distend enormously as we trace backwards to the first seconds of the universe—the time of the Big Bang, when the majority of activity occurred. Likewise, towards the end. Time will approach infinite duration at either end, from the viewpoint of an observer in our universe. Time will become meaningless, immeasurable. Indeed, time may be only meaningful *within* the processes of a Universe, but cannot say anything about the universe as a whole. For the total universe, there may be no passage of time at all. The Universe may best be regarded as a totality that is simultaneously, and permanently, present to itself. There can be no overall "arrow of time". Thus the future and the past may indeed determine one another, reciprocally; and the Universe can be self-determined by its contents—even if these contents only manifest themselves at a specific local time in its history from their own point of view.

So we are approaching a "goal-directed" view of the Universe. Some kind of "goal-directed" view of evolution is implied, also. Now, this is an idea that Jacques Monod for one, in *Chance and Necessity*, finds offensive and unscientific. According to Monod, we must guard against the feeling that everything real in the world is also necessary, rooted in the very beginning of things; that Man is necessary, that life is necessary—even though life, being goal-oriented by definition, appears to carry its own inbuilt necessity. "Destiny is written as and while, not before, it happens," writes Monod. The universe as a whole was not pregnant with life. Life exists by chance. Necessity may reinforce the initial lucky chance—but there was nothing necessary about that chance. A totally blind process can, by definition, lead to vision—purely by accident.

But, even ignoring the idea that such terms as "before" and "after" may be irrelevant for a simultaneously-existing, omnipresent universe, let us consider the genetic process itself. It takes 20 minutes to produce a single bacterial cell: from DNA to live organism. During this twenty minutes, about 4 million nucleotides have to be "read" and translated into proteins and so forth, with close to zero error. This is remarkable enough. But even more remarkable is the problem of how this gigantic sequence was ever arrived at. The DNA molecule that carries the code for the simplest bacterium represents one or few choices out of more than 10 to the power 1 million alternatives ($10^{1,000,000}$). Only the tiniest fraction of these could have been tested at random by nature during the total time-span of the universe to date. So there has to be some hierarchical principle of organisation at work: some dynamic of pressure and constraints on the basic physical and chemical level that leads, rather rapidly, towards living matter.

How do collections of matter produce their own internal descriptions? How does living matter describe itself, in order to perpetuate itself? Are genetic instructions simply ordinary molecules? No, they are more. They are ordinary molecules endowed with *symbolic properties.* It is not the structure of molecules as such, but the internal self-interpretation of their structure *as symbols* that is the basis of life. But what endows them with this symbolic property? What determines that they shall function as Language?

The answer, in the words of American biologist Howard Pattee, is that this is "a consequence of a coherent set of constraints with which they interact". Recent developments in theoretical biology—in particular the work of Réne Thom, who has applied concepts from topology (the branch of mathematics which concerns itself with the connectedness of shapes)—makes it possible to begin to explain how the interactions of the universe can dictate symbolic properties to matter; and in so doing, bring it to life. The publication of Thom's *Structural Stability and Morphogenesis: An Outline of a General Theory of Models* was reviewed in England as the only book comparable in impact to Newton's *Principia*. And indeed, Thom's theory of the necessary forms which are characteristic of our universe, and which will manifest themselves inexorably in any morphological process whatever (whether this is biological—or geological) is a daring and radical concept, that links up with the cosmological and linguistic questions we have been asking.

For Thom, language is an internal representation of space in the mind: a symbolization of the environment and of the phenomenological catastrophes occurring within this space. I quote: "It seems to me difficult to deny that before conceptual thought there once existed, and moreover still does exist in Man, a 'spatial thought' which controls all our movements in space. Now such a control necessarily implies that the brain makes a picture, conscious or unconscious, of the external space where mechanical activity occurs. In fact, to repeat this again, we can scarcely conceive of life without an internal picture of surrounding space, since competition for space is one of the most primitive of biological interactions. . . . What is the primitive function of language? It is to transcribe, in a form communicable by our organs, the phenomenological shifts in the external world." Following on from this Thom elegantly analyses the geometry underlying various language structures, which in his view are open to the same kind of analysis as morphological events in biology, or elsewhere; for there are only a certain number of such possible events, as a universal topological principle. (These ideas of a restricted number of mathematical "mother structures" is, incidentally, one that the group of structuralist mathematicians who publish under the pseudonym of Nicholas Bourbaki is also pursuing vigorously.)

Thus Man reflects Reality. Language reflects the basic shapes of Nature—and these are even susceptible to mathematical analysis. Thom even goes so far as to say: "The old image of

Man as a microcosm reflecting the macrocosm retains its value: he who knows Man will know the universe." Elsewhere he writes: "I believe that in biology there exist formal structures, in fact geometric entities, which prescribe the only forms which a dynamic system of auto-reproduction can present in a given environment". And the same is true, he maintains, even of the table of the elements. Sodium and Potassium exist because a formal structure already existed, corresponding to them.

So we seem to be moving in the direction of being able to talk of a topological grammar of the universe—which reflects itself in the grammars of actual languages. Dare we say that these same universal constraints, pressures, and necessary forms must reflect themselves in any languages anywhere in the universe?

Well, Thom is very careful to say that his "formal structures" or "geometric entities" only prescribe particular forms in a *particular environment*. How different, then, might be the forms —both morphological and linguistic—that might be prescribed for alien beings? Perhaps they might be so different that there would be no compatibility between us and them.

What is meant, however, by a "particular environment"? Does that mean a particular planet—a Jupiter as opposed to the Earth, a Mercury as opposed to Jupiter? Hardly! The particular environment we are concerned with is surely the particular universe we happen to be in, the universe whose mother structures prescribe the existence of Sodium or Potassium. We have every right to assume that these elements exist in the same form as we know them, in the furthest galaxies.

Now, to return to the point I raised earlier. I mentioned that all human beings possess a common market in meaning based on the biological systems of emotional and purposive behaviour they all share. I asked whether aliens would display emotional and purposive behaviour sufficiently similar to provide some community of meaning between us and them. Well, if language involves "a cerebral picture, conscious or unconscious, of the external space where mechanical activity occurs"—and if the pressures and constraints of the environment prescribe certain proper forms not only for biology, but also for intellectual structures, there may be a reasonable chance of compatibility on the deep level. The possibility, perhaps, of an Esperanto of the necessary forms involved in physical and intellectual development. These would determine the deep structure of knowledge of the Being. Deriving from this, in response to the particular environment, would be what Robin Fox and Lionel Tiger call the "biogrammar": the hereditary biologically-based patterns of behaviour, including the plan for the acquisition of actual languages. Then, on the surface, would be the languages themselves, in whatever form they presented themselves: by sound, by gesture, by patterns of lights.

You may object that it is a hopeless task to presume we could unpick these various layers. You may also object that, once having unpicked them, we might find that even on the deepest level there was sheer incongruity. Particle physicists are nowadays coming to the reluctant conclusion that while there *is* a regular underlying mathematical structure to Nature, Nature does not however properly obey its own laws. In the words of Steven Weinberg of Harvard, "Increasingly, it is believed that the symmetries of nature are in fact exact, but they are symmetries of the underlying field equations, and are not obeyed by the solutions to these equations." We live in a universe which only approximately corresponds to the formal structures and regulations that permit it to exist. The same may be true of the set of alien languages. They *are* related, yes—via the biogrammar, to an underlying set of necessary forms. But only approximately so. There will always remain a fundamental uncertainty and ambiguity—corresponding to the uncertainty with which the universe obeys its own laws! This may turn out to be the case. But that is no reason for not pursuing the idea of an alien linguistics.

To sum up, we must be prepared to entertain the idea of a self-creating, self-examining cosmos, in which life is somehow involved in the very processes which bring it into being in the first place; and that the nature of life's involvement is, in the broadest sense, a linguistic one: its double role of message, and observer or messenger. Since language evolves, we must also entertain the idea that structural evolution of language is to some extent determined by the demands of this participatory role; and furthermore that language may tend evolutionarily to yield up more of its nature, so that it will one day be possible to represent in language that which is mirrored in language. Or, that this is already possible, elsewhere—in languages which we would therefore have great difficulty comprehending. But, then again, such "ideal languages", which articulate Reality, might be quite impossible—in the same paradoxical way as the universe has to break its own rules, in order to exist. The ideal pattern only generates approximate realities. And this approximate feature is inherent in the nature of things. The idea of a universe pulling itself up by its own bootstraps, in the way I have outlined, is somewhat anathema. As Piaget puts it in his book *Structuralism*, "The *subject* cannot be the *a priori* underpinning of a finished posterior structure; rather, it is a centre of activity. And whether we substitute "society" or "mankind" or "life" or even "cosmos" for "subject", the argument remains the same." The cosmos cannot generate itself. And yet, strangely, it must do.

An English mathematician, G. Spencer Brown, has written a book called *Laws of Form*, in which he develops a logic to describe this situation: a logic for "operations taking their own results as a base." His logic demands, to make this possible, a universe which is so constituted as to examine itself—which divides up into Observer and Observed. So, once again, we are faced with a participatory universe: and it is *only* a participatory universe that *can* generate itself. Nevertheless, as Spencer Brown says, we are faced in such a universe with the situation of a dog chasing its own tail. "In respect of its own information, the universe *must* expand to escape the telescopes through which we, who are it, are trying to capture it, which is us".

Whatever the outcome of these speculations, it seems indisputable that we are witnessing nowadays a necessary convergence of what used to be regarded as the most diverse areas of knowledge: Physics, Cosmology, Biology, Mathematics, Logic, Linguistics. Each is needed now to throw light on the fundamental problems of the others. And this convergence—which demands some highly speculative "leaps into the Beyond"—is also something which the Science Fiction imagination can and should explore. The problems of this world here and now are urgent—the social, economic, ecological problems; and science fiction should deal with these. At the same time, I think it must find a way of dealing with these epistemological problems. For science fiction is a literature of the Beyond, as well as a literature of the impact of change on Man. It deals with the Beyond in an historical sense: the Future, that is rapidly becoming the Present. It must also deal with the Beyond of knowledge—without losing touch with a sense of the social base of Man, whose knowledge this is. For, just as we are here making our world and our society, so in another sense we are engaged in the making of the universe through that which is at the root of our social being: our language.

A linguistic fiction...

The False Braille Catalogue

So few real details seem to be available about Samuel Klossowski apart from the censored trial reports and the few anecdotes which the 'demon librarian' has chosen to make public that you might be forgiven for imagining Klossowski a figment of Borg's own imagination were it not for the existence of those one hundred and seventy-seven volumes in Braille, which time alone would have stopped Borg from composing and still attending to his other duties.

We don't often come across a case in reality of a tame crew of monkeys tapping away on typewriters to come up with some stochastic Shakespearian masterpiece; but Borg clearly had his own sedulous ape in Klossowski. Whether Klossowski comprehended the extent of his exploitation at Borg's hands is another matter; yet it has a bearing on whether we view Klossowski as the De Sade of this age of conceptual art, or just a chess piece in some complex game of Borg's which happened to involve Klossowski—albeit full-time for sixteen years—as scribe of his anger and frustration.

The volumes in question were typed on the prison library's braille machine at the rate of about one per month, and bear the titles of various edifying or nostalgic 19th century classics, novels by Charles Kingsley, Bulwer-Lytton, Mrs. Gaskell. They do indeed contain statistically significant samples of these works. But what they also contain, blandly bonded sentence by sentence, phrase by phrase, is an invitation to sexual madness, an entreé into a hypnotic incantatory world of psychopathology.

What blind person, forewarned, would be rash enough to isolate himself or herself within this obsessive antiworld that subtly, devastatingly, corrupts all the comforting realities of fiction? I learnt Braille myself just to read these one hundred and seventy-seven books and almost wish I hadn't. But then, I can *see* that things are not as he says. I can gaze out of the barred windows at the real world at the same time as I run my fingers over the embossed pages . . .

Klossowski thought every volume he typed would find its way to a vulnerable public through the Society for Blind Affairs. This wasn't the case—on the contrary, Borg was systematically diverting the volumes for his own private use, to be revealed only at the grotesque vernissage of last July when he proudly announced Klossowski's satanic achievement. Obviously Klossowski was convinced that nothing from outside the prison walls could threaten his literature programme, such being the hypnotic capacity of his books to usurp reality before the reader could defend himself, such their built-in coded traps and labyrinths.

How Borg rejoiced, in his librarian's heart, when he first discovered the nature of Klossowski's revenge against the world, his tactile rape of the blind! I remember how he described his ecstasy to me recently, still vivid after sixteen years, his airy puckish voice weaving a net of concepts to catch Klossowski in, fingers dancing as they juggled small faery balloons about his head, his seared displaced countenance looking like a humorous sandstone statue's eroded by years of acidic rain showers. He described too how he deliberately made things harder for Klossowski by instituting a quota system, keeping his prisoner constantly near the fringe of breakdown where he could refine his genius in the white-hot fire, where ever greater atrocities might be born, as he found out progressively fiercer incantations, as he laid the foundations for a new system of magic.

You may be wondering how Borg came to read Braille in the first place so that he was able to check through that first intercepted text. Well, Borg read every kind of script. He was as proficient in Egyptian hieroglyphics as he was in Chinese characters. And what could he read during the frequent power cuts of those years? It had to be Braille.

Besides, he was fascinated by the idea of being able to read two books at once, one with the eyes, the other with his hands. The dialogue of Babel was ever on his mind and the subversive implications of this dialogue.

"Suppose it were possible," he said to me a few months ago, "to develop a language which would seem to say one thing while really saying another: one whose sounds, or shapes, would contradict the semantics. Do you remember how Mallarmé complained that the sound values 'jour' and 'nuit' in French are the opposite of their meanings? So that we are plunged into darkness at midday, and the midnight is illuminated. What would the land be like where men spoke an anti-language that deliberately contradicted reality? What a fine project, don't you think, to escape from Nature into this ideal world!"

To this end Borg devised a whole theory of clashing signs over the years, isolating contradictions of meaning wherever they cropped up in whatever language; quizzing Hungarian, Jewish, Bantu prisoners about the colours of sounds in their languages and other paradoxes, tormenting them to get at the truth beneath the words.

"Why should I not prepare myself," he asked me, "to communicate with some interstellar being for whom all familiar terrestrial connotations may be inverted and reversed?" Certainly he kept a critical eye on the space adventure, over the years. Yet approaching it more in the spirit of a master forger who intends to let a wholly alien script be found carved in a rock on the moon where it will tantalise the human race to the end of time or drive it to despair long before then.

"I knew an amateur doctor many years ago who compiled a manual of imaginary diseases." He paused to savour the situation. The sun was shining in through the barred windows upon the thousands of books that served as a wall within a wall, a wall of paper within that wall of stone. "With the aid of a forged diploma he proceeded to get a job in a hospital where he could diagnose his own imaginary diseases and operate for them—bringing them into being with acids and scalpel. At the end of each operation when he sewed the patient up again there was the disease he had predicted, reconstructed before the amazed eyes of the nurses and anaesthetist. And this inversion of the usual time flow disorganised these worthy professionals to such an extent that it was some months, and some deaths, later before they began to challenge him. You see, each witness of the improbable operation took it for granted that the abrupt inversion of cause and effect was affecting him or her alone—some passing malaise induced by the bright lights of the operating theatre working on a latent trauma associated with surgery that they were not anxious to admit. Doesn't the imaginary strike you as much more *probable* than the real? It's still waiting in the wings, you see."

Denied the chance of planting forgeries in the Sea of Dreams or by the canals of Mars, Borg has, ironically enough, found his destiny as prison librarian and governor. By tradition the two posts are combined; he who can keep the books in order can perform the same service for criminals and misfits—for what are books but the miscreants of their time? Basically this governorship is a sinecure designed to let a man of letters get on with his own research, while the hard work of running the prison remains in the hands of a crew of bullies. Ironically, however, it was here that Borg was to meet the apotheosis of his theories, in the person of Klossowski. Dare one say that without Samuel Klossowski's activities there would be scarcely any reason to mention Borg?

At the same time I must admit that without Borg Klossowski's literature programme would have got nowhere and the world lost a magnificent if terrifying gesture, equivalent in our time perhaps of the Pharoahs' attempts to create conceptual time machines out of stone. How long would it have been before some appalled blind reader stammered out the truth about his welfare reading matter to a furious policeman or a gloating reporter? There is a dialectical relationship between Borg and Klossowski: each man negates the other and confirms the other.

Yet it was the genius locked up in Klossowski's mad head that actually realized Borg's lifelong scheme of a contradictory metalanguage: a galling thought for the prison director whose sinecure had perhaps been intended by the authorities to buy him time to develop this language of disruption and control for them (assuming that they knew about it or paid any attention to such subtleties—the truncheon and the thumbscrew are just as effective really). Was Borg's protection necessary? Would the blind victims have realized what was happening to them *in time*, before their fingers began to traverse the rows of dots helplessly as though they were magnetized—latterday Brer Rabbits caught in a tarbaby of conceptual pornography? An addiction so suddenly sprung upon them in their world innocent of the iconography of commercial sex which determines the gaze and gestures of the sighted! The whole waterfall would have poured on their heads at once, the whole wet dream of the modern world vexed to nightmare by Klossowski and transposed from predominantly visual into tactile, aural, gustal terms. Klossowski was determined to forge a landscape of pornography meaningful to the reader blind from birth. The missing dimension of so many sentimental novels with their passion for scenery, faces, glances, extended use of the pathetic fallacy: this missing *dimension amoureuse* Klossowski provided devastatingly, devising his own vocabulary of signs against which no protection exists. (It is perhaps the fact that I am sighted that saves me from the worst of Brer Rabbit's fate, though even I can sense how very *sticky* it is!)

"My detractors," Borg told me confidently the other week, "argue that compared with the authentic texts of those classics that Klossowski perverted, his books only deserve the status of footnote to a future psychopathology of signs. Yet surely you'll admit there are cases where the footnote deserves to be the text? And if sexuality is just a footnote to those books in the original—some critics suggest that precisely this constitutes their eroticism—in our friend Klossowski's texts this footnote progressively usurps the main text, elbowing it aside with a bland ferocity that compels assent! As it has done historically, wouldn't you say? All these memoirs and diaries of the Victorian sexual underworld! So that Klossowski writes the *true history* of those times, which did not then publicly exist for them. Truly the probable is more exact and demonstrative than the real! Don't you sometimes ask yourself: who is inventing *us?* And, what's more, if our destiny is to be invented, why all this fuss, this protest, this rebelliousness these days? It's no more than a rebellion among midgets that a giant dreams about as he sleeps in the sunshine while the flies buzz about him . . ."

But let me turn now from the conceptual, and outline the part that Klossowski's works played in Borg's own personal erotic life; something which you will not have heard about before: the brief ill-fated liaison that occurred many years ago, between Borg and the blind cellist Anna Soleri (whose death coincided with the revelation by Borg to the public of the Braille works of Klossowski, which he hadn't troubled to reveal on the occasion of Klossowski's death in prison the year before).

Undercurrents such as this 'invisible' liaison and its aftermath form the real content of history, Borg himself has written on more than one occasion. What takes place in public is essentially a subterfuge. (Thus the finding of a book that once belonged to you and has your name in it to prove it, but which you threw away in another city years ago, left on the next seat by a woman you only half paid attention to . . . you run out of the train after her in vain at the next station, as though she will be waiting there for you.)

Borg refuses to say anything personal to me about Anna Soleri; confines himself to criticising her virtuosity as a cellist. When I press him he shrugs his shoulders and smiles, upper lip twisting into a rictus of pulled flesh as though one or two of the muscles have been permanently severed in some accident which has left no visible scar—until he smiles.

I have pursued my own investigations.

Borg met Anna Soleri in April 1952 when they were both staying at the Pickwick Arms Hotel on East 51st Street—a hotel with an elegant European atmosphere (where virtually the entire Israeli delegation to the General Assembly has nowadays taken up residence). Borg was attending a conference on the Meaning of Art in a Time of Turmoil, Anna Soleri was presenting her incomparable rendering of Kaganovich's *Sinfonia for Cello and Strings*.

A psychoanalyst would surely have ascribed Anna's legendary 'purity' to dubious motives—the etherialization of hysteria, no less. For the single night she spent with Borg disappeared from her own consciousness the very next day in an amnesia so total and so perfect—with no ragged edges or nagging suspicions surrounding it—that nobody could persuade her she hadn't spent a perfectly tranquil eight hours asleep. Not only that, but she had somehow *tuned out* Borg's voice selectively from the spectrum of sounds reaching her. No one could persuade Anna that a Borg existed or was standing in the same room as herself begging for a word of acknowledgment. Alas, his own project had betrayed him: by becoming so real to her the night before, he had become totally improbable; and was henceforth banished from her own universe.

This scene was described to me by two former members of the hotel staff, brother refugees from Eastern Europe whom I traced to a motel in Reno which they now operate.

The motel is actually in the adjoining township of Sparks along Interstate 80, a couple of blocks beyond the casino known as John Ascuaga's Nugget.

I fed the 5-cent fruit machine in the motel foyer for a few minutes before introducing myself. I had no wish to seem to be a federal tax investigator. And I admired the replicas of the wooden leg inset with shotgun which Captain Coal Oil used in the Eighteen Eighties to back up his panhandling activities. Then I had myself shown into the brothers' office.

They were wary at first.

"Gentlemen, I am enquiring from anyone who was working in the Pickwick Arms Hotel during April 1952 about a love affair I believe to have been committed (I was not quite sure of my English) between the cellist Anna Soleri and a man of letters called Borg."

"Divorce case?"

Naturally I'd seen the many neon signs advertising quickie divorces along the main streets of Reno.

"No, nothing like that. I'm writing a biography."

They warmed to me then, realizing that I had nothing to do with taxes or crimes—except perhaps a metaphysical crime, Anna Soleri's subtraction of Borg from the space-time continuum...

They remembered that morning vividly.

"Crazy," laughed the younger brother, a tanned handsome creature with fat rings on his hands and black curly hair—I wondered how many marriages those rings represented, as he flashed them about like trophies of conquests, a big-time gypsy. "This stunning blind bitch—golden hair, no make-up whatever, wasn't so much as a lipstick on her dressing table, only perfume, a queer kind of herbal perfume, sharp and bitter—she was standing by the window listening to the traffic, her manager was there too and a number of admirers and some musicians among the vases of flowers. Then this small fellow, a bit dandified with a rose in his buttonhole, shirt open at the neck, two of the buttons ripped off, was weeping and begging her to pay attention to him—and she so cool, standing there listening to the cars and when her manager told this man to stop annoying her she turned to him and said calmly, Who are you talking to? Who are you talking to? I know where everyone is standing, by the echoes —and she pointed out one by one everybody in the room, even called some of them by name, though they'd been moving about and not talking much, she was as sharp as that at hearing their silhouettes. But she didn't point at the man who was making so much noise and in the end the manager took her hand and pointed it in the right direction and asked her 'What's there?'—but she said confidently there's nothing there, only the wall, the echoes are perfect. So then they told this man, Get out of here Mac you don't exist, laughing at him. They didn't treat it as serious, thinking this bitch was maybe just standing him up in a very cool way, but I saw there was more to it than that, she genuinely didn't know he was there. Now my brother and I, we know something about the Occult—séances, ectoplasm—and it was as if he was just a materialisation or ghost that she didn't sense because he was unreal. He called something out about them going to bed the night before—and I thought about incubi and they thought he was talking dirty and shouted at him to get out, angry now, and he left in a rage cursing them all . . ."

I turned to the elder brother who looked more like a professional businessman than his mercurial gypsy brother, but he too was a secret mystic.

"Surely you must have known who this man that claimed to be her lover really was? Wasn't he staying in the same hotel?"

The elder brother smiled thinly.

"There are many mysteries in the world. A man may be a professor staying in a hotel, and at the same time be an evil spirit. No one seeing that woman defending herself against knowledge of the man but would know that a good spirit was standing between the two hiding his image from her!"

Soon after this I excused myself. The two brothers' minds were twisted by mysticism (in the midst of that neon riot of materialism that was Reno!—but you will find the same thing all over California, whose cities are little more than vast outpourings of ephemeral ectoplasm).

Yet they had clearly seen more of what happened in that room than the other witnesses who could see no further than their own shabby lives of call-girls and one-night-stands. Something mysterious *had* occurred. A conceptual assassination. A casting out of heaven, in metaphysical terms.

Klossowski's mad vengeance on the world began approximately nine months later. No doubt Borg, already embittered, saw its applications as he scanned those first braille texts with his fingers, remembering the touch of Anna's body during that April night in the Pickwick Arms Hotel. But how exactly did he hope to apply the braille books? As seduction—or as revenge? Did he wish to punish the blind musician on some conceptual level? If she refused the direct acoustic signs of his existence he would provide her with the most indirect, yet powerful, tactile signs of it. Or did he mean to hew away at the texture of her amnesia itself, undermining its structure in order to win her?

By the terms of either scenario (and here's where I must temporarily interpolate an 'x' to account for that long delay till the time of Anna Soleri's death) the braille books would have arrived as anonymous gifts, anonymous so far as she was concerned since Borg did not *exist*—equivalent to those curious quests of medieval knights in the days of courtly love, when the search to placate the unattainable fair one (who may in reality have been some thoroughly commonplace hausfrau—but who only really existed for the lovesick knight on a plane of metaphor) could easily occupy a whole lifetime of hacking and hewing, riding, pitching tents, praying, torturing, chastity.

That such a medieval project might seem ludicrous today was beside the point. That it could only be carried through under a régime which permitted Borg to run his prison like a private torture farm of the mind . . . this must also seem beside the point to those international publishers whose agents are prepared to bid large sums for the right to transcribe and print Samuel Klossowski's tortured bran-tub of perversions!

"Please don't be naïve," Borg pleaded the other week, a strange rapture coming over his face as he recounted Samuel Klossowski's sufferings. "What does a lifetime in prison, a lifetime in solitary confinement even, what does this matter if it enables you to enter a wholly notional world, to reinvent the Nineteenth Century, and to believe till the very end that hundreds, thousands, of other people accept it as the very stuff of reality? That's surely something. What would our friend Klossowski have achieved with his freedom in the outside world? A few paltry rapes. But inside, he conceived the rape of a whole society and executed it with perfect tact!"

A few paltry rapes! What an understatement for the most ingeniously executed and protracted series of private atrocities that have ever shocked the press into censoring itself! But I suppose anything that actually occurred must have seemed less than perfect to Borg who had had endless opportunity to reconstruct in all its infinite details and variations on these details a particular night in New York when a greater artist had subtracted him from existence by sheer force of mind. She had undreamed him, and the rest of his life would be devoted to dreaming himself back, with Klossowski acting as amanuensis: to breaking the spell and unjinxing himself and laying the jinx in turn on her. For (this is the 'x' in my equation) Borg actually mailed all these braille books, one by one, to Anna Soleri; and just as surely one by one they were returned, unopened, refused.

I managed to trace a former trustee prisoner who works as a locksmith in Vienna nowadays and who was in the prison post office.

A sad doomed city, Vienna, with its vast empty buildings and echoes. All night long in the former palace that was my hotel pigeons flew up and down the stairs throbbing dolefully. Down in the yard repairs were going on like work on a hopelessly hollow tooth. The walls were peeling, with great ulcers of exposed red brick.

As the light faded, a blank-faced peasant woman shook clothes out of a third-floor window meticulously. Her white muscles looked like fish on a slab. Such mute devotion in the way she handled the rags and shook the dust off them! In another window behind geraniums a mother was teaching her child to count. Eins, zwei, drei, vier, fünf... but fünf was too much for the child, maybe he couldn't say the word, maybe five seemed like infinity to him. He waved his hand at me and the mother swung round abruptly, saw me, snatched the net curtains across.

And that night in the gloomy scabby palace I dreamt a savage story that seemed fearfully relevant to the Borgian aesthetics. It might have been put into my mind specially, as a warning...

I was with a party of tourists off the beaten track in Central America somewhere when we heard about the strange ceremonial of this tribe. It took place in a huge cave inside a mountain. There was only a tiny round hole to get in by, yet it wasn't dark inside there; the walls shone with a dull phosphorescence. We looked up from the cave floor, saw wooden rickety stairs running out from each side towards each other but not meeting by ten or twenty feet. It was the bell loft of a great natural stone cathedral. But the bells! Two savages moved out up the stairways high above us, then launched themselves towards each other over space, clashed great shells together, rebounded. Each held a living shell with some animal inside it and it made a booming music. At first we listened, amused, and took photographs. But the tempo began to quicken then. The savages hurled themselves out to meet each other, bounced violently back. Again. And again. Then they collided awkwardly, hung in mid-air for a moment, fell. Nobody paid attention. Two more took their places. Clash clash clash! The living music of the shells went on burrowing into our skulls. Another savage slipped and crashed down to the pit under the vault and I realized, the shells are the masters, the shells are driving them on. But what happened to the shells when they fell? They cracked apart, hatched their hideous contents which had quickened to the music of the wild percussion. The soft God of the savages mounted one of those dead broken bodies like a snail and the dead man rose again, to Godhead, his eyes closed and muscles twitching, and he walked about on his broken legs...

Next morning I went down to the Russian war memorial and walked about for a long time in the spray that freshened the dust of this dead city to cleanse myself, before calling on the locksmith.

Subsequently one of the questions I asked him was: "What was Borg's reaction when the books came back?"

The fat locksmith squinted at me through his thick glasses.

"The first one that came back, he tore it open and searched through the pages of the book looking for something. Well I said to him, nothing inside but you put it there, Sir; that packet hasn't been opened since it left here. And do you know, I really caught him off balance, he almost apologized to me. To me! 'Yes, it's funny, things that you send away become so estranged you don't even know them again.' Then he handed me another identical packet with the same name but a different address, Stockholm this time. And so it went on for as long as I was in the post office. One packet returned to sender, one new one sent out. Russia, America, Brazil, Lebanon. He used air-mail every time. If he'd have been trying to break out of jail, with his persistence, well!"

"But how did he know where she was each time?"

He shook his head, shrugged.

"Why did you think he sent her those books which she didn't want?"

"God knows. The man was mad. Some hideous things happened in that prison. Not to people like me, but there were politicals . . . That sort of thing leaves a nasty taste."

"Ever hear of a prisoner called Klossowski? Samuel Klossowski?"

The fat man considered, then shook his head.

"The name means nothing to me."

He didn't want to talk. But I had my missing link. The books had been sent.

That night, again, the emptiness of the city of Vienna horrified me. In place of its museums and parks of the daytime were great black holes surrounded by hacked-up roads like barricades.

Buildings were pockmarked with bullet richochets. It seemed an appropriate place to end my quest for information. Borg's life contained great dark holes too, which daylight revealed as parks and museums—aristocratic assemblages of concepts and artefacts with himself as their attendant and vampire, waiting for the nightfall of the soul. In his private park wandered the ghost of Anna Soleri, unable to see him, though he tracked her and tried to sink his teeth into her marble shoulder every evening, deaf to him though he whispered in her ear... On every pedestal rested volumes of Klossowski's braille encyclopedia, open in case one day she should accidentally rest her hand on one of them, one hundred and seventy-seven elegant tar-babies...

And then, one day, she died. Her plane crashed outside Cincinnati. Klossowski had died of exhaustion the year before. But as soon as Anna Soleri died, Borg revealed Klossowski's twisted genius to the public in a series of brilliant essays, and put his works up for auction as though they were his own, daring to argue that no one is in reality the author of a book, that of the new conceptual *Sense and Sensibility* Klossowski was no more the author than Miss Jane Austen. Why not consider Anna Soleri the authoress, for that matter! Authoress, too, of Klossowski's sufferings. Nature hates a vacuum, and her successful bracketing off of Borg from nature left a void in concepts that needed to be filled... Such clever arguments displease me now, after my trip to Vienna and my dream of the savages—which I believe gave me a truer insight into Klossowski's sufferings than Borg's pious words.

The auction is going to take place on July 22nd at 2 P.M. in the Galleries Paz. I am enclosing a copy of the catalogue. If you care to send a donation soon there is a chance of saving at least one of Samuel Klossowski's works from the indignity of a paperback edition, preferably his *Sense and Sensibility,* the new conceptual *Justine.* That will be something, don't you agree?

A limited edition in Braille can then be run off, for those who symphathize with the story behind this story. Klossowski can be read as he meant himself to be read: through the fingertips. And we will enter the maze of dots to confront the minotaur.

A fictional linguistics . . .

The Love Song of Johnny Alienson

How shall I sing my lovesong to you, Marianne? I'm dazzled by the numberless, nameless birds and blooms of this island of Tobago. I'm blinded by its white beaches. The soaring greenery of Pigeon Peak spears my heart with loneliness and homesickness. My palate is stunned by peppered pork, stuffed cascadura fish, fried iguanas. My throat burns with tots of rum. My ears are deafened by calypsos sung in my honour:

> What you tell the man from the stars?
> Lots of boys got Mas and Pas
> Talking to them in all sorts of lingos
> Aliens can't speak ours, there's the stingo!

Is a catalogue of bewilderments, exile and muteness an adequate lovesong? Can I woo you all in negatives, Marianne?

Nameless is what most flowers and birds of Tobago will remain for me, no matter how long we live here as man and wife. Likewise our love must become something nameless and unexpressed—just as soon as our first child is born. Thereafter, in our cottage by Turtle Beach, I may speak your Earth-tongue no more; I shall only talk in the speech of Homestar's world, which you have no means of mastering, Marianne.

I shall talk to our offspring in my alien speech, and they will learn it after a fashion; and they will learn your own Earth-speech too. They'll become somewhat bilingual. But to you, my love, I shall only speak through them; our babes will be our interpreters. Our bodies will talk to one another, Marianne, but not our mouths. Our lips will kiss, but won't communicate. So here and now is the honeymoon of our voices, yours and mine. Here and now we can exchange the selfsame words such as *you* and *I* and *love*. Very soon the entwining of our limbs by night and the setting of the seed and its swelling inside of you will deafen us to one another. So let me now gush out this flood of Earth-speech, in adieu to all earthly words. Thus let me empty my throat of human sounds—as I shall empty my loins into you, my love.

At last I'm starting to appreciate how it was for my alien Dada and my human mother light years away on the world of my birthing.

Self-sacrifice? Supreme dedication? Greater love hath no person?

Or: a life of insanity?

Which?

I well recall the day when mummy-Sarah first broached the how and why of my existence; and of hers and Dada's.

I was eight years old then, Homestar-style, and nothing about my home background struck me as extraordinary—for what did I have to compare with it?

Mummy had wedded Dada. Nothing weird in that. Nothing odd about the fact that my mother like me was softly white-skinned with auburn hair on her head, and brown eyes; whereas my Dada and everyone else in sight had hard yellow bodies without a wisp of hair, though their tall thin heads were crowned with stiff cocks' combs, and the pupils of their eyes were amber bars.

Nothing exceptional in the fact that we dwelled in a great ceramic cradlehome slung from the branches of a stick of broccoli the size of the tallest earthly tree. Didn't eveyone else dwell likewise, thereabouts? (Save for Cavern Clan, and Raft Clan moored on Unspeakable Lake.)

"It's very very hard for Earth-humans to learn alien languages," mummy-Sarah said to me. "It's just as hard for aliens to learn Earth-speech, or the speech of any other alien race."

"What's an alien?"

"Dada is an alien." Sarah frowned. "That's to say, *I* am. You are. Here, we're the aliens."

"Oh."

"Dada isn't your body-father, Johnny. Your body-father was a human just like you and me. I arrived here impregnated."

"But I talk to Dada and anyone else . . ."

"I don't," she murmured.

"It's always kind of hard and it gives me headaches now and then and I say the wrong things in the wrong ways. But I manage."

"You're the *best*, Johnny."

If I'd thought this through a bit more deeply, I might have worked out then and there that other human children were being raised on Homestar's world in other marriages of human mother and alien Dada—and vice versa on Earth.

I could have had playmates just like me!

Oh no I couldn't. The experiment had been tried. The growing human infants had drifted into speaking idioglossic languages, private mishmashes which were neither chalk nor cheese.

"Let's take a walk, Johnny."

"To the golden wall? To the spikes? To the bottomless pool? To the creeping waters?"

"How about to Pumpkin Center?" (That was Sarah's name for the place.)

"Okay."

"And I'll try to explain."

Remember the market in Scarborough, Marianne, where we went last week? All those stalls in the sun piled high with gourds and marrows, purple eggplants, orange peppers, mangoes flushed like hot cheeks, bright yellow pumpkins and bananas?

Suppose you scatter all those fruit and vegetables across a rumpling plain and swell them up to the size of houses. Then you plant groves of broccoli-trees in between, and hang ceramic cradles and home-pods from the branches. Next, hollow out some of the largest marrows and pumpkins for workshops, bodycare centers, mindcare centers, admin, what have you. In the distance, rear up golden cliffs. Erect a cluster of crystalline spikes. Sketch a misty mauve lake far off. That's the landscape I knew and loved back home.

Pumpkin Center was about a half Earth hour's walk away. It was a multiple com-center nexing with the other main islands of Homestar's world, interfacing with the space platforms up in orbit, databanking for the comp-terminals in local cradle-homes, feeding programs to the mindcare centers locally—one of which, carved within a great green-banded marrow, I attended, always struggling along at the bottom of the class. Yet always included, always bespoken and teamed with, wrestled and raced and riddled and all else.

On the way to Pumpkin Center that day mummy-Sarah tried to reconstruct my personal universe somewhat without upsetting it.

*

"A couple of centuries ago on Earth," said mummy-Sarah, "the blessed Rupert Sheldrake fathered the principle of formative causation."

"The what?"

"Patience, Johnny! Listen and learn. The blessed Rupert discovered that all shapes and patterns of activity of everything in the universe are guided by kin-patterns in the past. So a solution of chemical salts knows how to crystallize quickly in a particular way because of what's called 'morphic echo' with similar events somewhere else in the past. Or suppose you put a little rat-animal into a maze with a tasty tidbit to find at the center; once the first rat has solved the maze, all other animals of the same kind will be able to solve the same maze faster in future. And an embryo animal in its mother's womb knows how to make its body unfold in the way of its kind because kin-foetuses have done so likewise in the past. Persons on other worlds already knew this principle. We Earth-people came by this knowledge rather late, but then the blessed Rupert realized the truth."

"He guessed because of morph . . . because of the echo?"

"No, that's just the trouble. If a rat learns a maze, that helps all other rats. But it doesn't help dog-animals or fish or mice."

We were passing by Slark's Hollow, where you could valve down into the long-distance undertube. A couple of persons popped up out of the ground-valve. Spying us, they bowed to mummy-Sarah and enquired of her stability from me; which I answered as well as I could, whilst Sarah smiled sadly and mutely at them. The two trotted on their way in the direction of Unspeakable Lake.

"Tell me, Johnny," mummy-Sarah riddled me, "what's the easiest and the most complicated thing a child ever learns?"

"How to walk, and not fall over?"

"No, how to *talk*. How to communicate. So how does a child achieve this?"

"By listening to its mummy and Dada? Then echoing them?"

"No, that isn't how. If it was so, the child would never know how to put words together for itself. It would never be able to make up fresh sentences of its own, which other people can understand straight off. A child learns to talk because all human languages have the same deep structure. They have the same underlying general grammar rules—and the child only has to map what it hears on to this deep grammar. Let's call that deep structure the 'speech-maze'. No matter what the words are, or how they're put together, or what language they belong to, the paths of the maze are the same. And that maze has been solved successfully a million times before, so it's child's play to solve it again."

"So why is it hard to learn alien languages? Why can't you talk to Dada? Why can't he talk to you?"

"Because we both belong to different species. We have *different* mazes in our minds. This makes it damn near impossible for an alien to learn the language of any other alien even halfway fluently when their two species first meet. There's no morphic echo to help, none at all. And in fact, the strong morphic echo from your own species really gets in the way. You just can't grasp the alien pattern."

"But can't machines help out? Can't comps crunch words like they do numbers and exchange them between different . . . species?"

"They can. But it isn't good enough! Persons have got to be able to talk to each other directly. They have to be able to think along with each other. Back in the old days on Earth before the stargates opened, people used to fantasize about yacking on to strangers from the stars—buying them drinks, swapping jokes, telling tales. But the mazes don't match. It turned out well-nigh impossible to think or speak an alien language naturally."

"But what about me?"

"You. Yes, you. Indeed. The only way real communication can get going, Johnny—the only way all persons in the galaxy will get their act together—is if morphic fields can be established. Somehow we have to set up echoes of human people learning alien tongues from birth, in addition to their own. Learning languages is much easier for kids; but even so it's ten times harder for a human child to learn alien speech, than it is for it to learn any human language. Still, it's possible. And in time it'll become easier, because there'll be morphic echoes. Even adults will find it possible to learn."

She ruffled my hair. "You've done *well*, Johnny—and your kids will do even better. In a hundred years we'll all be able to communicate quite easily with the persons of Homestar's world. Then we can really go out and buy them drinks and natter and tell stories. Till then, we're verbal cripples."

"Oh."

"This is how alien races have learned to talk to each other in the past. Every time, every damn time. And every time it's new and different. A new species: a new maze."

"Could there be some sort of, well, super-maze? A maze of mazes?"

Mummy-Sarah looked so pleased that I felt proud. "There may well be, Johnny. We surely hope so. But none of us have found it yet."

So that was it.

Of course, the implications didn't sink in all at once: the grandeur, the perversity, the life-warping sacrifice for the sake of a future when men and aliens could swap yarns like buddies, and bargain and philosophize together . . .

Perversity, did I say?

Marianne, before I ever met you I already loved you. One day I would need to meet somebody just like you and mate and raise kids. We would have to be willing to stick it out together unflinchingly through years of dumb wedlock: you the human mother, and I the pretend-alien speaking only in alien. (And not especially well, at that! However, my infant successors on Homestar's world would find the exotic word-maze easier to master, than I had; and my own kids would make better progress too.)

I would have to bed a human wife and stay with her as spouse. So I had to be properly motivated, to this end. Mummy-Sarah saw to that as soon as I reached puberty.

Consider: I was reared amidst aliens with amber bars across their eyes and crests upon their heads, and whose bodies were smooth hard yellow china.

At puberty I had to be, um, exposed . . . to the expectation of human sexuality. I had to be nudged firmly in the right direction. I needed my libido fixing on the right erotic images. Yes indeed, I was to be focused from afar—light years afar—on such as you, my dusky darling Marianne.

Attentive dutiful mummy-Sarah duly provided me with porno-pics and tapes for me to play with.

So I was conditioned to love and lust for such as you, my Marianne, just as I suppose you were trained for me. You're dusky; mummy-Sarah was white and auburn. Musn't focus my libido on mummy; must avoid incest or homosexuality. My pics and tapes saw to that.

Truth to tell, that day when we visited Pumpkin Center was (you've guessed it) to pick up a nicely graded, well-tailored package of human pornography for me. It wasn't something to transmit to our comp-terminal. Private and personal. Anyway it wasn't all electronic. In the package were real pic-books for me to amuse myself with.

Such is the quality of passion I lay at your feet, Marianne, here on the isle of Tobago. Such is the depth of my desire for you. Oh it's deep—eighteen light-years deep, or so.

Your calypso minstrels aren't always very delicate in their praise-singing:

> How you love a man from the stars?
> He's from a globe where girls' eyes got bars!
> Girls got no bosoms and their skin's hard as wood
> But our boy does know how to give it to you good!

Or how about this one?

> Man from the stars come to wed a woman
> He'll be an ET and she'll be human
> He knows his stuff but his Ma's come too
> In case their wedded life needs fixing with glue

(Oh yes, mummy-Sarah returned to Earth with me, cold-sleeping through the stargates for a year or so. Now she has a fine beach cottage up by Speyside fishing village; a decent distance away, nothing too obtrusive. As I understand it, arranged marriages and mothers-keeping-an-eye-on-things were common enough situations in the past . . .)

Marianne, you and I are going to be a sort of Holy Family (to add to the roster of other holy families secluded on various pleasant isles around the world). Johnny and Marianne: Mary and Joseph! Oh yes.

For didn't a strange star shine over my own nativity, namely Homestar? What's more, through our love we'll help spread the Word. The alien word.

And so the calypso bards of next century, sporting bold names such as King Tutankhamun, General Mandigo and Captain Kidd, will be able to carol out their witty satires in alien patois in star bars out by Homestar or Arcturus or wherever.

Or wherever . . . We only know two alien races so far at first hand; those know a few others in turn. No doubt the *real* problems lie ahead when humans have to wed intelligent snakes or things that breathe poison gases; wed them somehow . . .

Do you know what I think, Marianne? There *is* something holy here. There's something sacred about our love. I'm perfectly serious.

Listen: we oughtn't to view the huge initial difficulty of speaking alien languages as some sort of malign barrier, some wicked way the universe has found to fox and hamper us. Look on the bright side. We're obliged to wed aliens; or to do whatever passes for spousing or kin-bonding on each alien world. We have to live with aliens as if we love them. We have to become family to them; they to us. We have to become kin. This, I think, is something holy. Don't you agree?

Thus, Marianne, our marriage is a sacrament; a love-pledge between Sol and other stars.

I'm glad I realized this. I feel a lot better about the whole thing. So let the calypso singers have their bit of fun.

> Man from the stars got himself a wife
> On our own Tobago for the rest of his life
> Raising his kids in an alien way
> His whole damn time's a carnival day!

Precisely. I'm the King of the carnival, and you're the Queen, Marianne. We're King and Queen for life, or at least for the next twenty years. But I won't wear an alien masquerade costume. I shan't shave off all my hair and stain my skin yellow, or stick a crest on my head or wear lenses with orange bars across them. That would be going too far. Yet I shall speak with the tongue of an alien.

I do miss Dada. Considering our differences, we had some fun times, him and me. I'd say he was one fine father—and he must have been a fair spouse as well. I wonder if mummy-Sarah misses him too? I don't suppose she and Dada could ever have . . . ? Well no, I don't suppose they *could*.

Sarah must have had the dedication of a nun, during all my years a-growing. She's making up for it now, I hear. I, of course, had to be pepped up by porn to assume my proper erotic place in human society . . .

I'm going to try to emulate Dada, Marianne. I'm going to be him *exactly,* to our kids. I'll be just the sort of Dada he was to me; that's the least I can do.

Oh my adorable Marianne, cynosure of my desire, target of my soul, our marriage was made in the heavens where the alien starlight shines. Accept my wedding gift of these few human words before my tongue becomes inhuman! The rest will be silence. The rest will be incomprehension, and alien jabber on my part. But one day because of us world will speak unto world. One day we'll all buy each other drinks—ranging from rum to hydrochloric acid—and swap stories and puzzle the riddle of the cosmos and be family to one another from here to forever, stars without end.

At last I know how to sing my lovesong to you, Marianne! How else but calypso-style? (I'll show them.)

> Man from the stars he's no more than a boy
> But we wish him and Marianne lots of joy
> It's urgent we all get to talk to each other
> So we all embrace every alien like our brother!

Now I'll kiss you.

SCIENCE-FICTIONAL

I wrote science fiction for a *reason*. Being a good European (culturally, if not politically) I sought for a theory of what I was doing . . .

The Crudities of Science Fiction

During the last decade the best Anglo-American SF has grown up. The bounds of the so-called genre 'ghetto' have burst. Its puberty is past; sex and human relations can be freely discussed. There is a reasonable awareness of political and social dimensions. Today's new vintages (as opposed to the vin ordinaire which continues to be pressed out) are—to be paradoxical—mature ones. University presses aren't ashamed to print critiques of SF; on the contrary. And these critiques deal with SF as a literature, not merely a peculiar sociological phenomenon. Meanwhile, many of the 'best' writers increasingly condemn the commercial classification 'SF'—so convenient to publishers, so artistically constraining to the writers. Thus Harlan Ellison refuses to let the term 'SF' appear anywhere on the covers of his books; Malzberg quits the field because he feels that the label and the preconceptions implicit in the SF format hamper the imagination impossibly; Silverberg ceases to write since he considers that his best books haven't, and by definition can't, be appreciated within the field. There is a round of applause whenever a 'superior' SF novel is marketed as a novel for the general reader. The best future is seen as one where SF is simply part of general literature, where general literature (already borrowing devices and metaphors from SF) absorbs its prodigal son—ghettoized by the devilish Gernsback and other pulp magazine editors—back into its body, till there is again simply literature, fiction, in all its multifarious diversity. (The term 'SF' may be kept on, perhaps, as a convenient label for Perry Rhodan and suchlike adolescent immaturities.)

SF writers are supposed to be pleased about this. But I for one am not very pleased.

Why not, when we obviously have a new improved SF? Well, let us compare the old SF with the smart new literary model. Compare, for instance, the grandiose cardboard inanities of E. E. Smith with the artistic kind of story that often appears in original anthologies these days (I think particularly of Silverberg's *New Dimensions* series). In Smith, bright young heroes invent starships that skylark through the cosmos, saving kidnapped girlfriends from falling into dead stars (by firing morse-code messages through space by machine gun) followed by valiant cuddles in space armour. Blasters roar, crypto-science jargon jangles evocatively, galaxies collide. It's gawkish stuff. Yet there is such sheer passion for science, discovery, space; such wonder (even though the human and social dimension is missing and the stuff is frankly unreadable beyond the age of 14 with its lumpy style, minimal characters and histrionic plots) that I turn with some sadness to some more obviously mature, adult, artistic SF of today.

Take a typical *New Dimensions* story. The piece is called "The Mothers' March on Ecstasy"; it is by George Alec Effinger. In it the resident anti-hero proclaims:

"Oh, that I could enjoy anew the conscienceless

freedom of those long-dead days. But I am sure it is impossible. I am not a scientist now. Perhaps you have noticed from the loveliness of the words that I have become a poet. It happened overnight..."

This story is rather symptomatic of what is happening in SF today, now that the ghetto walls are tumbling down. Sadly, the science ideas of genuine SF, and science itself too, become all too often a form of stylish kitsch, reflecting a self-indulgent Western disillusion with science, wonder, hope, the future, and their replacement by a sophisticated Silver Age rococo. Wry tragedy glitters. The future—that is all too rapidly becoming the present—is kitschified, as SF dons its laurels of respectabililty. (So Vonnegut—not that he would wish to be termed an SF writer!—reduces alien communication methods to farting and tap-dancing, and Malzberg's entire opus is almost all parody.) This is not true of all writers, certainly. Le Guin is writing authentic exploratory SF that is mature, literary, politically relevant and positive towards our future. Philip Dick *believes*—perhaps hectically, perhaps crazily; but he has vision. John Brunner cares. Frank Herbert too. Yet the autumnal Silver Age elegance is there in Silverberg's later books—which are far from being kitsch themselves, yet the imaginary cultural museum is being paced by a fine connoisseur before the barbarians breach the gates, before Death's sickle reaps. It is there in Chris Priest's *The Space Machine*—accomplished exercise in literary nostalgia that it is. It is there in Brian Aldiss's recent *The Malacia Tapestry*, again not kitsch certainly, but a patrician private world. (And of course the barbarians are within *us* too). This is a literature of personal aesthetic statement, the solution to the founderings of the Western episteme being sought in sophisticated private craft, in formalism rather than idea content.

However, SF is founded upon the exploration of ideas, rather than stylistics. It is a community of ideas; in its sum, it composes what one might call an 'idea-myth', the idea-myth of man in the universe, of future-humanity (alien to ourselves at present), of the alien future, of life other than we yet know it. When, long ago, Michel Butor (*"The Crisis of Growth in Science Fiction"*, 1953) remarked that "The power of SF writing is based upon one common dream" yet bemoaned the incoherent disagreements about the shape of the future, proposing a conference to sort things out, he was wrong in proposing such a syllabus for the future—for the very strength of SF lies in its contradictoriness, its multiple vision—yet he was quite right in seeing SF as a powerful mythology of potential liberation; and in reality such a conference did already exist—in the shared conceptual outlook of the genre. SF is already a mythology, in total; though unlike the hieratic mythologies of antiquity, it is a multiplistic mythology, with as many worlds, futures, heroes, Gods as there are writers (the sources for these), though with certain shared structural motifs: the sense of future time, the sense of future humanity, the sense of radical change, the sense of the alien. SF is a mythology of change—which we sorely need today. The old mythologies, as Mircea Eliade points out, were ones of cyclical renewal of the *same* world. And it is the very content-centredness of SF that makes it this mythology; the communal act of thought about future and change.

In *Myth and Reality* Eliade discusses the survivals of myth amid the secularisation of the present day. In humanity resides a deep urge to generate myth, to apprehend the universe and to renew one's being within it. In fiction (one such myth survival—for when old myths are exposed as fictions, fiction may become myth) the reader steps outside of normal time into a foreign universe, a mythic universe, the universe of sacred time. The urge to novelize, even though it arose amid the bourgeois enlightenment and typically concerned itself with things of this world, nevertheless reflects man's (thwarted) mythic thinking. Yet we are now emerging from a period of this-worldly secular myth (perhaps one should call it anti-myth)—into a time of ecological awareness, future consciousness, consciousness expansion; we must, or our world crashes. We are at a transition threshold—from secular, national man to planetary beings, to man-in-cosmos: a return to the old concern of myth, you may say, *except* that there is no possible return to primitive, static thought processes where all events of importance occurred in the beginning. Technologically mediated, the new episteme must concern itself with vital future events brought about by our own scientific activity.

Mainstream art which senses this new, barely definable episteme (as opposed to mainstream art which merely perpetuates the realist tradition of the past two centuries) seeks a tabula rasa upon which something new may be inscribed, seeks a new personal language of expression, a new metalanguage of reality, a reduction of discourse to its minimals to cleanse the dialect of art (Joyce, Beckett, Abstract Art, Action Art, Stockhausen...). Yet this project remains largely a private aesthetic one, wherein the artistry is sanctified rather than the matter. For the 'myth' of general literature is ourselves; while the myth of SF is the other, the alienness confronting us. Other beings, other times.

SF, because of its subject matter—and despite its crudities—has a vital and serious collective mythic function, which I see as socially and imaginatively healthy (even though the politics of some SF writers may leave something to be desired). Yet it is not an aesthetic thing-in-itself, a private communion. For SF writers to hope to become individual writers within general literature, creating their own personal masterpieces, would be a false sublimation of the genre from which they emerge—injurious, after a time, to their own creativity, to their ability to create significantly; a sucking of energy into the maintenance of an artistic and psychological status quo, in this time of changes. Plainly market pressures and reader expectations tend to force the SF writer to support a consumer status quo of mere entertainment and formula; yet at the same time I believe that the genre has a different, and deeper effect within society by presenting the idea of future man, future alien experience, as something conceivable, encompassable. Collectively, it generates myth—of our future.

In a recent newspaper interview, British novelist John Fowles remarked that all novelists are sick, obsessive creatures who have experienced some infantile trauma that generates but one thing in common: the need to create an alternative world. The SF writer, I would suggest (perhaps one should speak hesitantly, after reading Malzberg's *Herovit's World* on the sickness of the SF pulp artiste!), is in a healthier situation, despite all the moans; is less isolated since he is engaged in this communal mythic creation, is engaged in something that undoubtedly *matters*—for the future certainly matters.

Yet what of the immaturities, the childishness and crudities of the genre? Franz Rottensteiner jibes (aiming at Philip Farmer in particular) that SF creates whole worlds and universes—and what does it do with them? It plays billiards. It uses them all too frequently as ping-pong balls in a shooting gallery. What is SF doing, though, but creating myths which are games and toys? Let us not sneer at games and toys. They are very necessary; and we must admit that humanity is still in its infancy. What do children do but play with toys? *And learn from them.* SF—the collective myth of SF—is such a learning toy. To strike out for a spurious sophistication within the bosom of general literature is to place these toys in a connoisseur's art gallery, at the very time that epistemic shockwaves are shaking the foundations of the gallery.

This is why SF can have its crudities—and still be of great

value; why the creation of SF *as SF* is a collective enterprise which we cannot, perhaps, properly grasp the importance of, as yet. Why SF, strangely—given its economic market background—is a revolutionary literature.

Of course, this is no reason to praise its being written badly or carelessly! A horse runs best when it runs most elegantly, most stylishly. (Yet it must still be a horse.) SF should be written as well as is in the writer's power; and I am aware that market and genre pressures frequently make this hard—though frankly I would say that there is a lot of rather good SF around, much better than one would expect. The cry for the acceptance of SF within general literature and the erasing of the label appears at first to be a plea for culture against barbarism (the barbarisms of 3 cents a word, deadlines, garish packaging, inane blurbs, a forced catering to cardboard adolescent power fantasies—'How I saved the Universe in my spare time with one hand tied behind my back'). Yet, underlying this, is a dangerous rejection of the positive well-springs of this mythic literature. SF should be written with a respect, rather than a loathing for the genre; and there is a bit too much loathing of it about now.

Perhaps this reflects the years we are living through. The Seventies, so far, have been an austere and gloomy, if still prolific period. One would like a safe haven, free from storms—and personal art (by our cultural conditioning) is apparently such a haven . . .

Yet of course Art was not a private haven in the past, before the Romantic view of the Artist stamped it as such. SF is really akin to older literature, before literature was santified as a thing-in-itself. It is mythic—and didactic; it is content-directed, as Art traditionally was. It is the collective conceptual framework of SF that counts, and gives strength to the individual works. Within that framework, one should obviously write as well as one can; but one must not forget the framework, since it is this that lends SF its strength and potential, not yet (let it be added) fully realized.

Personally I look forward to the SF of the 1980s: a fiction that acknowledges it is science fiction. It is this that will be relevant, socially and humanly.

IAN WATSON

In my satiric (though, I hope, affectionate) story "The World Science Fiction Convention of 2080" after the collapse of civilization SF fans continue their old pursuits, freed from the realities of on-going science and technology. Here is a companion piece, in which history takes a different turn . . .

The Big Buy

Well, friends, you all know how it happened. But since it's the most important thing that ever happened to the world, I guess it can bear one more retelling!

Three weeks after the aliens put their big ship down in the middle of the Simpson Desert, a couple of hundred miles south of Alice Springs, the world had got its trade fair assembled as requested. None too easy at such short notice, way out in the Australian Outback! But our aliens—chitinous, gem-encrusted, exoskeletal critturs that they were—happened to favour very hot and dry conditions. They weren't about to put themselves out unduly. It was a buyers' market, you'll recall.

But what were they about to buy? And more important for the whole future of the Earth, what were they prepared to go on buying? They would install their robot credit bank and matter transmitter mail order satellite in geosynch orbit if we came up with a good long-term deal; but that was the whole trouble—their technology was streets ahead of ours.

"Bring us your best," they said. "You decide what is your most appealing. Technics, ceramics, songbirds, examples of the jeweller's art, quantum gravity equations, patents for perpetual motion machines, chic fashion suitable for aliens going to a party, weapons systems, picnic ware, intoxicants, hang-gliders! We shall decide what suits us and our trading partners, best. If anything. We shall set a fair price and if nothing particularly suits us, we'll certainly drop by in another thousand years or so to see whether you've come up with something really special."

"But," said the Secretary General of the United Nations.

"But nothing," said the aliens. "How can we say what we want, till we see it? How are *we* supposed to know? *You're* the aliens, after all! We're not. We're us."

So, in national teams, the world and his wife scrambled to the Simpson Desert. There was a kind of cargo cult hysteria—in reverse. The idea was to get your goods on board the big metal ball. And of course people died of heatstroke, and the Libyans cut the guy ropes of the Egyptians' best marquee, and a tank of hundred-year-old Japanese carp had ink dumped in it, and the Chinese dwarf trees were sprayed with defoliant by the Vietnamese. And suchlike incidents.

And day by day the stately, jewel-studded aliens strolled up and down the desert avenues, admiring a cage of birds of paradise and shaking their heads, and trying out a sub-machine gun and shaking their heads, and viewing a Modigliani reproduction and shaking their heads. A certain Arab emirate even offered human slaves, but still the aliens shook their heads. (I might add that the sense of revulsion produced by this offer among all right-thinking nations—which led to a sponsored revolution in that emirate shortly afterwards—went hand in hand with a certain feeling of peeved resentment that apparently homo sapiens was not even worth buying as slaves! Though perhaps the aliens' ethical sense prohibited their trading in intelligent flesh . . .)

How was I, Bob Butler of Fantastic Universe Bookstore, present at that world fair in the outback? Well, my huckster table had been at every major Stateside SF event for years too many to recall. At least twelve or thirteen years. How could I pass up the opportunity of touting my wares at the first genuine alien fair, even though it meant putting the shop in hock? The U.S. Government's position was simple. Since we had no idea what these goddam aliens wanted, and were in a hell of a hurry, anybody who put up the highest tender for an export license in each single trade category could pay for themselves to go to our patch of the Simpson Desert.

I must admit that the officials reviewing my application (at great speed—there was some doubt whether I was in a separate category from the literature trade at large) had a few jitters when they saw samples of my wares: a few old *Planet Stories* and Ace Doubles, for nostalgia and sensawonder, and paperbacks of a broad band of the more literate moderns for class and insight.

They stared at the covers.

"This is like offering Cowboy and Indian stories to the Apaches!"

"It's like peddling a cartoon edition of *Mein Kampf* around Watts!"

"But," protested I, "the aliens are the goodies in the best new SF!"

"It's like telling anti-Jewish jokes in Tel Aviv!"

"Oy veh, don't they do that all the time?" said I.

"It's like auctioning porno to Nuns!"

"This is a respectable, insightful literature, Mister! Look here, it says on the cover of this one, 'SF may be the only true literature of our day.' "

Fortunately, they didn't believe me, or I'd have been bundled in with Books (Lit.) and never could have afforded a license.

"Okay, go waste your money," they said. "Just don't get in the way of any genuine artistic or commercial deals!"

Came the twentieth day of the Fair. It was a hundred and ten in the shade, and nothing had been sold. I had put up with quite a few sneers and threats, mainly because I'd had the wit to bring an icemaker and a battery fan with me—though of course the sneers were directed at my wares.

"Look, Butler, I'll buy one of your cretinous magazines myself for a thousand bucks, just to fan myself with, if you'll throw in the battery fan too."

"You don't know what a *true fan* is, Mister," I retorted blandly. "You don't know the meaning of the word." Implacably I sat there.

Finally, on that twentieth day, one of the bejewelled chitinous aliens circulated by my huckster table—having shaken its head at programmable calculators, bottles of Southern Comfort, Cruise missiles, videotapes of *Oklahoma* and such.

It peered at *Planet Stories*, then it picked up a paperback. *Mazeworld*, as I recall.

"What are these?" it asked in a rattling voice, which may have conveyed threat (had it been a snake) or (in retrospect) excitement.

"These are our alternative histories of the galaxy," said I. "Since we had no contact with you star people, we had to imagine it all. These are our histories of you aliens."

It gazed across my crowded table.

"All of these?"

"Not every single one. Alien SF is a kind of sub-genre—but it's probably *the* major one. Oh, I can think of five hundred titles off the top of my head. People are writing it more and more. And I guess they'll carry on. When we landed on the Moon, people said, 'What'll you write about now?' Look what happened: we had the biggest writing boom ever. I guess the same thing applies now that you star people have turned up. I guess . . . "

The alien cut me short, to concentrate on reading the first chapter of *Mazeworld*. Then it read a chapter from another novel which I handed it, and then a third.

"This is quite *unique* . . . Mr., er?"

"Butler. Bob Butler."

"Nowhere else in the stellar worlds has a sapient species done such a strange thing as inventing other species they know nothing about. And so relentlessly too!" Its arm swung over the masses of books, like a crane jib. "I am tempted to think that this is your unique peculiarity. If only our customers could scan these words, they would be enthralled. Titivated!" (I suppose it meant 'titillated', unless their customers dressed up in fancy costumes or fluffed their feathers out when they read a book.) "Convulsed, enchanted!"

"We can sell translation rights," I said, quick as a flash.

I could indeed. As soon as I got on a phone, the major agents would instantly forgive me poaching on their preserves. The phones were mostly standing idle, since there was nothing to negotiate—until now.

"We shall need to negotiate a sample contract quite carefully. Particularly, we will need to include binding provisions to guarantee the quality and uniqueness of our supply."

"But of course! I'm not selling 'All Rights', though, you understand? We'll do it on a language by language basis. Vegan rights, Sirian rights . . . "

"Nobody inhabits the system you call Sirius."

"Well, whatever!"

" 'All Rights' would be simpler. There are approximately five thousand major planetary languages, and proportionately many sub-languages . . . "

Now it was my turn to shake my head. A great moment for Earthmen.

"Very well," it conceded.

And you all know how it went from there. I was the only human who sold anything to the aliens, and what I sold them—I can say it between friends—was that crazy house of images of themselves, seen through an SF eye weirdly.

So the aliens put their satellite in geosynch orbit. Soon the space shuttles of the USA, and Russia too, had all their time cut out ferrying up my SF submissions and ferrying back the signed contracts and the goods we've bought with our credits via the matter transmitter: the force-field patents, the pan-immunity drugs, the 100% conversion solar cells, the whole shape of the now-world.

As you all know, I'm a billionaire just from my ten per cent commission. And in the face of such clout as the SF authors of alien unrealities now carry, we have seen the rather rapid demise of old-style political governments. ASFW, the Association of SF Writers, whose sole membership criterion is an alien sale, *is* the world government today.

I thank you all for your attention to one man's reminiscences. I thank the staff of the U.N. building for running such a fine convention. And my thanks to the Madame Vice-President of the U.S.A. for introducing me so kindly. My hearty congratulations to her on her recent sale of Arcturian and Canopian rights to *Shawl of Stars* for a ten-figure sum!

Is that a question from the audience?

Clause Thirteen in the contracts? What about Clause Thirteen?

Infamous to some, my friend! Caviar and champagne to others!

No, let him have his say!

You are naïve, Sir. We have a duty to our readers that goes way beyond the provisions of Clause Thirteen. Clause Thirteen is the cornerstone of this duty. Without that cornerstone, where would the world be? This world—I say this without fear of contradiction—that we have saved and remade? The very quality, Sir—the purity, the unbridled *spontaneity* of our product, and the sanctity of our imaginations—crucially depends on our allegiance to Clause Thirteen. Of course we must agree, and keep our agreement, never to try to leave the Solar System. Should we ever actually travel to the stars or find out one substantial fact about the real alien community, why, we'd be ruined.

And don't you forget it.

Thank you, all.

The German authoress Gisela Elsner wrote a novel called *The Giant Dwarfs*, a phrase which comes to mind when we consider the heroes of many SF tales...

Who Can Believe in the Hero(ine)?

"James Tiptree Jr." once remarked, *à propos* narrative technique: "Start from the end and preferably 5,000 feet underground on a dark day and then DON'T TELL THEM."

This comment has a curious, askew relevance to so many SF heroes and heroines—for after reading a lot of SF, one becomes aware of a curious feature, which may be intoxicating at first, but which may eventually drive one screaming far from the domains of SF, or may compel one to ask a few searching questions. And this feature, I would say, becomes even more agonizing to the writer of SF than to the reader—who can always shrug and turn away. The writer is up to his or her neck in a narrative for weeks or months on end; the reader only for a few hours.

The curious fact is that, in book after book and story after story, it always happens to be the darned, ahem, *protagonist* who turns out to be central to (a) the explanation of the universe, (b) the rescuing of space-time from collapse, (c) the salvation of the human race, (d) the detection and defeat of the ravening mind-horde from Ursa Major—even if said protagonist is a nitwitted thug, or someone marooned on a space derelict near Arcturus, or somebody stuck in a space ark in mid-journey, or someone who has lived all his life in a deep cave, and who consequently starts out full of the most absurd notions about the nature of the world.

How often, and how arbitrarily, does the central enigma of the cosmos thus converge upon the central character, whatever his or her qualities! How seldom is the protagonist marginal to the events unfolding—as nearly all of us are, nearly all of the time, in the real world.

One may, of course, invoke such critical concepts as "cognitive estrangement" and "conceptual breakthrough." Yet how often we feel: what a wonderful concept, yet what mental and social cripples inhabit it! And by what awkward contrivances are they jerked up by their bootstraps! Indeed, how often is it the case that by their blunders alone the plot is kept moving along, to be salvaged at the eleventh hour by something *ex machina.*

SF is a heroic genre, by and large, given its subject material. One might even say that it is in the business of heroes (and heroines). But oh dear: how many of its protagonists can really live up to it? And those who try to often provide the direst examples. (Better, perhaps, simply to get on with the hijinks—even if this is obviously a cop-out with regard to the material.)

I have a theory about this.

Any writer worth his or her salt knows that if a book is to be any good at all, one has to let it grow organically, as a separate living entity—whatever one's prior vision of it. It has to make its own decisions, rather like a child growing away from the parent.

(Worth his or her sodium chloride? Ah well, we now know that NaCl is a subtle poison, to be avoided at all costs... But the metaphor lives on.)

This raises strange questions about the relationship of the

author to the world which he or she creates, and the characters so created, who should likewise establish their own independent existence. It raises questions about the responsibility of the author toward those creations, and questions about the relationship between the book-reality and the consciousness of the author.

These are questions which are perhaps at the root of artistic creation—and which, if we posit for the moment the existence of a God, no doubt constitute a fundamental dilemma at the root of Her creation of a cosmos.

We are all little Gods, cobbling together our own little cosmoses, pocket universes in imitative variation upon the real thing. Well, most of us. Some writers, like Barrington J. Bayley, manage to come up with entirely different cosmoses—made, say, of solid stone with world-bubbles of air in them . . .

Anyway, Godly creation (whatever a God might be; and frankly I don't know, though a number of my own books—in common with quite a *lot* of SF—are concerned with what a God *might be*) and artistic creation do have in common the paradox of the relationship between one's creating consciousness and the reality created: a paradox, incidentally, which has become central to the cutting edge of modern scientific attempts to explain the universe coherently.

SF, which includes within its domain attempted explanations of the nature of the universe—and of the nature of mind and reality—is in fact particularly well-adapted to address this problem central to artistic creation.

Hence, indeed, there are many novels and stories which concern themselves with what we may call "the reality problem"— from such as Daniel Galouye's *Counterfeit World* through to most of the works of Philip Dick.

In a sense, a lot of SF is already *meta*-fiction: fiction about fiction, fiction about the process of creation.

And I hazard the guess that so many SF heroes and heroines are deficient—no match for their material—because of this reality problem. Yet the convergence of the central crux of the universe upon the protagonist in so many tales is more than just a genre cliché or contrivance. It is a reflection of the reality problem, and of the artistic problem, tuned up to fever pitch in SF precisely because in SF one can invoke the whole rest of the universe—and indeed, once one has started, often one necessarily must do so. (Though, it being logically impossible to describe the totality, inevitably one fails.)

Yes, tuned up to fever pitch—and sometimes exaggerated almost to a point of parody or absurdity. (And how easily SF writers concerned with Big Things can produce self-parody! See some recent examples.) Consequently we may find the honest or desperate writer from time to time beating his or her brow and expostulating: "How the hell can I *believe* this shit I'm writing?" "How can this jerk possibly solve the riddle of the ages?" "How can this fool save the universe?" (But often it is only due to the protagonist's "folly" that enough scene-setting can be introduced, to get the story under way.)

Yet, precisely what makes some SF unbelievable—even occasionally to the writer who is producing it—is one of the most potentially valuable and productive aspects of SF: the attack on the reality problem.

The writer who grows aware of this, in the course of a career, is now faced with a *meta*-problem: the need to incorporate awareness of the problem into the texts that reflect it.

Or the writer can try to ignore it entirely. Or hit the bottle, to stave off impending insanity and disconnection from the real world. (As in the case of Jonathan Herovit, in Barry Malzberg's novel; indeed this is a dominant theme in Malzberg's work.) Or one can refuse to believe it fully, as a deliberate strategy for carrying on—whilst accepting it in practice. Thomas Covenant the Unbeliever is able to function because of chosen, sustained unbelief—which is why Donaldson's books, to my mind, are so powerful, sustained and successful. Donaldson addresses the reality problem very skillfully and honestly. He does this by making *his* problem into the *hero's* problem. But he does not—so far—let Covenant resolve the problem; which is just as well, since the problem is ultimately unresolvable. Putting it another way, Donaldson's hero succeeds as a hero by refusing heroism—whilst nevertheless conducting himself heroically. (I think it was Schopenhauer who said something like: "On this firm foundation of unyielding despair must the soul's salvation henceforth be safely built"—a fitting motto for Covenant.)

To speak personally for a moment, looking back on my own novels in this light, the first four were "innocent" ones—innocent of the problem, though admittedly the aliens in my fourth novel, *Alien Embassy*, had to be pretend-aliens, for me to believe in them fully. By the time I wrote my fifth novel, *Miracle Visitors*, the problem of the reality of events themselves demanded to be explored—which seemed best done through the UFO mythos, wherein events seemingly occur which hover tantalizingly between reality and irreality. By the time I wrote *God's World*, published in England in 1979, the journey to the stars in that book was presented (and presented itself to me) necessarily as a journey *through imaginative space*. And I was able to reach an actual, "objective" alien world precisely because I envisaged a physical journey to it in a starship as also being a journey through the imagination—a journey which the characters had to create for themselves, as much as the author himself had consciously to create it. If the characters had suffered a failure of imagination, they would not have reached their destination. Thus, in a sense, the problem involved in the cry, "How can I, the writer, possibly *believe* this?" was shouldered by the characters. Thus I, and they, arrived at journey's end, and returned.

I think that SF writers who decide that they are no longer really writing SF, or are no longer interested in writing it, or who can no longer *bear* to write it—SF writers who can no longer persuade themselves of the authenticity of what they are writing, or of the credibility or adequacy of their heroes or heroines—are in fact suffering from an unresolved reality problem, an affliction as dire as prickly heat or poison ivy rashes; and that this will be much more acutely evident in SF writers—particularly in the best and most thoughtful of these writers—than in writers in other fields . . . because of the nature of SF itself.

That SF presents this problem of belief—in authenticity, in a genuinely adequate hero or heroine—at its very heart, isn't for me a cause for bemoaning the inherent deficiencies of the genre; but rather of excitement at the prospect of tackling the problem. For it's a problem that lies at the heart of art. As, indeed, it is at the heart of the existence of the physical universe as such.

One cannot exactly *solve* the problem—any more than one can define the nature of God, or pin down an actual UFO. There's no ideal SF novel which balances all the terms of the equation self-consistently and demonstrably, equivalent to Flaubert's ideal of a novel which could sustain itself entirely by the power of style alone. John Crowley's *Engine Summer* may seem, on the surface, to be a perfect example of the Flaubertian SF novel. Yet it isn't really, since its crystalline perfection comes from its perfect mapping of the reality problem—by means of a technology—on to the text of the book. And of course Rush sets out to become a Saint—a Hero—and succeeds precisely to the extent that he is no longer a real person by the end of the book; and never has been.

This is, of course, to ignore a whole dimension of 'heroines and heroes' in the sense of childish wish-fulfillment figures—not to mention the whole side issue of heroic fantasy—in favor of the more encompassing notion of the protagonist. But I think that here we hit on the reason why so many heroes and heroines presented *as such* are actually far from adequate, in real terms; since as soon as one sets out to invent a problem-solving or action-resolving heroic figure in an SF tale, one is immediately involved in a race of the tortoise, trying to catch an unattainable Achilles.

Achilles, of course, was a genuine hero fortified by being dipped in the Styx. Yet that is not to suggest that so many protagonists and heroic figures in SF are ultimately sub-standard simply because we mostly dwell in the literary sticks. Our protagonists, including heroes and heroines, measure themselves against the universe—or at least a reflected part of it—and the universe flattens and dwarfs them.

At least, that's one theory.

Here is one such ill-equipped hero, adrift in the void, suddenly pitched into one of SF's cosmic struggles . . .

Showdown on Showdown

The miracle that saved me from madness in my survival capsule in the deeps between the stars represented odds that no gambler would ever have accepted. A trillion to one? Who could even calculate it?

The quasi-mass detectors of the Highspacer *Euclid* noted, momentarily, the faint echo of my capsule adrift in Low Space. The Highspacer dropped back down into the ordinary continuum two lights short of its goal of Eta Cass, the forbidden system of Ruby-Hoyle, and fished me in to human society once more.

Since the explosion of the Highspacer *Herschel*, I had spent nine months pitting my wits (and staking my sanity) on chess with the mini-comp, and on all the varieties of solitaire I could remember: Klondike, Canfield, Golf, Spider—and Napoleon at St. Helena, this last being the variety that Napoleon reputedly played to while away his last exile. I too, though no Napoleon, had met my Waterloo and was in exile, perhaps forever.

The pecularities of the *Euclid*—the sense of oddity—I attributed at first to my own nine months' estrangement from human society. There was the lavish Games Room *cum* Casino that I thought I glimpsed: surely a fantasy distortion, a projection of my own late lonely rituals? There was the intent preoccupation of the crew, as though they were playing some sort of telepathic chess with each other. And there were the exhaustive mind-tests administered by psychofficer Rosamundi Bjornson almost as soon as I was brought aboard (instead of a slap on the back, and congratulations on my deliverance).

But then Rosamundi Bjornson led me to Highcaptain Wang's cabin.

The Chinese Highcaptain regarded me with prim anxiety, well masked but not entirely. (I was hypersensitive to human faces after my time in the void without them. By enhancement of my own trade-agent's skill at reading unwitting expressions, now every faint rictus even of a tight-stretched Chinese face seemed magnified a hundredfold, cartoon-like.)

"I am so happy to hear you are sane, Mr. Cortina," he said by way of greeting. "We could not, of course, leave a distress beacon unheeded, but even so . . ." He let a hint fade away, that circumstances might have required that I be tucked back into my pod and jettisoned—or euthanased. "I am happy, too, to hear of the manner in which you occupied your time while shipwrecked." (Was he being sarcastic? No . . .) "I would dearly love to place you under arrest for violating the forbidden space we are now moving into. However, all of a ship's complement must play a role in the Hoyle system to dig us out of the mess our first expedition thoughtlessly got us into. That is how things are. Sit. Drink," he ordered sharply, in a high-pitched voice.

Drinks appeared from the dispenser. Little cups of burning mao-tai, Chinese brandy.

"How much do you know about Hoyle?"

"It's the brighter of the two suns of the Eta Cass binary. I've heard rumors that it's got two or three habitable worlds with intelligent aliens on them. Maybe that's why the system's off limits?" I searched my memory for some celestial facts. "Hoyle's a star like Sol. It's named after a twentieth-century astronomer."

"*It is not.* That is a convenient coincidence. The truth about Hoyle's human name—dreamed up by the fancy and folly of the first expedition—is that it is named after a certain Edmond Hoyle, who lived from the late seventeenth to late eighteenth centuries."

"Hoyle's *Rules of Games!*"

"Precisely. The human names of its planets, three of them inhabited and a further one terraformable, as frivolously selected by the first expedition, are Chip, Pair, Flush, Showdown, Straight, and Jackpot."

I coughed as the mao-tai caught in my throat. Rosamundi Bjornson regarded me unsympathetically.

"To give them their due, the first expedition chose appropriate nicknames. Chip is just a chip of hot rock, and Pair is number two—big, but hot and airless." Wang paused.

"Showdown is . . . where it's all happening?" I guessed wildly. "Between Flush—and Straight? For the Jackpot?"

For the first time Captain Wang smiled. "Very acute, Mr. Cortina. There is hope for you. Though you don't yet know *what* is happening . . ."

And he told me.

"Three intelligent species co-exist in the Hoyle system, inhabiting Flush, Showdown, and Straight. Both Flush and Straight possess space travel on the interplanetary level. Straight is a cold, ice-girt world of low mass with spindly six-limbed hairy natives that look like dancing spiders with a couple of legs missing. The dominant species of Flush, a heavy, hot world, are six-limbed too, but burly and scaly like golden pangolins who stand upright. Showdown, however—in between the orbits of Flush and Straight—is a water world with only a few crests of land peeking above the deep world-ocean; its dominant lifeform resemble giant squid. *Very* giant squid: krakens. They communicate by light signals at close quarters, and at a distance by a kind of modulatable empathy, a sense of their placement around the globe.

"Dominant species, did I say? Already we are going haywire. No one is dominant in the system, as such. In fact, the Spidermen of Straight and the Pangolins of Flush are forever playing an intricate game between their two worlds—without war, without aggression or killing. They play it for stakes of territory on little Marslike Jackpot. The actual moves in the Game are enacted for them three-dimensionally throughout the world-ocean of Showdown—by the Krakens. Showdown is the games board; the Krakens are the willing pieces, and umpires. What *their* motive might be in turning their world into a games board, we have no idea.

"The Game has been going on for a very long time, though in recent E-decades the play has extended to take in Janus too: the solitary 'double atmosphere' world of the companion star Ruby, a world with primitive lifeforms of different biologies in both its hemispheres. Its territory is also contested now, far from Janus itself, in the oceans of Showdown."

"But how does that affect us?" I asked.

"The first expedition got involved in the Game. Maybe they thought they'd dropped into a Las Vegas of the sky."

"So what's wrong?"

Captain Wang stared at me with a pained expression. "The fools lost us Ganymede, Mercury, and Luna. To the Krakens, as stakeholders for the Game. They lost us the Moon, man. The Moon."

For a moment I too stared at him. Then, of course, I burst out laughing. Oh, they were marvelous. They'd been leading me along all this time. Cruel to a spacewrecked castaway, I suppose!

But perhaps it was intended therapeutically. Perhaps I was showing signs of alienation, and needed a gigantic dig in the ribs.

Neither Wang nor Rosamundi followed suit, though. And the Highspacer *Euclid* was indeed fitted out with a kind of casino...

"That's unenforceable," I said. "It's utter nonsense. These Spiders and Pangolins don't have space navies, do they? You said they don't fight."

"They don't. But then, neither do we."

"They haven't any way of *getting* to Sol system! And even if they could—well, I mean, Spidermen or Pangolins or Giant Squids dropping in on the Moon to collect rent! It's a fantasy. A joke. Why are you treating it so seriously? Surely they realize that you can't play board games with *worlds*?"

"But these aliens do. They play on Showdown, for Jackpot and Janus—and whatever any visitors choose to stake."

And then I saw the flaw—or read it in their faces.

"You're afraid that you'll spark off an interplanetary war between Straight and Flush if you back out? You'll have kicked the board over. Straight will beat up Flush, or the other way about. You'll have destroyed an intelligent species. Yes, I see, instead of playing they'd do it for real! Tear each other to pieces."

"We're glad you're quick on the uptake," said Wang. "Yes indeed, we might trigger the mutual annihilation of two intelligent species who have found a crazy *modus vivendi*—a way of getting on together—and possibly even the trashing of the Krakens. We have to *win* our way out of this Game—and win it in such a way that we don't win: one inch of Jackpot, one centimeter of Janus."

"Of course, there's a further problem," added Rosamundi. "War greatly stimulates technical advances. If the Game turns into a war, Straight or Flush, or maybe both, will be hugely optimized technically. We're going to drive the winner into Highspace—we've shown them it can be done—and we're going to rue it, because they'll *own* Luna and Mercury, according to their rules. Preposterous as it is, we'll have to build up a defense force ourselves. That'll ruin everything. We'll poison our souls."

"Surely this game will have to come to an end some day? There'll be the same problem. Put up or shut up."

"It wouldn't go interstellar, Mr. Cortina. That's what the risk is now."

"So get yourself down to the casino," ordered Wang, "and limber up your wits. Everyone has to be in this, according to the umpires. The rules of the Game we'll hypno into you presently. But you can regard it as something like planet-wide, role-playing Go in three dimensions with spherical topology. The number of possible plays five ahead at any moment vastly exceeds the number of electrons in the universe. We play," sighed the Captain, "highly intuitively. With WorldGov's blessing. We play, not for Luna, but for the survival of two or three alien species—and for our souls, as Bjornson says."

He raised his hand as though blessing me. But he was only waving me from his cabin.

Touchdown on Showdown: on a single island in blue ocean, up in the northerly temperate zone. No other land is visible. Our nearest neighbors—excepting the Krakens—are the Spidermen up at their Arctic station two thousand klicks further north. The Pangolin station is on the equator, round the other side of the world from us.

The tiny nugget in the ocean swells into a cratered, eroded peak with skirts of lichen green and a thin ribbon of cliff-high coastal plain. Where a subsidiary crater has collapsed into the sea is a deep wide bowl-like harbor; that is the harbor of the Krakens. Above, is the Earth station.

It is another kind of marooning for me: a marooning with forty other people, true . . . but it bears a resemblance. It bears a resemblance.

So then, in the harbor roosts a shift of half a dozen enormous Krakens, like tentacled submarines at anchor. [Beware those tentacles. They can reach all the way up the cliff and sometimes do so, toying with the rock, stretching themselves—it seems—during the relative immobility of duty; or are they perhaps idly exploring the rather rare (to them) sensation of solid surface—the grain of the board which Spidermen and Pangolins and Earthfolk alike inhabit? We do not expose ourselves in the open.] The Krakens' oval purple eyes watch underwater comscreens—installed by Spider work teams. Their phosphormantles pulse color mosaics at the sensors around the screens. An interfacing of Hoylish decoders displays the changing state of play up in the Games Room, on the crater lip, as symbols in ranks of curved viewing tanks arranged in the shape of a great globe. We sit at our input consoles on tiers around this globe, like Olympian gods or perhaps like so many personified signs of the Zodiac brooding down upon a world. As do the Pangolins and Spidermen in their own stations. We are surveyed by Hoylish vid-eyes—tiny ornithopterous sensors flitting about like flies—for infringements of the Byzantine rules. The vid-eyes feed down by radio to a multiscreen in the harbor, watched by a Kraken amidst its other duties; Krakens have a pretty awesome channel capacity for information.

A million dots, red, white, and green, pulse in the viewing globe: the placement of the Kraken players skirmishing and wrestling notionally in the seas of Showdown—thickening, thinning, pincering, probing, massing into arabesque formations, three-dimensional patterns which my pre-hypnoed brain almost, but never quite, grasps.

I sit on tier three, above the eastern quadrant of the Northern Hemisphere, scanning my pieces. Real-time play is fairly slow, but not as slow as I'd imagined—and far subtler. By the rules, we aren't allowed a pattern-seeking computer.

This is all a terrible fantasy! Krakens have no power over us—apart from the addictive compulsion of the Game—yet here we are ceding chunks of real estate in our own solar system eighteen light years away. And if we renege or back out we'll cause a war that could wipe out one, two, or three species—and reap the whirlwind of that war ourselves. Yet if we go on playing, the Spidermen or Pangolins—or the Krakens as stakeholders—will some day *own* us, in some abstract way. And one day they may, just may, come to collect. Which, of course, they won't succeed in doing—because the whole idea is ludicrous—yet a splinter will have entered our souls once more: the splinter of defense, of the military.

All we know is that if someone from the other side of the world steps into your backyard and says "I own it," however ridiculous this is, fierce ancient territorial reactions are going to be triggered, subtly altering the parameters of human society for the worse. Once you start building precautionary Highspace warships you might just start using them. How indeed do you train a military arm—unmilitaristically? Whence comes their *esprit de corps?*

Time to begin reinforcing a salient . . .

"Player Cortina," I voice into the record. "Am staking zone two of Io, moon of Jupiter." Much good may it do them to win part of Io, a moon they knew nothing of . . . until our first expedition blithely told them of all the moons and worlds we hold. I have to stake rather a lot of Io on a trivial move because Io is so bloody useless and dangerous. I could stake a couple of square klicks of Earth, instead; but WorldGov won't let us.

"Rosamundi?"

Euclid, of course changed hands—and captains too—when we

relieved the previous team. Another helpful rule. So here is Captain Wang, and Rosamundi Bjornson too. Rosamundi and I have time for a little gossip—overheard by a roving vid-eye—as we snatch an automated meal . . .

"Mr. Cortina?"

(*I love you. I'm your wild card. I'm the joker who jumped into your pack from the void* . . . Do I really love you? It's madness! I've merely imprinted on you, like a duckling newly hatched from the egg of my survival capsule . . .)

"Is this *travel?* I haven't even *seen* a Pangolin or a Spiderman except on screens—and I daren't go down to see the Krakens! We're on the outside—utterly on the outside of things. We're outsiders! Locked up *inside* this station like some kind of topological joke—in a goldfish bowl rotated through Highspace so that the outside is the inside."

She watches me circumspectly. Is the goldfish bowl of my own mind cracking? Is water dripping down my face? No, it's just sweat, that's all. A sweat of love.

"I wonder whether there could be some higher arbitrating power in the universe—some court of cosmic appeal—that could conceivably rule in favor of the Pangolins or whoever is owning Luna? Some superbeing that could swoop down out of the Magellanic Clouds and hand over the title deeds? Having first written them, of course!" The notion of title deeds to moons and worlds so amuses me that it is only with difficulty that I avoid breaking up.

Rosamundi eyes me warily. "Consider, Mr. Cortina—"

"Victor, please, call me Victor."

"Actually, Mr. Cortina, as you might have guessed by now your first name is one reason why Wang kept you on the *Euclid*. Gamblers need a spot of luck. What better luck than stumbling upon a man named Victor in the middle of the void? But it's such bad luck to articulate your luck, don't you think? Like telling a wish when you snap the wishbone. So I think I'll call you Mr. Cortina, if you don't mind."

"So I'm just a mascot." (Bitterly—full of self-pity.)

She shrugs. "Also a player. Now consider: we have no idea how the Krakens achieved their twin role of umpires and pieces in the Game. Their culture—if that's the word for it—is hidden by miles of water. We don't even *know*, Mr. Cortina, that the state of play represented in the view-tanks bears any relation to what the Krakens themselves are actually doing! Are one million Krakens *really* cruising the ocean at all those co-ordinates, or are they just simulating it? Perhaps they really *are* devious superintelligences."

(Ah, your bright red hair, Rosamundi! The blood courses through my veins when I see you. And you cannot call me intimately by my name, or it would spoil our luck!)

She fans her hands: a hand of cards. Long slender tactile fingers . . . they will never touch me. She wears several synthdiamond rings, and nailpaint the same color as her hair. Red diamond fingers, a suit of ten. Unheartlike fingers. Heartless.

"They may be stakeholders—but they can't set a tentacle on dead, dry Jackpot."

"Maybe it's like the collector who has his treasures locked up in a bank vault which he never visits? He knows he owns them. He masturbates over the knowledge. The knowledge is important, that's all. The fact that the Pangolins and Spidermen *seem* to be the territory-collectors is the really clever part. They aren't, no matter what the state of play seems to be. They're both on a winning streak. But in the end the bank always wins. They've banked Jackpot and Janus. Maybe in the end they'll have to start staking bits of Flush and Straight, then the whole damn shebang."

"It doesn't sound like superintelligent conduct to me. It sounds plain dumb."

"No doubt a rabbit watching a human being swing a golf club to wham a little ball into a hole would think it was pretty dumb, if it could think so much. But actually, compared to the rabbit's 'sensible' activities, the golfer is superintelligent—in a context of ritual behavior. Who knows how the superintelligent might amuse themselves?"

I nod at the hovering vid-eye. "Maybe they amuse themselves by watching us try to figure this out? What does WorldGov think of the superintelligence idea?"

"Not much. They're mainly worried about us triggering war and genocide—and the aftermath. Plus the slight nuisance of bunches of aliens nominally owning bits of the solar system."

"The Game's hollow. Hollow," I moan. (Moans of love for Rosamundi, whose diamonds trump my heart.)

She pats my hand—at last! "It gets to us all. But we have to persevere."

The vid-eye loses interest in us and drifts away, disappearing through an air duct.

Yes, the game is hollow—but nobody has ever played it *from the inside of the hollow!*

Down to the Games Room go I, awakened by buzzer, haunted by hollowness, unfulfilled by Rosamundi's love. I shall do something grand—a knight tilting at a dragon. I am holding a black box.

I clap my hands for attention.

"I've decided to play *inside* the sphere. I'm going to roll a viewtank out of the assembly and operate my pieces from inside." Modestly, I display my black box. "I want to see the state of play from inside out."

"That's a bright idea," says Wang. "In fact, that is one hell of an original idea. But—"

"If you're worried about the isolation factor, I already spent nine months playing solitaire in a pod that was pretty much like a sense-dep tank by the end of the experience!"

Matsumoto, the second officer—a black belt or something in Go—searches his hypno-memories of the rules. "There does seem to be a loophole here."

"Sure there's a loophole," I grin. "It's in the center of this viewsphere, that's where."

There is even a round of applause. Of course, I haven't told them the second part of my plan . . .

Around me the viewtanks of the waterworld, now concave, scintillate with a million sparks of red, white, and blue. My chair swivels, rocks, powers up and down. My own particular screen is tagged with gold tape to remind me which it is.

I'm in the survival pod again, alone in the void, playing for my sanity. But not *quite* alone: a vid-eye hovers, ornithopterically, behind me—always keeping behind me. A guy could go crazy locked in a room with a fly. But this is a discreet fly. It keeps out of the way and never buzzes, though I fancy—I fancy—it is inching closer to the back of my head.

I scan the pattern in all directions. Damn it, I still need eyes in the back of my head.

"Player Cortina," I voice into the record. I rap out a whole series of plays, to build my network of Kraken-pieces (if they're there at all, at the co-ordinates!). "Am staking subcrustal Luna, 5 klicks to 10 klicks depth."

"Hey," cries my earphone, "we've already *lost* Luna, dummy."

"Can't you hear? I'm staking *subcrustal* Luna. We've lost the surface, but who says we've lost the interior?"

Somebody is scrabbling at the outside of the tanks. I see the ghostly shape undulating through the sparks of play, like the shadow of a Kraken rolling in the depths.

"*Reminder!*" comes a synthesized umpire voice. "*No player may be removed during the course of the Game by force majeure."*

The scrabbling ceases.

And my pieces begin to shift position ever so slowly in the tank, jetting streamlined through the sea at three or four hundred klicks per hour. The Krakens have accepted my stake. It's all legit. Looney legitimate! You can stake the insides of worlds. This is a whole new dimension indeed!

Rosamundi purrs in my earphone. "Mr. Cortina . . . *Victor*, you must stop. This is a very delicately balanced game. You've just unbalanced it almightily. That isn't *fair*." So the fair Rosamundi appeals to my better nature, does she?

I swing round in my seat, rocking it up and down in a sine curve like a satellite track orbiting the interior of a world rather than the space around it.

"You've destroyed the whole rationale of the Game, Victor. Perhaps you can withdraw your moves and your stake, if you appeal to the umpires personally?"

Actually, I am on the point of winning us back a few million square klicks of the *surface* of the Moon. I'm Victor, after all.

Wang's voice cuts in. "The Pangolins and the Spidermen have both just protested most hotly. The Game is about territory. They can't occupy stretches of the *interior* of Jackpot."

"The Krakens are allowing it!"

"Because it's never arisen. Only a madman would think of . . . I'm sorry, Mr. Cortina, I take that back."

"If not a madman, then a genius?"

"If you like. But listen, this is a conflict-*prevention* game. *Please* request your moves and stakes withdrawn."

"I'll discuss it with the Krakens. That's all."

"Good man," coos Rosamundi.

I push a blue button, which lights up—interfacing through Hoylish equipment down to the lightshow in the harbor.

"Umpires, I am staking *interior* surfaces. Please confirm that this is permissible?"

There is silence for a while. Then I get my synthvoice reply.

"It is permissible, because it is not specifically prohibited. But to compensate for your internalization of the Game, you must now provide a corresponding externalization capacity for the other competitors. You have opened a gateway to the insides of worlds; now you must open a gateway to what lies outside of the space occupied by worlds. For the sake of balance you must provide an entrée into Highspace for the other competitors."

"*What?*"

"This, upon penalty of forfeiting the entire planetary surface of the Earth. You will still, of course, retain the interior below a depth of five kilometres."

The blue button winks out.

There's a lot of shouting outside the sphere of viewtanks now. Shouting for my blood. My God, they sound as though they've gone berserk out there. We don't really *have* to forfeit the Earth . . . I mean, it's all a game. I think I'll let them cool down for an hour or so. Or would it be better to get it over with soon? Before positions get hardened?

Of course, WorldGov expressly prohibits the export of Highspace travel technology. So Captain Wang has little choice in the matter. Now the Earth is gone, from shore to shining shore. Down to a depth of five kilometers. (Do we still own the Marianas Trench and the Tuscorara Deep? No. The five klick depth follows the contour lines of the solid surface.)

I was pretty worried when I emerged, into the midst of the lynch mob. Even dear Rosamundi was baying.

Court martial me and shoot me? Tear me limb from limb? Neither of these. Worse, far worse. They *have* all gone insane.

"Five years' work ruined!" Wang screamed at me. "By a piece

of void flotsam!" They don't care about any umpire penalty now, for removing a team member. Not with the Earth gone.

I still wouldn't have believed it possible.

They're going to sacrifice me—to the Krakens. They're going to feed me to them.

And they proceed to do it.

Two robos hustle me out naked, bar a loincloth and an air pressure mask, from the Station and frog-march me to the edge of the cliff. A third robo abseils down the face of the cliff, twenty, thirty metres. And I am lowered, to a tiny ledge. My ankle is chained to a ring, driven into the rock. If I try to bend over to test the strength of the chain I'll tumble headlong. Either the chain will snap, dropping me into the harbor, or I'll hang here upside-down.

The robo abseiler doesn't make it back to the top. It falls past me, narrowly missing dislodging me, and splashes into the waters where the great shapes lurk, alerting them. I'm sure its fall wasn't deliberately contrived. I'm sure my dear friends would prefer me to have to wait a long time at this dizzy height—time to brood upon my crime—sunburnt by Hoyle, staring madly at the blue horizon or else squinting down my nakedness towards the pack of living submarines with their long, long suckery flails wafting like anemone tentacles far below.

Presently one tentacle quests upwards, higher and higher. It fumbles at the outcrops and ledges, feeling along them. Another tentacle follows it up. A third. A fourth. All six. Oh God, oh cosmic meta-intelligences (if there are any of you), save me.

The Kraken's head breaks surface. Its purple eyes squint upwards. Can it see me, up here in the air? Between its suckers is a maw, a black hole.

The tip of the first tentacle reaches my ankle. Wavering, it creeps up my leg.

I suppose I scream and scream and kick and try to tear free, heedless of falling. The tentacle loops around my chest. It holds me firm. A second tentacle probes my ankle, then the chain. It tears the ring piton out of the rock. My knees buckle.

And I am hoisted out from the cliff. I am borne down towards the water, towards the purple eyes, the maw. The Kraken's mantle is phosphorescing wildly across the spectrum, underwater and above too. It sings a color song of appetite.

Coiling back, the tentacle holds me up before its eyes. The purple ovals stare at me. Oh let it bite my head off! Let this be a fast death. Anything but slowly stifling and dissolving in its stomach, in the darkness.

Suddenly it whisks me up and away from its maw. The tentacle bears me higher, higher, up through the air! Another tentacle snakes up alongside it, wavering beside me.

Extending incredibly, it hoists me over the lip of the cliff and sets me down on my bare feet. The crushing coil around my chest ... slackens. It frees me. It whips away. The second tentacle hovers above me briefly. Very gently it pats me on the head—the way you pat a puppy.

I stumble back to the station—where else can I go?—highly unsure of my reception.

But Rosamundi meets me on the other side of the pressure doors and throws a towel around me, as though I am a racehorse back from a brisk canter.

The others are waiting for me. Perhaps shame-faced is too strong a word. A sense of chagrin shows, let's say.

After glancing around to confirm that, for once, there is no vid-eye about, Captain Wang breaks the ice—as though he has not just recently allowed his crew to hang me up as bait.

"You'll never guess what friend Kraken pulsed while he was hoisting you, Mr. Cortina."

"I don't suppose I will. I don't think I'll *guess* anything ever again, Captain. Do we have to play guessing games now?"

"He—or she, or it—said this. Quite poetic, but maybe that's in the translation . . .

'A ripple in the water;
'A man upon the cliff—
'Redemption.
'The offer of his own self
'To pass within my self
'Erases the internalizing of the Game.
'Now Earth is other than a stake.
'Play resumes, at the earlier stage.
'Thank you.' "

"I wonder how they can have the concept of honorable sacrifice?" asks Matsumoto.

"Ah, they don't really," says Wang. "They have a sense of symmetry. It thought that Cortina sacrificed himself *symmetrically*. Inside the Kraken's belly, to balance the insides of worlds. Two insides cancel out. I suppose swimmers in deep seas need a deep sense of symmetry in three dimensions. Pressures within, pressures without, and so on. It's what the whole Game's really about—balancing off. Flush against Straight. I suppose we represent a three-body problem for the Game . . . Which corresponds to something very basic to the Krakens' minds. The Krakens are our pieces? Hell, no, we're *their* pieces. I've suspected for a while that Flush and Straight have both *won* the Game, maybe many times—and started playing all over again. Obsessively. Best of three. Best of five. Or the Krakens slid them into a new game without their being able to realize it, by right of umpire! The Krakens don't want Earth or Luna or anywhere, for themselves or for their players. They want symmetry. We're their poem, their song. Their art form. As are the Pangolins and Spidermen."

"It must have been bloody boring for them before Flush and Straight achieved space travel!" say I.

"Isn't it odd, though," remarks Wang icily, "that the Spiders and the Pangolins are both six-limbed creatures? Who would dream up intelligent land dwellers with six limbs, except something that had six limbs itself? Six tentacles, for example. They'd expect there'd be a terrible fuss balancing on less than four legs —if they'd never seen it done."

A chill descends on the room. "Wouldn't it be a very singular situation," he continues, "if the Krakens had *designed* the Spiders and Pangolins, with a genetic vector to come to Showdown to play the Game? And continue playing it?"

I can see the flaw in that. "The Krakens would have needed space travel. A marine species can't have space travel. They can't *build* things. Anything."

"Then how can the Krakens conceive the heavens at all? Stars and moons and worlds ought to be meaningless to them. Maybe there's some other way through space. Some other way of establishing connections between space-time loci . . . If you brood about it long enough. If you play games with networks, spatial patterns, dimensions." Wang waves his hand in the direction of the Games Room. "Speaking of which, enough of this intermission. We're getting seriously behind. Mr. Cortina, kindly resume your place. And the rest of you."

"What! But just an hour ago—!"

"I hope it has been a salutary lesson. At least all is well again. You have undone the harm you caused. I think I shall reward you. After our tour of duty, I will recommend your secondment for a second tour."

But today, only twenty-four E-hours later, a Highspace signal from WorldGov informs Wang and all of us that a fleet of giant squidlike creatures is cruising the Pacific Ocean of Earth east of

Australia. These bear a startling resemblance to the Krakens of Showdown. Some of them seem to be sick from the salinity of the terrestrial water, but they forge ahead regardless. WorldGov is most uncertain what to do about them. If they *are* Krakens, how did they get to Earth except through some dimensional gateway of their own devising deep in their own ocean... a gateway devised by superintelligence? Does one argue with superintelligence?

At least *I* know what the Krakens are doing.

Earth isn't a stake any longer. Earth is a new gamesboard.

The Krakens are surveying their new board.

Author's Note
The planetary system in this story was devised by Harry Stubbs (Hal Clement) for the Galileo's Worlds *project, and is used with grateful acknowledgement.*

INEXPLICABLE

IAN WATSON

In 1979 Cutty Sark Scotch Whisky, in association with *New Scientist* magazine, offered a prize of £1,000 for the best "scientific paper" on any aspect of the UFO phenomenon—as well as a prize of £1,000,000 to anyone who could produce any artefact acceptable to the Science Museum in London as of demonstrable alien manufacture. The winning essay was a predictably sceptical assessment of Ufology. This was my attempt to win a million Pounds...

UFOs, Science, and the Inexplicable

The notion of a 'scientific paper' on the UFO phenomenon begs a couple of important questions. Firstly, we're to suppose that this phenomenon will yield to scientific investigation as generally understood. We're to suppose that the evidence can be collected, sifted and analysed to yield an irreducible core of data (or even no authentic data at all, in which case success comes early!) and a hypothesis developed which will succeed in 'explaining' the phenomenon and even perhaps provide grounds for experimental or observational verification.

One can imagine a number of excellent scientific papers, and one could even write these—though they would be rather like reviews of imaginary books. Here is the meteorological explanation, or the plasma cloud explanation. Here is the antimatter particle explanation. Here, even, is the explanation in terms of actual alien spacecraft powered by gravitational field inducers which produce ionisation effects. When even the BBC nature programme *The Living World* chips in with its own hypothesis (namely, clouds of bud-worm moths) it's obvious that everybody can see the matter quite clearly from their own special angle—no less so the 'alien spacecraft' aficionados, though since their own particular obsession lies outside the bounds of current conceivable technology to explain the data they must extrapolate or invent a possible future technology and attendant scientific theories of gravity, space-time, lightspeed constraints. (Yet why not indeed, when one can talk blithely on the fringes of 'real' science—as does Adrian Berry in *The Iron Sun*—of diving our starships through the midst of toroidal black holes?)

Obviously, if we don't provide an explanation of this order—whether it be bud-worm moths or gravity drives—can what we are suggesting be rightly labelled 'scientific'? Science, as we all know, strives to explain things. Science unravels the DNA; it takes us back to the first microseconds of the Big Bang; it analyses the basis of matter as a dynamic interplay of quarks and gluons. Some day science will explain everything, and already we know the right sort of questions to pose. It's our scientific duty to explain this phenomenon too.

But—and here the second question is begged—does science really operate this way? As physicist Geoffrey Chew has pointed out (" 'Bootstrap': A Scientific Idea?" in *Science*, 23 August 1968), the whole history of scientific endeavour is one of an increasingly close approximation to the 'truth'. The number of *a priori* concepts embedded in scientific theories may certainly lessen as time goes by, yet *a priori* concepts as such—something taken for granted; some unquestioned framework—are essential to science as we understand it. All natural phenomena are ultimately interconnected, yet science only works by a partial approach—provided, of course, that the part currently being ignored is sufficiently small for the partial approach to work. Thus we have today a cosmology that ignores quantum effects, a particle physics that ignores gravitation, a natural science that ignores the mechanism underlying consciousness; and so on. "Semantically," as Chew says, "an attempt to explain all concepts can hardly be called 'scientific'. " May we presume that one day the *a priori*, taken-for-granted elements will diminish to zero by scientific attrition? Not so. For a 'total self-consistency' approach would inevitably involve the concept of observation and thus the enigma of consciousness itself—and it would thus move outside physics into a domain "that will not even be describable as 'scientific'. " Capra concludes thus, too, at the end of his book *The Tao of Physics* when he declares that we will one day move beyond a 'theory' to a 'vision' of Nature—and this isn't something that is definable along the rational, analytical lines of science as we know it.

How about making a start on the groundwork for this 'vision of Nature' now? For it happens that the two questions which are begged may in fact answer one another. The necessary incompleteness of scientific method and the unidentifiability of the UFO phenomenon may perhaps be brought together fruitfully in a new approach which does not so much seek to 'solve' the UFO problem as to use it as a probe into the necessary incompleteness of our approach to physical reality—an approach, moreover, which draws into the equation a theory of that consciousness which, in the long run, must be 'bootstrapped' into our understanding of the nature of reality.

How to proceed? One sure feature of the UFO phenomenon is its unidentifiability. Another is its ubiquity. Here, we must side with the 'revisionist' Ufologists (such as Jacques Vallée, Aimé Michel, or a recent addition to their ranks, Bertrand Méheust). We aren't simply talking about 'flying saucers'—

apparently alien craft—which have been buzzing around the Earth and even landing on it since 1947 or so. We're also talking about the rash of phantom rockets seen over Scandinavia in the Thirties. We're talking about the dirigibles observed over the Middle West of America in the 1890s—sightings all of craft that were conceivable within the 'belief structure' of their period, yet which were technologically somewhat outside of it. We're also talking about flying ships that snagged their anchors in church steeples in the Middle Ages and aerial battles witnessed then—events outside of normal reality yet compatible with the belief structures of the time.

We're also talking about the menagerie of Ufonauts reported by UFO contactees, people who prove under hypnosis to have sincerely experienced something. We're also talking about the structurally similar encounters with fairy folk—who abduct, as do the Ufonauts; who promise great things then cheat and hoodwink, just as the Ufonauts offer evidence which evaporates into trash and nonsense. We're talking about a phenomenon with many guises—sedulously adapting itself to the belief structure of the time, which today in our consensus world of CETI and space travel presents itself in terms of alien visitors from the stars.

We're talking about a phenomenon which has been collectively experienced—mutating sociologically—for a very long time, and which is thus of the psyche, yet which is also of the objective physical world since it leaves actual traces such as radiation burns, marks in the soil, or blips on radar screens. We're talking about a phenomenon which bridges 'reality' and the consciousness that structures reality for us. In so doing, it questions what existence is: what the relationship might be between consciousness and reality.

A fascinating analysis of the problem appears in Méheust's (as yet untranslated) *Science Fiction et Soucoupes Volantes*—which I am happy to cite since I arrived at some of the same ideas and extrapolations beyond them independently in the course of writing a novel on the UFO theme entitled *Miracle Visitors*. Méheust's unique contribution to the debate is his proof, from a dedicated dredging of pulp fiction of the past 100 years, that exact details of UFO phenomenology and exact experiences of contactees have been prefigured by obscure SF romancers years before they took place 'in reality', in Brazil or wherever, to people who could have had no access to the long-forgotten 'originals'. These filter through into the phenomenon, as per text. But from what do they filter?

Méheust favours the idea of an "objective mythical web" which organises, in the domain of reality, UFO events and in the mythic, psychic domain organises the preferred imagery from which the fictional tales arose. He relates this back to the archaic substratum of human thought from which arises dream imagery and likewise the transmutational symbolism of alchemy so aptly analysed by Jung.

Jung insists in *Psychology and Alchemy* that a 'symbolism as rich as that of alchemy invariably owes its existence to some adequate cause, never to mere whim or play of fancy.' The alchemist 'projects' his inaccessible unconscious—with which he is striving for union—upon the objective world (upon his retorts and alembics and chemicals) which will simultaneously validate his projection for him, and deny it ultimate proof since it is only a projection. Rumours of success abound, of course. Like the UFO contactee, the alchemist is widely known to have succeeded, but no one can prove it.

Yet alchemy was 'only' a projection. What are we to make, then, of the objective evidence left over by UFO events? The answer to this takes us even further into the process of projection of unconscious forces onto the outside world—to a zone where the observer actually modifies reality, or more exactly where a symbiotic interplay occurs affecting both domains.

As Méheust shows, UFOs do obey rules. Hard evidence and duration of sightings vary inversely with the possibility that observers can get close enough to pin them down. 'Holes of impunity' would seem to be known to them in advance. Yet they continue to show themselves, and it has been demonstrated statistically (by the astrophysicist Poher) that the observing consciousness is 'necessary' to them.

Impossibility of proof, coupled with ostentatious intrusions, is therefore an essential characteristic. What scientific theory can tackle this inherent indefinability?

We may genuflect here to Kurt Gödel with his proof that the axioms of a particular system cannot all, by definition, be validated within the terms of that system. A metasystem is required; but it too will carry its own inbuilt logical restriction. We may nod at Geoffrey Chew with his statement about the necessarily partial nature of science.

Yet an avenue is open by which we can approach this particular psychophysical enigma—not from the mystical side, though there are techniques there, in Sufi thought particularly—but closer to our rational scientific paradigm: namely in a discipline that is in its own (highly fashionable) infancy—the study of altered states of consciousness, or transpersonal psychology.

American psychologist Charles Tart is the pioneer in this field, and in his *States of Consciousness* he sets the groundwork for the analysis of discrete states of mind which diverge from ordinary baseline consciousness (in which we normally operate and where, perforce, we perform the work of science—*pace* the dream discovery of the structure of Benzene by Kekule). These are states of mind which are wholly 'irrational' and aberrant from the viewpoint of baseline consciousness, yet which possess an internal consistency and coherent logic *while one is within them*. What Tart hopes to develop is a method for working *within* these states rather than, as heretofore, from without them objectively. A means may exist since there may be overlaps between some of the mental structures of one ASC (Altered State of Consciousness) and those of another: between, say, certain trance conditions under deep hypnosis, and certain structures within an LSD experience; or between mystical apprehension and, say, ethyl alcohol intoxication. A stepladder of intersecting states can perhaps be erected—and thus a reportability achieved across the psychic boundaries, so that the investigator can bring genuine internal information back to the baseline.

I would suggest (as indeed I do in my novel *Miracle Visitors*) that here is a potential way to tap into this UFO phenomenon which is partly of objective reality and partly of the psyche. Let us suppose that there exists a hitherto unrecognized ASC which I shall term 'UFO-consciousness'. This is an ASC in which UFO experiences—of sightings, landings, contact with 'aliens', abduction by them, instruction by them—occurs. It is an ASC that is very far from ordinary baseline consciousness, yet it is one into which we can—as yet inadvertently, yet often collectively—transit. Let us probe its boundary conditions and internal structure by 'states of consciousness' techniques, and it may become one into which we can *experimentally* transit, even though its validity will necessarily remain suspect in baseline terms—just as mystical apprehension does.

UFO-consciousness is an ASC, I believe, which is tied into the roots of our cognition—our 'construction' of reality, and thus the roots of the world as we can possibly conceive it. We exist in a participatory universe which is as it is because we are here to observe it, and in it the activity of the experimenter must have an actual physical effect upon the reality under investigation and can never be divorced from it. So that we here enter an area of exploration of the actual intersection of mind and reality which, in the case of UFO events, is upon a macroscopic rather than upon a microscopic scale.

Might there be a *reason* for UFO events—along with their insistence coupled with their observational impunity? Perhaps higher orders of consciousness—reflecting, as they evolve, a more precise convergence upon an understanding of the universe—evolve *because* of the 'suction' of the psychophysical unidentifiability which is embodied in UFO manifestations? Maybe here is the hint of an evolutionary dynamic towards higher orders of awareness?

If it is true that reality cannot wholly be known to any discrete level of consciousness, then this fact may well be reflected in our own psychic structures which have evolved within this reality—as indeed it is in the fact that consciousness arises from preconscious psychic structures which, by virtue of being unconscious, cannot come within the domain of conscious scrutiny. And yet unconscious structures project themselves upon the outside world constantly, in a dynamic aimed—in Jungian terms—at reintegration. Just as, in mystical or theological terms, the universe represents a separation of a 'God' from Himself—a theme which accurately projects our own psychic dilemma.

And yet the UFO phenomenon cannot consist solely of projection, since evidence (of an elusive nature!) is indeed forthcoming. UFO events may then be, not merely a key to the evolution of our own psychic structures, but also to the 'transscientific' problem (in Chew and Capra) of the actual interplay of mind and reality.

If techniques of ASC research can be developed to embrace the psychophysical zone that I have called 'UFO-consciousness', then here—without prejudice to my point about inherent unprovability—is an idea that is potentially testable. If we could set up experimental conditions to transit into, evoke and explore UFO-consciousness, to be flippant for a moment, then one could even win £1,000,000 from Cutty Sark by producing a demonstrably alien artefact—summoning it, as it were, into existence.

Only it would not be an alien artefact—it would be something far stranger. This will not be a research area that can be tackled from baseline consciousness—in the way that UFO 'research' has been so far. It will have to be undertaken somewhere up the 'transit ladder' from baseline consciousness to UFO-consciousness, within the logic structure of the latter state. However, the tools for thinking about this project do exist, and it may bring us one step closer to Capra's 'vision of Nature', as well as one step closer to our psychic reintegration with the hidden areas in ourselves.

It would be a scientific enterprise necessarily leading outside of 'science'. It would be a psychological exploration that would lead beyond the individual mind. It would not be an enterprise that could 'succeed' in the sense of nailing down once and for all the will-o'-the-wisp of the UFO. It would, however, open a door into a possible future science of transpsychic reality, one that would integrate and subsume so much that has eluded us, yet constantly nagged at us too, like a toothache. It would be a genuine way, available to us all as we are here and now, of thinking about the unthinkable (what a pity that Kahn captured this phrase for his megadeath scenarios), and operating within the inexplicable—not 'explaining' it, but envisioning it and reporting back, as the benighted contactees who are snatched up for a 'saucer flight' report back, but this time with our eyes open, aware where we have actually been.

In *Broca's Brain*, Carl Sagan speculates as to whether all our theories of the origin of the universe have psychological roots in how we ourselves are born, as human beings. So what cosmology would sapient kangaroos—who crawl almost embryonically from birth canal to pouch—conceive of . . . ?

Horrorscope

"Your partner is pregnant," observed the Kangaroid officer. She looked extraordinarily pregnant herself. But then, from out of her pouch, poked a smaller replica of her own head. Its little face twitched and sniffed and blinked at the swollen alien human being, searching for the slit across the belly where she must surely keep her infant child. Its eyes focused on her navel—like the little, plugged crater of a volcano under pressure; and it wondered.

Determined to expose her future offspring to all possible cosmic influences, the Lady Carla van der Woort only wore a glitter-dusted silver brassière and shorts and jewelled sandals. Her belly bulged hugely, resembling one of the domes of the observatory somewhere over the horizon out in the desert, well away from Sweetpouch Shuttleport.

"Do you engage in intercourse during pregnancy until the final moment? Do you thrust your shaft into the chamber of generation, to burst the waters of life? And has it ever been the case that a jealous sire has tried to prevent the emergence of his offspring by holding it in place with his penis?"

Jeff Lunaliho had been warned to expect such questions from aliens who were certainly not ill-informed but who might well feel mischievous, since he and the Lady Carla were not visiting their world as cosmo-seers but as tourists. Carla refrained from looking scandalised.

"The Lady isn't my partner," said Jeff. "I'm merely her hired escort and—"

"Chaperone?"

"And bodyguard, and general factotum and courier. And midwife."

"Ha!"

The Hawaiian rubbed his nose, to conceal a grin as he thought up a bastard *haiku*.

"And as for your impertinent questions, let me ask you this:
May the universe not be
An explosive hernia,
Erupting from the intestines of Eternity?"

"Ha! Very good. I appreciate." The Kangaroid thumped her tail on the floor.

But this particular alien officer was only Immigration & Customs—with the accent seemingly more on customs pertaining to birth, copulation and afterbirth. She had paid scant attention to their matching synth-crocodile luggage or to Jeff's black surgical bag. No doubt he and the Lady Carla would meet stiffer challenges presently, if she was to succeed in her mega-rich, zany dream.

The Kangaroid dictated whimsically into the desk computer's microphone:

"Lady in silver bikini, plus eight-and-a-half month foetus contained internally on bio life support system. Accompanied by burly cloned servant, wearing floral shirt and chastity codpiece—"

Jeff grinned openly.

"I'll have you know that these are *lederhosen*, made of finest imitation Wallaby hide. And I'm not a clone. I'm a direct lineal descendant of William C. Lunaliho who won the first election as King of Hawaii, but unhappily died of consumption thirteen months later—"

"Due to over-indulgence at his celebration feast," dictated the Kangaroid. "Purpose of visit?"

"To have my child born at the confluence of theories of the universe," said Lady Carla, airily. "I am a devotee of astrology, so therefore—"

"Shhhh!"

"Really, Lunaliho—you whose name encompasses the Moon, encouraging me to employ you on my journey from the sublunary into the supralunary sphere!—"

"Not in Hawaiian it doesn't. 'Luna' means a plantation foreman."

"Why did you never tell me that before?"

"You never asked, my Lady."

"It doesn't matter. The Moon you are to me, with your round cheese face. Now really, Luna, having successfully come all this way—"

"Just don't blow it, on the wrong side of Immigration."

"Have you two quite finished quarrelling, like frustrates during a year-long menstruation? Yes? Good. I'm not stupid, you know, and as it happens I can help you, in return for a certain you-know-what."

The Kangaroid typed enquiries and scanned its screen. Suddenly she shadow-boxed the air in satisfaction, while Jeff hastily interposed his bulk between the flashing furry fists and the Lady Carla's belly.

"You came here to have your baby born in a significant locus, my Lady." (Now that the official was soliciting a bribe, she was slightly more polite.) "Now of course this is all nonsense to me—I mean, your primary fantasy about the positions of the stars and planets at birth. I apologize for my obtuseness in not appreciating the rationale for it. And you indeed must share some of my scepticism, since here you are light years distant from your home worlds, and all the constellations are entirely different. But you have had a bright idea."

"Kind of you to say so," said Carla icily.

"This world is Thraith, home of the Interspecies Institute of Comparable Biocosmology."

"Comparative," Jeff corrected her. "And we *did* look at our tickets."

"No: Comparable. Some cosmologies are comparable, whilst others are incomparable. Ours is particularly incomparable—beyond compare! Let me tell you about it. The embryo kangaroid is born prematurely. Heroically it toils, hand over fist, through the cold blinding light from birth canal to pouch—which is the second womb of warmth and darkness. Therefore the cosmos that we can best conceive of is one which begins with a whimper, certainly not with a Bang, when we ooze out with hardly any trouble at all into Radiation which is diffused everywhere equally in space. If we fail to enpouch ourselves in matter, we die of the radiation. But if we reach the Second Darkness, then how sweetly the universe springs into being subsequently! Translated into the math of higher physics this is represented by a cosmological equation of the form—"

Lady Carla fidgeted.

"I'll simplify. Look at it this way: it's just like the explosion of a nuclear weapon. The fission bomb goes off first, *pop*—but that's just child's play. But then the *implosion* of the fission reaction acts to ignite the fusion bomb—and the real business gets under way. Though this isn't a very gentle example, unless you happen to be a race of thermonuclear weapons, who breed by... but never mind." The Kangaroid's hands cupped the air. "Little bang, *out*; then a quick collapse back in again; then *whoosh*, the real universe gets under way."

"That's all very interesting," said Jeff, diplomatically. "But you'll realize that it's hard for the Lady having to stand around like this, after the shuttle trip down, and all. She's been on two-thirds gravity on the way out. She's within two weeks of giving birth."

"My apologies. So where were we? Ah yes: here you are on Thraith—where zodiacal signs and ruling planets shall not preside over your epochal birth-giving, determining the fortune and character of your child; but rather instead, whole *cosmologies*, whole universes as envisioned in mystical drug-recall of the uterine and natal state, by teams of alien cosmo-seers and metaphysicists out at the observatories in the Desert of Gesh. Out there, where one observes not so much the galaxies themselves, as the foetal gestation of thought concerning Cosmos! You intend, in a word, not to choose the right stars for your child—but rather the best universe! A universe model for him or her, so that he or she becomes in turn the fornicatress Queen of Fornax, the Sculptor of Sculptor, the Strongman of Hercules—"

"Don't be ridiculous," interrupted Lady Carla. "It's just that—"

"Nay, these are mere clusters. But we are speaking of Cosmos itself! How about the Statesman of the Steady State . . . ?"

"It's just that, well, terrestrial astrological influences strike me as a shade *démodé*, for a child of mine. Here on Thraith is a focus of all the deepest thoughts about the birth *of the whole universe itself*. Here is where cosmo-seers decide what influences preside over the nativity of the Cosmos, determining the course of *everything*."

"Ah, but it all depends on the *means* of birth."

"My child," said Carla grandly, "will be born in all possible ways. He alone, or she alone, will grasp the whole. He, or she, will write the equation which spells reality. And when she, or he, casts horoscopes these will be the utter truth, a true foretelling."

"Hmm," said the Kangaroid. "You'll need a *laissez-passez* to the Observatories at Gesh. Idle curiosity or informed curiosity are alike amply satisfied by the guided tours, departing twice daily. But you, in a sense, wish to work there. Or at least," and the Kangaroid produced a noise midway between a sneeze and a whinny, which must have been a Kangaroid laugh, "or at least to *labour* there."

"I can pay a generous donation to the Institute," said Carla indignantly. "I was told this would be simple."

"Oh, the Institute is funded by whole worlds."

"I own worlds. Small ones, true."

"But you do need a rapid *entrée*, to one of the high cosmo-seers, if only to cut corners. As it happens, I know that a certain alien cosmo-seer is developing a research programme at this very moment—which involves presenting the foetuses of various species with the birth-experience of other quite alien species . . ."

"I had heard something about that. My agents, my informants . . . But the creature's name kept on escaping them."

"It's a touchy subject. Highly sensitive. You see, everyone's cosmogony is so basic and personal. It's like, well, sex. I happen to know the cosmo-seer's name and call-number." The Kangaroid said no more.

"Luna," said Carla gently.

Jeff reached into the pocket of his floral shirt.

"Slip it into my pouch," suggested the Kangaroid, idly examining the ceiling. "A gift to my child, as we say. That way, no one sees. It is taboo to see. The pouch is the sacred place of refuge."

A soft, wet nose nuzzled Jeff's fingers.

He tickled the infant Kangaroid; and it bit him sharply.

"I'm glad we paid the extra bribe," said Jeff. "It's always worth it to find out what kind of character you're going to have to deal with. No doubt you've heard of a pig in a poke."

"Would that be some Hawaiian banquet, such as where your noble ancestor over-indulged himself?"

"No, that's *kalua* pig: whole pig steamed in an underground oven." Jeff licked his lips. "You skin it, scrub it and shave it, then you rub it inside and outside with soy sauce and rock salt. Next you stuff it with red hot stones. Then you lower it down on chicken wire into a pit lined with banana leaves . . ."

The crimson desert sped by them, like an inflamed griddle plate; though actually it was rather cool out there—the eye was simply tricked, achingly, by the livid colour. Though the monorail car whispered almost silently, nevertheless the desert seemed to be putt-putt-putting, like a heart-beat amplified by a doctor's ear-trumpet. Jeff leaned closer to Lady Carla, alert for a moment, then relaxed. Inside her, the baby was cooking away nicely, ready to emerge sweet, fresh and succulent; though, unlike *kalua* pig, alive.

The sky was a perfect eggshell. A faint, tiny, irregular moon flew by from West to East: the egg-tooth of a chick tapping to crack its shell. The chick was invisible; only the tooth orbited overhead.

"Anyway," he said, "what a pig in a poke is, is a pig in a bag: you can't see what it looks like. Five legs, two heads, whatever. But *Haupt*-Seer the Unpronounceable is none of these. He is a colony of organisms that arise, God help me, by what is claimed to be spontaneous generation! Of course, being a man of Polynesian stock myself, I sympathize. Till the white missionary man hit our shores, we all quite happily believed that babies conceived themselves spontaneously. Sex had *nothing* to do with it. Sex was just fun. So we had lots of it. Captain Cook was quite amazed at how unreservedly a *wahine* opened her legs, if you'll pardon the expression. Alas, the facts are otherwise."

Lady Carla patted herself.

"I know."

"Mind you, we're all still in the womb in Hawaii. Those islands are one big womb. The Pacific Ocean is the amniotic fluid. No wonder there are no Hawaiian geniuses. We're expelled from Eden, straight back into Eden. In fact, we're so relaxed there's a law says you can lie down in the middle of the road, and the traffic has to wait till you get up again."

Carla pouted.

"I didn't hire you as a chatterbox, Luna. Will you please be quiet? We're getting closer. I'm trying to concentrate on the influences." And she stretched her belly forth, to gather these in. Like a neutrino detector, full of fluid.

The seventeenth observatory was the province of the *Haupt-Seer* (Unpronounceable) from Capella 1V: a social organism, or rather congregation of such organisms, resembling *in toto* a blue jellyfish the size of a small whale.

The Medusoid floated in several million gallons of saline solution, its physical needs attended to by a host of slave organisms tailored for each occasion. Some were free-floating tentacles resembling eels, others were nets and scoops. And several were androids of blue translucent flesh which clambered, dripping, out of the great pool in a caricature copy of whichever alien race the Medusoid found most handy at reading particular instruments in the adjoining laboratory—though these androids needed to return to their pool before too long, or they would begin to dry out and die. Humidity was high in the Capellan observatory, after the dry desert air; even so, once out of the parent amnion, these bodies would only last a matter of hours.

One of these lumps of slave-flesh slapped wetly across the tiled floor to greet the visitors from Earth. It wore the approximate shape of a human woman, who was no more attractive than the prehistoric Magdalenian Venus—no Mary Magdalen, she. Perhaps her shape was chosen out of courtesy. But equally this could have been intended as morphological satire.

Developing a mouth, the amorphous Magdalen addressed Jeff and Lady Carla in space pidgin.

"So, as I understand it," said Jeff briskly, after hearing her out, "what you're suggesting is to drug the Lady Carla and her bloodstream, placenta and foetus with tailored psychochemicals akin to the oxytocin hormone which induces labour. Thus she—but more importantly her child—will hallucinate coming into the world as a tiny, premature Kangaroid foetus rather than as a full-blown human baby. Then one of the Kentauran empaths will enter the baby's fledgling mind to examine the psycho-template of two natal cosmological models superimposed?"

"Yas, boss," said the sloppy Venus.

"Well, this isn't *quite* what the Lady had in mind. It isn't ambitious enough, you see? The Lady wishes to experience *all* known birth-cosmologies at once, so that her child is born under the influence of all the biological variations on the Cosmos known to the Institute. Can you fix it?"

In the pool, the Medusoid's tentacles seemed to quiver with excitement.

"We been working on dis now coupla years. The machines can whomp us up a cocktail, chop-chop. Fills us with curiosity, dis birth business. Us not being born, jus coming together in de Amnion Ocean of Capella. So we know dis Cosmos jus comes together too. Jus happens for no reason."

"But out of *what* does it happen?"

"Outa de fluid of eternity. Time is de sea. We's all made outa bits of Time dat turn inta matter."

"Can you include your own world-view in the, er, cocktail, noble *Haupt*-Sir?"

"Some of de psych-chemo-links dat attract us togeder? As our cells emerge, all over de sea? Couldn't dat be teratogenic? Misshape de foetus?"

"No problem. This human foetus is already fully formed, about to be born. Just you give it your own spontaneous coming-together experience, too."

"Okay, boss. So dat's fifty-two biocosmic birth experiences, programming da view of de cosmos, divided into a dozen main types."

"Fifty-two weeks, and twelve zodiacal signs!" exclaimed Carla. "How perfectly horoscopic! I knew we were right to come here." She went so far in her enthusiasm as to squeeze Jeff's hand.

The Venus observed them, meltingly, then slopped back towards the pool.

The Medusoid also 'whomped up' a team of jelly-blue nurses for the delivery. *Wet nurses*, thought Jeff as he presided, noticing how they tended to ooze and drip.

A large space had been cleared for the birth-bed in the laboratory. Even so, this was crowded with alien observers and mechanical extensions from other observatories, since the Medusoid had invited its colleagues as though to a vernissage.

There was considerable tension in the air, as though today something crucial to all intelligences in the travelled galaxy was about to be demonstrated or refuted. Certainly it might also represent something important to the fortunes and funding of the Institute on Traith; something, too, whereby the Medusoid *Haupt*-Seer gained much status, or else was shamed in the eyes of its peers—if not in its own eyes. The Medusoid always had sufficient blue slave jelly-eyes in attendance, ready to dote on it. When one pair of eyes grew bleary, it could always conjure up a new pair.

Amidst the Kangaroids, Avoids, Arachnoids, Batrachoids and others, one anthropoid observer was present in the person of the *Haupt*-Seer Marcus Desmond-Campbell. A firm proponent of the standard Big Bang Cosmos, his skull still bore the faintest grooves from the surgical forceps which had assisted his own cork-in-the-bottle delivery. Till now, he had refrained from comment.

The Kentauran empath, Chlippa, was an Avoid and thus inclined by nature towards one particular Cosmic Egg model of the universe. Yet Chlippa was broad-minded enough to digest other viewpoints, no matter how eccentric. Kentauran empaths were invaluable in the presentation of evidence uncovered at the Institute. They were the psychic translators of those deeply held, yet biologically biassed, preconceptions which in the past had generated whole towering structures of scientific theory that proved on later analysis to have their foundations firmly rooted in the birth canal. Or the egg-shell. Or the amnion. Or the pouch.

The Lady Carla writhed in confusion on the birth-bed, while a jelly-nurse ineffectually mopped her brow.

She was giving birth to a human baby, she was breaching a Delphoid into warm water, she was laying an egg, she was oozing the merest slip of a foetus as though in a miscarriage, she was venting strings of Batrachoid spawn, she was . . .

She cried out, she croaked, she gurgled, she whistled, she clucked . . .

Jeff inspected her actual dilation.

Now the head was presenting nicely.

Chlippa stood beside Jeff, her eyes shut by her nictitating membranes, her wings rustling faintly to ventilate herself.

Meanwhile the baby—which sported a thatch of wet black fuzz—was no doubt being born as a human child, and slipping out as a Kangaroid, and pecking its way out of the shell, and chewing its way through a membrane, and spontaneously combining with itself...

Easing out the spindly legs, Jeff held... *him* up.

"It's a boy, Carla! It's a boy!"

He payed out the birth-cord then wiped the baby and laid him on his mother's belly, where the newborn clutched and swam and flapped for a nipple. The baby wailed, to clear his lungs.

Deep in the infant's mind, Chlippa rocked from side to side. She spoke in a dazed tone.

"The bright light... the darkness. Up, down... in, out... inside, outside... Ah, now I see the overlay! Now I know the truth!"

"Yes?" asked a jelly-nurse, on behalf of the Medusoid.

Chlippa flicked her nictitating membranes open, like gauze curtains whipped aside; but the windows of her eyes were empty.

"The one... cancels out the other," she chirped. "One by one, they all cancel out each other... Because there's no cosmogony at all. *There isn't any universe at all!* The universe doesn't exist. It's all an illusion of ours! Birth is an illusion, life is an illusion, the Cosmos is an illusion!"

"Obviously you're hallucinating in rapport," said the *Haupt*-Seer Marcus Desmond-Campbell coldly. "That's all the baby's doing: hallucinating. It stands to sweet reason, if you try to superimpose fifty-two different—"

"*No.* The jigsaw fits together perfectly now, *Haupt*-Seer. This is the first time we've ever seen it whole and entire. But it contains *no picture.* It only possesses the shapes of the separate pieces. When you put them all together, there's *no shape left*—there's no picture. Just a perfect blank."

The baby boy managed to turn his head, stickily, upon Carla's chest.

"Mama," he said, quite clearly—but to the Kentauran bird.

And that was all that he ever said, though for several months humans and aliens hoped that he would say something more.

And he shut his eyes, and refused to open them again.

But he sucked milk, lustily.

So, in the seventeenth observatory on Thraith, under all the biopsycho-zodiacal signs of the Cosmos, a wilfully blind, dumb Buddha had been born. But in his mind (as the Kentauran empaths knew all too well) he conceived a whole universe which, compassionately, he meant to care for, at least until he died—though he cared little about the specific details of it.

Except for the milk.

The milk was good. It squeezed from one or other of two nipples—just as (he began presently to decide) the cosmos of white light sprayed forth alternately from the twin paps of non-existence, forming the matter that was his flesh, the worlds that were his blood cells, the stars that were his neurons.

In baby Buddha's sixth month, against all advice, the Lady Carla van der Voort decided that he really *must* be weaned. Since the Lady Carla was the only human female currently on Thraith, her decision was final.

Quite final.

IAN WATSON

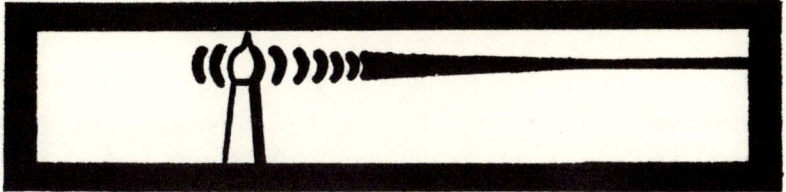

With a title as long as the following, what more need one say . . . ?

Some Sufist Insights into the Nature of Inexplicable Events

SF has a strange paradox implicit in it (if one may generalize the genre for a moment, lopping off a few toes and fingers which don't fit, as on Procrustes's famous bed). SF concerns itself with the unknown and unpredictable (the future; alien life forms) and even the unexplainable (the nature of the universe; the nature of reality), yet at the same time it has an obsession with explaining things 'scientifically'.

Sometimes the answer to the problems posed by the chosen story and milieu is genuinely implicit in the story (as in, say, Stableford's *Daedalus* series)—the veils are penetrated and the solution laid bare. At other times the answer is simply pulled out of a hat—a *deus ex machina* is trundled on from the wings to wrap things up. (An extreme case of this is when it becomes increasingly impossible to find a big enough *deus* to fit the bill, as in Farmer's Riverworld series: who *are* the makers? By now, nobody's going to be satisfied; yet the original conception remains a magnificent one.) The tension between scientific rationality and mystery is one that pulls at many writers, and is actually responsible, I believe, for some of the crudities of the genre—the writer goes for 'mere' adventure as a resolution of the dilemma that will hopefully coast the reader past the dilemma so that he doesn't even notice it. (This dual strain is evident in Arthur Clarke's novels: on the one hand technological supremacy solves all; on the other the Star-Child or the Overmind sweeps such toys aside, utterly transcending them. This contradiction is rather neatly resolved in Clarke's culminating novel, *The Fountains of Paradise*.)

So, as SF writers we have to develop some tools for handling this paradox (as well as researching our backgrounds and the far frontiers of modern science), if we aren't merely going to blat people over the head with a trumped-up *deus* or seduce them with runaway adventure.

Unfortunately these tools don't appear to be available within science, which of course 'explains' things—explains increasingly more, but never everything, about the universe. Actually, by definition they aren't available *within* consensus science, because science is really a process of ongoing convergence upon the truth, or a set of truths, by a method of partial approximations. The partial approach is essential to scientific method; some hypotheses must always be taken for granted. Also, any eventual total explanation is going to involve the nature of consciousness as well as the nature of matter and will necessarily move outside of rational science—from theory to vision, as Capra puts it in *The Tao of Physics*.

Where can one find the tools to think about this? We surely need them, since scientists can take basic things for granted in their theories (such as the gravitational constant G: valid for all epochs of the universe?), but if we story-mongers take too much for granted the reader might justifiably feel cheated. Of course, we do cheat all the time; and the modes of cheating—FTL drives, time travel etc.—are the very conventions of the genre. A genre based on cheating? Well, yes—and necessarily so—for here we are trundling our technology into unexplainable areas.

How about turning to some theologies for help? (Using the term in its broadest, least dogmatic sense.) Well, of course, theologies and mythologies have been pillaged along with the best of sources. But most theologies are absolutist ones. They tell The Truth. What we want is a 'theology' that doesn't tell The Truth, that seeks instead to provide us with thinking tools for the area of indefinability.

Zen? No theology, Zen, of course. But in any case Zen hits you over the head with the begging bowl and in the moment of concussion you may perceive a flash of light; Zen is the very opposite of an analytical method; and we really need an analytical method for thinking about mystery. This is *science* fiction, after all.

One such analytical method for handling inexplicability exists in Sufism, of which I first became aware around about the time I was starting a novel on the UFO phenomenon (which emerged as *Miracle Visitors*). While I was penning the manuscript (in real live handwriting) I stopped and scribbled some notes to myself in the back of it (which I left out of the printed text, not wishing this to be a metanovel, a novel about writing a novel—things were complicated enough, anyway), for I was up against the Paradox. (Particularly in this book, since UFOs are precisely that: unidentified—and, I believe, unidentifiable in essence.) One of the notes ran as follows: "If one writes a novel on the (true) scientific premise that science cannot explain everything—and that it would be unscientific to believe that it could (against its own tenets *as science*), is this a science-fiction novel? This book is described as science fiction. Which it is. Yet if the events of the book cannot be explained scientifically, how can this be so?"

Sufism: the mystical tradition in Islam, home of some of the keenest thinkers of the last thousand years. (Or a mystical tradition that merely wears the robes of Islam for convenience?) Isn't this rather unpleasantly trendy—jumping upon the newest bandwagon? If you want to know the colour of their oil money, you'd better know the colour of their thought.... If the Ayatollah Khomeini can overthrow the Shah, what's he all about? Alternatively, Jim Blish as a good Spenglerian would have cried 'Shame! Syncretism!'—which is the cobbling together of other cultures' philosophies from every which where to prop up our autumnal declining Western world view.

I must confess to a tension here, since I strongly dislike what I can see of the public face of this emerging grassroots Islamic revival: the re-introduction of the veil, the stoning of adulterers, people scourging themselves with chains. Yet the Sufi tradition is a fluid one, that takes of the colouration of the bottle it is poured into, and historically that bottle happens to have been Islam.

The works of Idries Shah—variously hailed as an axis of the age, or decried as a kind of Castaneda of the Middle East, a suspect person (by some scholars; but there's too much scholasticism in Sufi studies—the tracing of endless genealogies of sects)—are a useful start, in a discursive, allusive, 'teaching parable' way. Inexplicable chains of cause and effect are embedded in funny anecdotes—shockers, designed to knock us off our linear rails. Symptomatically, his major 'history', *The Sufis*, lacks an index—it isn't a book designed to be used that way. (While his *Book of the Book* contains about 23 pages of text and another 200 blank pages—designed as a serious joke to make us think about what we are hoping to do when we quarry books for aid and instruction.) His works are also anthologies of major Sufi writings by such as Jalaluddin Rumi and Ibn 'Arabi.

Turning to the original sources, and some major commentaries upon them, one enters a world of thinkers whose ideas about the nature of the universe, and of causality, and the inexplicable, of timelines, of perception and cognition, of ontology and cosmology, of evolution (oh yes: in Rumi, A.D. 1207-73), of the intersection of matter and consciousness, are highly apposite to what SF is up to—and of course to the basic paradox, of explanation and inexplicability (which is perhaps why a fair amount of Sufist philosophy appears in the form of fictions, and poetry).

Fascinating texts are, for instance, the *Discourses of Rumi* (translated by A. J. Arberry—my U.K. edition was published by John Murray) and Ibn 'Arabi's *Wisdom of the Prophets* (Fusus al-Hikam), a partial translation from Beshara Publications; also the complex yet highly rewarding commentary on this and on another book of Ibn 'Arabi's by France's premier orientalist Henry Corbin, *Creative Imagination in the Sufism of Ibn 'Arabi* (Bollingen Series XCI, Princeton University Press).

For me, this material is more than just another eclectic grab from other cultures. Alexei and Cory Panshin are already well aware of this rich vein; and I have noticed in *The Dark Design* a Sufi, Nur (whose name means 'light' in Arabic), stepping on stage making knowing noises. . . .

But be careful. The Sufi sources are not merely material to be used. They will use you too—and that's the only way in to them.

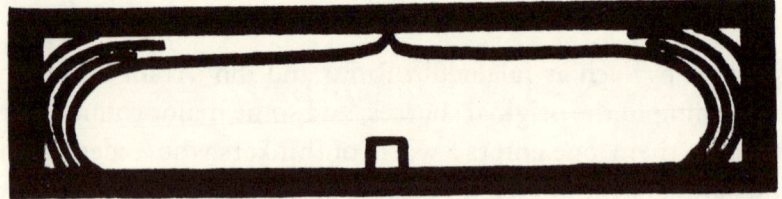

Here is some Sufism camouflaged as science fantasy. *Istinbat*, in Arabic, means "mystical interpretation"; *Wakil* is "custodian of a mosque, or Sufi order"; *Tasamma* is to "claim a spiritual relationship"; and so forth. *Suf* (as in Sufism) is "wool", and wool is sometimes pulled over the eyes . . .

Dome of Whispers

"Welcome to the Dome of Whispers, star-stranger. I am Istinbat. Please let me assure myself that you carry no recording devices or other instruments. The visitor to the Dome of Whispers may bring only himself, or herself. . . .

"You may leave your wrist computer here. No-one will touch it."

The burly man shed his bracelet, and Istinbat placed it on a shelf. The shelf was otherwise empty; there were no other visitors yet. Perhaps there would be no others.

Istinbat looked out from the doorway briefly, imagining the splendid view of the Dome, golden in the morning sun, that this stranger must have enjoyed as he approached up the road from Wakil City. The Dome rose three hundred metres at its zenith, and was a full kilometre around its base. The area immediately surrounding it was paved in turquoise marble, well worn by the scuff of countless feet down the millennia—though this was one of those centuries when the number of feet was more easily countable. Just off the marble stood a line of hutches, where vendors—poor brown folk with flashing teeth—were only just now putting up their shutters, to hawk their holopictures, spiced buns, wine flasks, fresh fruit, bowls of goat's meat stew. Mainly they supplied the guardians of the Dome with food and drink; tourists were only a sideline. A stall concession at the Dome was a rare prize for a poor man; and only to a poor man would it go by tradition. The stall holders would bring the food and drink over when a bell tolled. Istinbat himself had not stepped outside of the doorway for perhaps a year.

The burly man fidgeted.

With a shrug, Istinbat turned from the doorway to the outside world. He pulled a cord which would summon another guardian from the catacomb quarters underneath the Dome. Twitching a taper alight, he preceded the visitor down the flight of steps into the long downward tunnel leading to below the mid-point of the Dome.

Istinbat was a tall thin man, with a long nose, thin pursed lips and eyes of a startling violet hue: the face of a sucking insect. His head was shorn, and he had a creamy skin, much lighter than the norm on this world, blanched by long attendance in the Dome. He held the taper high, and thus they proceeded down the tunnel in a cocoon of light.

"Will you be staying in the Dome with me?" asked the visitor idly enough, though the answer obviously mattered to him intensely.

"A guardian has to stay—though not intrude. I shall station myself a fair way off. You may take as long as you like. All day, till dusk. I shall not get bored, with all the voices speaking to me. I have hardly heard the same one twice, in all my years since I was a boy."

"Hmm," said the visitor. Obviously the answer pleased him.

What private message was he hoping to hear—or to leave—in the Dome? Yet this was no concern of Istinbat's, except in so far as it had been a very long time since anyone had come to the Dome from another world with a specific purpose beyond simple curiosity.

As they walked, a second cocoon of light approached them. A similar tall robed figure—the woman Tasamma—glided past, with a nod to Istinbat, as routinely as an ascending funicular railway cab passes a descending one midway.

The tunnel opened into a large circular chamber, with several brass-bound doors beyond which were the labyrinths of living quarters, and burial places. Once, there had been a hundred guardians. Now there were scarcely twenty.

A well-worn spiral stone stairway led up into the Dome itself. Istinbat held the taper well clear of his body to illuminate the steps; there were a hundred of these.

He noticed that the visitor did not puff or wheeze as he climbed.

As the man stepped up into the centre of the great bare floor of the Dome, Istinbat twitched out the taper. It was luminous enough inside. Light diffused from the translucent eye of the Dome, and from similarly translucent blocks inset at regular intervals high around the walls—or rather, the one wall. Faintly, from that all-encompassing wall, the massed echo of the whispers came to their ears like the distant sussurus of the sea. Istinbat wondered what the wall would say to him today. . . .

In the southern hemisphere of the planet Suf stood this famous Dome of Whispers: famous in the sense that it was the only thing by which most star people remembered the planet Suf these days. Much turbulent history had flowed through Suf down the millennia—and ebbed away again, leaving Suf to its own private weave of events, of which nowadays only a few threads remained. Yet Suf still ticked on, even though the clock (as they said locally) had no hands; and the old Dome endured, though comparatively little visited except by those native to Suf.

While it still stood, the Dome remained one of the most remarkable buildings in all the star worlds; for it had the most peculiar acoustics of any building ever raised.

Whispering galleries existed elsewhere: places where you spoke softly and your companion heard you clearly hundreds of metres away around the building. But in the Dome of Whispers, alone, no utterance was ever lost. Whatever was spoken there continued on around the Dome forever, quietly, undiminished.

This building of perfect proportions acted as a superconductor —not of electrical current, but of sound waves. Perhaps there really was something superconductive about the unique quartz-veined marble of which it was built—and something piezoelectric too; perhaps the slight compression caused by the impact of sound waves set up a current which stored and reproduced the spoken word again and again around the Dome. Perhaps. The guardians of the Dome had never permitted anyone to take the smallest flake of a sample away nor bring any kind of mechanical or electronic instrument into the Dome. It was all that the Sufish had, this Dome. Better that it should remain a prodigy, a marvel, than be explained away.

For millennia past the people of Suf, both common and uncommon, and intermittently the people of other star worlds (generally uncommon) had come here to whisper the secret of their lives or a confession or a prophecy. They had come to swear a binding oath or a love pledge or a vow of revenge. They had come to immortalise—for as long as the Dome endured—their own insight into the meaning of life.

During periods of Sufish decadence, the Dome had been used as an oracle. . . .

*

Around the perimeter of the floor stood various mobile ladders resembling pieces of ancient siege-gear. Their wheels rested on a track running right around the circuit of the wall. These ladder-towers leaned backwards precariously, balanced on a support leg which wheeled along an inner track.

"I expected it would be noisier," said the visitor. "Uh . . . should I speak?"

"It's all right to speak here. Beyond the black marble line, three metres from the wall, is where the effect occurs. You can speak anywhere within those three metres, and be recorded at that very point in the air. We don't really know how large the capacity is—certainly not infinite—therefore each visitor may make only one statement, and then he must withdraw."

"But you said that I could . . ."

"You may *listen* for as long as you like. With sealed lips. When you remove the seal, you may speak just once. Most people only have one real thing that they need to say." Istinbat plunged a hand into his robes and produced a strip of adhesive bandage. "I am accustomed to silence, but I must ask all visitors to seal their lips during the Listening, till they wish to speak."

The visitor nodded. "Only one real thing to say . . . or to hear—it's quite true."

And what is your real thing? wondered Istinbat.

The visitor stared around the Dome. Twelve metres above the floor was a continuous inscription cut in an angular script; it ran around the whole circuit of the wall. The inscription was repeated exactly in the black marble of the boundary line. The visitor pointed at it, sweeping his finger along.

"It is the whole of the ancient poem known as the *Ruby Yat*," said Istinbat, "in the old script of Suf. A poem on the theme of mutability and eternity. Very few people can read the old Sufish script these days. Lovers sometimes match up the angles of the letters, above and below on the floor, as a way of marking where they pledged their love. They copy down the piece of text, without understanding it. Even so, it might take them quite some time to find the exact point where they spoke, and the exact angle of their lips."

"But can you read it?"

"Oh, yes, that is something else that we guard: a knowledge of the sounds of those letters."

"Will you read some of it for me? Please. I will pay you generously."

"Why should I need money? But I will read it, if you wish. Come, we will walk to the beginning."

"No, I already know the *Ruby Yat* by heart. I am looking for one particular passage."

"So, a friend has been here, perhaps? It's unusual, to know the *Ruby Yat* by heart."

"It's handed down . . . in my family. But this is the only example of the old script left."

What family would that be? wondered Istinbat. Was this man a scholar?

Historians from off-planet had, from time to time, eavesdropped on one voice, then another, then the one after . . . sifting the equivalent of a ton of ordinary potsherds to find, by chance, one golden brooch or King's insignia, one historic confession or vow. They soon gave up, their heads full of peasant love-words, verbal graffiti, portentous statements by the totally forgotten.

"What passage?" he asked.

And the visitor recited:

*"Of my Base Metal may be filed a Key
That shall unlock the Door to Paradise."*

"But that's wrong," said Istinbat. "It should be:

*" Of my Base Metal may be filed a Key
That shall unlock the Door he howls without." '*

The man's face darkened. "Yes, yes, of course it is. How stupid of me."

"But if you memorise the whole poem, in your family . . . ? I suppose changes creep in. Corruptions of the text."

"Yes, yes, they creep in."

"But you knew you had made a mistake." Istinbat thought briefly. "Where the text diverges, is that where you expect to find the message waiting for you?"

"Just show me where those words are, will you?"

"I am doing you a favor, star-stranger . . ."

"And you don't want money. What do you want?"

"Why, I am curious. Events do not happen on Suf these days. I have a feeling that this is an event." Istinbat felt a curious sensation, of *power*. It was an unusual sensation, and not one that he particularly cared for. This burly visitor was, perhaps, accustomed to power . . . or else he remembered power. Here, however, amidst the tide of voices he was powerless.

"But aren't you vowed to silence . . . Istinbat?" The visitor had named him, to forge a relationship.

"Yes. But at the same time a guardian feels curiosity about the myriads of voices he hears."

"If only he could identify one of them, is that it?"

Istinbat chuckled dryly. "Most people identify themselves. Right here is their immortality. I will show you. Seal your lips. You may reflect upon the phenomenon of the Needle and the Haystack."

"But you said you would stand a fair way off."

"And now you have involved me."

Once across the black marble strip, it was like dialling through the air-bands of an enormous radio; catching a word here, a phrase there, half a sentence—switched away by the least movement on their part. Here was the archeological deep litter of thousands of years, compressed into three metres of whispering air, every millimetre of which clamoured for attention, begging to be heard.

Yet unlike an archeological site, here there was no depth yardstick of time. So here was a plea out of the deeps of time... perhaps. Here, next to it, was a promise from last year... perhaps again. There was no discernible difference in the signal strength. It did not matter whether the original speakers had cried out loudly or murmured most quietly. Each whisper had the same strength as the next. Nor did they overlap, however crowded together they were. No-one talked anyone else down. Each whisper was equal.

The visitor moved as if he was moving through treacle, though actually there was no resistance except for the drag of fascination.

He moved his head in tiny quantum jumps from one whisper to the next. Ah yes, one heard with the left ear or the right ear... but never with both at once. One heard *inside* the ear.

"*Orelda, thee I love forever...*" Dust.

"*... yaum el-nnushur...*" Unknowable.

"*... anda klath impto hoptu vendi saa...*" what language? An alien hissing and croaking, never from a human throat...

"*I swear my vengeance upon Satpat and all his heirs, by all of mine, for as long as our revenge is renewed in this iota of ever-air...*" How long did that blood feud last for? Or had it merely just begun?

A nervous giggle: "*Well, what do I say?*"

A crisp voice: "*This is Sully Hoberman from Alpha C in the Suf year 5079. The proof of Galois' last theorem, which I have now found, is as follows...*" Was Sully Hoberman right or wrong? Who knew? Who remembered?

A primping voice: "*I, Marquis Enderby, will now recite my prizewinning ode which placed first in the Concourse of Poetry at Middlestar...*"

"I'll marry Lala whatever her Dad says . . ."
And on. And on. An infinity of voices.
Well, not an infinity; but very many.
Istinbat let the stranger listen for ten or fifteen minutes, then laid a hand on his arm and nodded him back across the black marble strip. Gently, he detached the adhesive strip from the man's lips.
"Now will you satisfy my curiosity, star-stranger?"
The visitor glanced around the Dome again, confirming that it was still empty but for the two of them. He flexed his hands. Strong hands they were.
"I suppose I shall have to!"
And this the stranger proceeded to do; and it began to dawn on Istinbat that he had put himself in danger of his life. Surely no-one would attempt to murder a guardian in the very Dome itself? Still, as the man spoke, Istinbat measured himself against him . . . unable, even so, to bring himself to call a halt to the stranger's words. For this was the Event, and it seemed as though Istinbat had been waiting out his whole life to connect with this moment . . . of History.

The Empire of Tajalam, at its height a thousand years earlier, spanned seven worlds in the Praesepe Cluster, that mass of stars five hundred light years from old Earth for which the fanciful old Earth-Chinese name was 'the exhalation of piled-up corpses'. Regarded with an unromantic eye, Tajalem's Empire seemed amply to merit the Chinese description. Yet, despite his barbarities, Tajalam had been a remarkable character who persisted in sending out expedition after expedition into deepest space long after all other exploration and pioneering had slowed to a snail's pace.
He was searching for no less than Paradise. A Paradise planet, which he believed must exist somewhere among the millions of

suns.

Perhaps it had to exist, simply to counterbalance the hell of Praesepe.

And Paradise had been found...somewhere...by the last and smallest expedition. No doubt it spoke volumes for the loyalty that Tajalam inspired, or the terror he induced, that the expedition came back at all to tell him. Probably the former, since by then his Empire was crashing about his head, and he was on the run. Apparently he ran by way of Suf, before eventually committing suicide with his ritual ruler's sword in the city of Qalb on Usul. From some personal quirk—which those of his descendants who survived the pursuing wolves had enshrined as a tradition—Tajalam had adopted the *Ruby Yat* as the basis of his private battle-code and cipher system.

It was a strict part of Praesepe culture that a dead ruler's sword should be preserved in public for ever more. In Tajalam's case, his enemies might have felt like melting it down—but not when it was stained with his own blood. That final act of his had sealed the sword into the stone of history forever. Thus his victorious enemies took the sword back with them to Praesepe Prime, where it lay in their central museum these days.

That sword had an inscription on it: the words which had pierced his heart....

"We didn't find *that* out, Istinbat...not for nine hundred years. We were scattered to the stars, as far from Praesepe as possible, living under new names, often living in poverty."

"We?"

"The direct line of Tajalam. It's *unusual* for a ritual ruler's sword to have an inscription on it, you see. We believe the words were inscribed shortly before he killed himself, and some time after he passed through Suf. They were a message to his heirs, which his immediate heirs never received."

"They were the key to the paradise planet?"

"Exactly. And it's here. The celestial coordinates to Paradise are here. Now I've slaked your thirsty curiosity, perhaps you would tell me," the visitor gestured impatiently, "*approximately where?*"

"I will have to remain alive afterwards," said Istinbat, hoping that he did not sound as though he was begging for his life. Though how could he ensure that he remained alive?

No doubt, in the last thousand years, Tajalam's line had become more settled in their ways, less inclined to produce exhalations of piled-up corpses. In some not-unpleasant respects, the human galaxy had run out of energy.

The visitor laughed.

"We shall see, Istinbat. We shall see."

"You will swear it, by . . . yes, by the blood of your ancestors. Or I will not tell you where to listen."

"Oh, very well. I so swear that you shall live . . . if you can call this living."

"Do not despise the Dome, star-stranger. Has it not kept Tajalam's secret for you for a thousand years?"

"Yes, actually that's the only good reason for its existence! Plus, I suppose, the luring of a few scraps of trade to this backwater."

Istinbat shook his head.

"There's more than that. Much more. Here is the essence of hundreds of millions of people. Here is the last surviving breath of their souls, now that they are dead. True, some are vain and some are fatuous, but it is what they were. And that's enough."

"The door, man! Unlock the door. Now!"

Istinbat considered the inscription, then led the visitor half way around the Dome. With his foot he tapped the end of one word in the black marble. With his finger he pointed to the corresponding word above. With a mocking grin, the visitor retrieved the bandage from Istinbat's hand and stuck it back over his lips. Slowly, very slowly, he moved forward.

Supremely alert, the burly man sifted through a thousand voices—confident, petulant, brash, boastful, yearning—before one harsh, regal voice spoke to him; and he froze utterly. Until now, for an hour and more, he had been moving in infinite slow motion. Now he did not move at all. He was a statue.

"I am Tajalam," said the voice. "My son! My heir Tajasanid!"

But Tajasanid, son of Tajalam, was dead a thousand years since—caught by the wolves, in disguise, on Praesepe Prime itself.

"You seek the key that will unlock the door to Paradise, as I sought it too. Meanwhile, the enemies increase. The assassins bestir themselves. The carrion fowl gather. I know you, my son, and I love you. How to save you from yourself, as I was never saved from myself? Let me tell you, Tajasanid, that the forging of an empire is simply *forgery*. It is the production of counterfeit —whereas a single man may become true gold himself. Remember our battle-code command for wreaking havoc and laying waste a world: 'Wilderness is Paradise enough!' There is no alien paradise planet to inherit, my son, except for the Paradise that you will make for yourself in the wilderness of exile, and simplicity. Howl now, my heir, but heed my words in time. I hope you will learn how wilderness may be truly paradise enough. I learnt it too late—but I shall write it in my blood for you to find. This is my legacy. Farewell—and blessings!"

The visitor tore the seal from his lips, and howled. He hit out at the air, as though he could strike Tajalam himself across the face, but his blows only met air.

Before Istinbat could intervene, the visitor stepped back across the black marble strip of his own accord.

Controlling himself, the visitor said to the guardian, "Didn't I say that there was only one good reason for this Dome's existence? Well, didn't I?"

"What did Tajalam say to you?"

The visitor spat on the floor.

"Barbarian wisdom! Now that the single reason has gone, my friend, and now that the reason for my own life has gone together with it . . . well, I did promise you your life, and there's small reason to break my promise now! So be warned, do not remain in this Dome today. This Dome is a trap for fools—for millions of idiots. Here is the temple of folly of all the galaxy. I do not suffer fools gladly, even though I am one myself."

The visitor strode away towards the mouth of the spiral stairway.

"What do you mean to do?" cried Istinbat, hurrying after him.

"I shall put an end to folly, honourably, as Tajalam put an end to his own folly. Stay out of this Dome!"

"But I *guard* this Dome."

"Guard it from the outer doorway, then!"

"What can one man do?" Istinbat laughed. He twitched his taper alight again. "I am a fool too. I thought this was an Event. It is no event at all. Nor are your threats an event. You did not even speak them aloud, so that future visitors can hear and wonder. You only howled like a beast. Your howl whispers round the wall forever, now, until time wears the Dome away."

Istinbat reached the base of the stairway, where the visitor was necessarily forced to wait for his way to be lit. Istanbat led him quickly along the tunnel.

"I have told you," the visitor repeated. "You, who wish for an Event. I promise you there will be an Event."

Ignoring the woman Tasamma, sitting inside the doorway, the visitor retrieved his computer bracelet and strode away, brushing aside a few brown people with flashing teeth who rushed to him from their stalls.

Istinbat watched him go. The visitor did not look back.

*

Half an hour later, still sitting together in golden silence, Istinbat and Tasamma saw a small hyperboat rise up into the cloudless sky from the desert beyond Wakil City. But it did not shrink to a speck, disappearing into space. Instead, it arced above the city on a tight parabola, curving back down towards them.

"It's out of control!" cried Tasamma.

Istinbat dragged her down the stone steps into the darkness of the tunnel. They huddled where they fell.

A moment later, came the crash of the explosion: an almighty thunder-shout. The tunnel floor ripped under them. A single brick fell onto Istinbat's back. Dust choked their lungs.

Coughing, they staggered back up the steps again and out onto the turquoise marble space, where vendors were running and crying out, though all apparently unhurt. The rise of the Dome above them was intact. However, as Istinbat and Tasamma ran together around it, keeping a long way from its base, they saw that the whole western quadrant had been demolished. Pieces of marble had been tossed about the sands by the force of the explosion. The remains of the hyperboat, scattered widely, were recognizable only because they were steel not stone. The Dome was a great yawning cave, now—a broken golden egg.

As Istinbat trotted towards the great hole, a voice assailed his ears, fleetingly.

"I'll marry Lala whatever . . ."

And another: *"Khalwat dar anjuman . . ."*

And a third: *"I, Seloose of Vega, swear . . ."*

He stopped, appalled, bewildered. Tasamma stopped too, cocking her tall thin head.

The voices were all escaping into Suf, flying out of the hatched egg of the Dome as though from a Pandora's Box, spreading and reproducing themselves throughout the suddenly increased atmospheric volume. The phenomenon was as enigmatic, to Istinbat's mind, as the Dome itself had been.

Alone, he scrambled over the banks of rubble in the face of a tidal bore of voices, into the mouth of the cave.

He was nearly driven back by the pressure of noise, but then quite suddenly the voices became a trickle, and ceased—the flood had flowed past him.

Istinbat stepped down onto the floor of the Dome, and hurried towards the nearest intact stretch of wall. He crossed the black marble strip, and found only silence there.

Which is why the planet Suf is known as the Whispering World, or the Ghost World, nowadays; and why the brown people with flashing teeth wear plugs of wax in their ears and converse in sign language; and why more tourists pay visits to Suf, to be haunted. Generally the constant haunting is too much for the curious tourists, so that after the first five or six hours they will seek refuge in the inappropriately-named Dome of Whispers, where alone in all that world there is utter silence.

That silence has its guardians, who will not as a rule let visitors so much as whisper anywhere inside their fractured holy place. Though sometimes, for a truly golden consideration, they will allow a person to shout aloud and hear his or her voice vanish utterly without even an echo.

Nowadays there are a hundred guardians. People are eager to escape all the whispers in the world.

METAPHORICAL

IAN WATSON

The Recession Strikes Back! The jam disappears from one's bread and butter, soon followed by most of the butter. How long will the bread last . . . ?

Down the Mine

Last week I received a fan letter from George Turner in Australia, about my novel *The Gardens of Delight*.

A fan letter from George Turner is an unparalleled event, and must be recorded in the annals of the universe, or at least of my own universe.

Now, *The Gardens of Delight* appeared from Gollancz under the rubric 'Gollancz Fantasy,' and George duly noted that "despite the Gollancz pigeonholing it does fulfil the most necessary qualifications of sf, though it stretches them to the limits." While Brian Stableford, reviewing the same novel in *Arena 11*, wondered why "the author and/or publisher should have chosen to distinguish it from his earlier novels." Because, of course, the book does possess a perfectly solid sf rationale.

So why, then, is *The Gardens of Delight* labelled 'fantasy'? From the publisher's angle I would surmise that, having established a fantasy line, it is necessary to bring some books out in it. While I must confess to having been seduced by the prospect of a real live illustrated dust jacket.

When the novel went out to reviewers, however, great and

perhaps predictable confusion ensued. The 'straight' reviewers, who can count fantasy within their domain, were sorely puzzled.

"In *The Gardens of Delight*," wrote one, "Ian Watson has unwisely foresaken SF for FF (fantasy fiction)." A second, seeking a neat antithesis, wrote: "Watson has already written a string of science fiction but this is his / / / strangest and most compelling tale to date." (The phrase following the slash marks is, sigh, merely lifted verbatim from the jacket blurb.) While *The Observer* opened with a whole column discussing the nature of fantasy before deciding that, by virtue of being fantasy, the novel under review "transforms itself into something more interesting than 'ordinary' SF."

An interesting case study in confusion, this. And incidentally it resulted in the least favourable bunch of reviews I've ever had, for a book which George Turner, doughty critic, says makes him "jump for joy." But George Turner, of course, knows perfectly well what sf is.

At a time when a fair few writers and critics deplore the existence of the label and the category sf, one might feel inclined to draw the moral from all this that the label and category are no bad thing. This wasn't a case of an sf book being let loose in the wider world to take its chances, and succeeding or failing, whichever. Rather, it was a case of the mainstream critics desperately trying to understand it *by means* of a label, and failing utterly—establishing false antitheses, proclaiming it to be worse than sf because it was fantasy, or to be better than sf for the same reason. The 'outside' critics actually yearned for the label, and simply couldn't understand what they were reading when it didn't fit the label. Particularly, none of them—while making knowing noises about sf—knew enough to say: this *is* sf.

So should we simply call an sf novel 'a novel'—or even perhaps 'a book'? The confusion would probably be worse compounded then, since the critics wouldn't even have the term 'sf' or 'fantasy' to react against. Yet again, if *The Gardens of Delight* had simply been labelled 'a novel' I'm fairly sure that the reviews would have read quite differently: "Now we turn to a science fiction offering which has slipped into the pile..." Because the novel has a spaceship and an alien planet in it. So now it could have been mis-reviewed, with all prior prejudices intact. (At this point I fantasize about issuing normative definitions of the universal, multifarious plenty which we know as sf, to all newspapers and weeklies.)

But this is really a rather obvious, first-stage thought about the current anathema regarding the genre label. What I want to write about in this particular column, instead, is what the writer who writes and loves sf ought to do, particularly in a time of economic recession, to pay the bills and maintain him or herself as a writer.

For one immediate hope, or temptation, is to diversify. We are wordsmiths, after all; and words can be written about anything at all.

Surely we can dash off a quick Romance (under a pseudonym, of course). And how about all these horror novels which now seem to share the shelves 50/50 with sf? (Last year it seemed more like 25/75, in favour of sf.) I refer to *The Squirming, The Slithering, The Foreboding, The Presage, The Yucking.* How about a quick children's book? And how about TV? Or how about a quick ook, rather than a book? Supposedly publishers are on the lookout for writers with a good track record of published pages, who haven't made it big, with a view to hyping them into orbit through an artificial book, an ook. How about contributing to other kinds of artificial books, 'marketing books' such as *Great Interstellar Dreadnoughs of the Sirius Class*?

I have the information sheets for one such current project before me, kindly sent by a friend in California who heard that I was broke. It is undoubtedly a nobler venture than *Alien Crimi-*

nals to Beware Of, but it's still a wholly artificial book. It's *The Dune Encyclopedia*, and the idea is to invent fictitious entries on everything mentioned by Frank Herbert in the Dune books, from the Aba Hood through to Zombie-Katrundo, without ever mentioning the name Frank Herbert. Thus the result should seem to be a genuine encyclopedia of facts.

I admit to being tempted, since it would be quite easy to pull down from my shelves books on Islamic theology and Sufism, and write entries for *Baraka* or *Dar al-hikman* or *Fiqh* or *Ilm*, giving these a cosmic future twist, and so performing a double displacement of the original material which Herbert drew upon.

One deterrent is the fact that his project is a 'Work for Hire' which means that you give up your copyright on your own words immediately. But the other deterrent—working against the prospect of $40 per 1000 words payable immediately upon acceptance—is the thought: Why the hell? Why the hell write marginalia to the Dune Quartet instead of writing fiction of one's own?

Likewise, why the hell propose to write *The Yucking* or *Spock Goes Schizo* or *A Guide to Extraterrestrial House Plants*?

One mistake, if I did this, would be to try to do it fairly well. To take too much time over it. (Perhaps any time taken is too much?) Actually to care for it. To believe in it 100% at least 5% of the time.

And the book would just drown. Vanish.

There *are* nuggets of gold in the midst of crappy hack projects. Take Laser Books, universally scorned. I read one pretty good Laser Book: Jerry Sohl's *I am Aleppo*, and one really stunning one: Ray Nelson's *Blake's Progress*. And what mention is ever made of these? They are tainted.

Even in the Marvel Novel Series—another way of picking up extra cash by novelizing the superheroes—number 7 is pretty good. The cover proclaims: STAN LEE PRESENTS: DOC—

TOR STRANGE, MASTER OF THE MYSTIC ARTS / / IN A NOVEL BY WILLIAM ROTSLER (much smaller capitals) / / NIGHTMARE. I bought this because I was always intrigued by Doctor Strange, and knew Bill Rotsler's name, and thought that he would turn in a rather good book; and he did.

And who cares?

Yet as advances sink to historic lows, not always paid in advance, one needs the money.

So, in the past year or so, I've been tempted by several bright ideas for diversifying.

The first lightbulb lit up overhead when *TV Times* announced that they had run out of Roald Dahl stories for the *Tales of the Unexpected* series, and were offering a prize for a story. Not much. About £200, I recall. But I reckoned I could blitz Anglia TV at the rate of two pretty good 1500-worders (this being the limit) per day. After all, I had watched the series—which I always thought ought to have been renamed *Tales of the Expected*. So I sent in six specially written rural horror stories with suitable twists in the tail (or perhaps they were unsuitable: too unexpected?) A year later I can say with a fair degree of objectivity that they were all rather good. And I heard of another sf writer who sent in fourteen stories.

As I should have realized in the first place, this was an utter waste of time. What news value was there for *TV Times* if they handed the cash over to a full-time writer? With no disrespect intended, the winning entry just had to be a first story by a chiropodist's secretary.

My next foolish project was to try to float an ook, about our feathered friends who fly around my windows, in the great tradition of epics about rabbits, moles, barnyard roosters, cockroaches and earwigs—and get paid to write it. I wrote a bloody good chapter and outline, and these were really well pushed for me at the Frankfurt Book Fair. And nothing happened. (Thank

God.)

So then I launched into a brief children's book. And nothing happened.

By now friends across the globe were working furiously for me, trying to hook projects. Thus in due course I heard that Playboy Paperbacks were really keen to consider *The Woman Factory*, which has only appeared in French so far (and in Portuguese, I believe, but the publisher has defaulted on the second half of the advance, any complimentary copies, and the copy of the typescript which I loaned him). I hauled out the last surviving blurred xerox of the typescript, and decided with the hindsight of ten years that it could well do with being entirely rewritten. So I typed out the first eighth of the book as it was, as a sample, and outlined the rest and my further plans for it, and airlifted the package to Playboy Paperbacks, who were so keen. Silence. The silence continues, despite enquiries.

I also wrote the story for a proposed film maker, at his request. Gratefully acknowledged, then silence.

Now all this may seem par for the course when one is trying to hack it as a wordsmith. (I suppose I had better except *The Woman Factory* from that, since I wrote it with full commitment originally. But is the book *actually* clamouring to be written—rewritten—ten years after)* And no doubt I should have hustled a lot more, in a lot more places. But anyway, after quite a lot of working hours wasted here and there, I decided: sod it all—and went into an sf story blitz. The repressed material

---

* (The silence has now been tentatively broken. After a mere six months. Immediately a new and greater *Woman Factory* blooms in my mind, with a larger and even more dramatic plot, which I could fully commit myself to, as a fresh writing experience within science fiction. Will there now be another silence, equally long?)

(*Footnote, added three years later.* And lo, the novel was rewritten, and bought enthusiastically by Playboy Paperbacks. And lo, the Playboy empire lost its gambling license in London, and got rid of PP to Berkley; who refused to publish. Currently, publishers are passing the typescript from one to t'other like a hot potato or live hand grenade, warmly wishing it luck elsewhere, and murmuring that if *they* published it, they would get their lungs torn out.)

erupted like Etna. *Fantasy & SF* bought, *Omni* bought... Out of the blue came a phone call from Germany asking for SF stories.

So there's a moral here, to me at least. It isn't the moral that one should write the same darned old stuff as ever, stuck in the same faithful genre groove. (Since in fact I feel that my fiction is altering, mutating.) But it is an argument, to me at least, for writing *organically*, out of oneself, rather than arbitrarily—as a wordsmith of any old thing due to economic pressures. Somehow one survives. Usually. One hopes.

"Depend upon it, Sir," said the redoubtable Doctor Johnson, who knew all about the effects of poverty on the author, "when a man knows he is to be hanged in a fortnight, it concentrates his mind wonderfully." I would add that it is important to concentrate on the right things.

In a publishing scene where relatively easy money can be picked up from Dune Encyclopedias and novelizations of *Blake's 7* or whatever, and where an original creative act is much less certainly rewarded, there's a great temptation to pick up on these peripherals, or to generate others—ooks *et al*—to survive as an independent writer. Though if someone offered me a UFO film novelization tomorrow, what would I do?

Down in the hot dark mine of the creative process, labours the miner with little job security (since someone might close his mine down or foreclose on the loans to run it). He works a long day, carving out ore or coal or whatever for pay that just ensures the roof over his head and a pint of beer or three; but not always. The ore or coal or whatever is trundled off, and the value and energy are transmuted presently into highly-advertised profitable toys of the moment, from which the miner receives little joy. One day the miner is offered a job in the secondary-products factory. Then all the other miners are offered jobs there too. And lo, the secondary factory proves to be self-sustaining, even without the original ore and coal. The products circulate through an abstract causality loop, and no longer need the raw materials. One day the first miner has saved up enough to return to the true mine. But he has forgotten how to find the veins of ore, and can only dig up fool's gold and cardboard coal—which still glitter and burn, though.

And one day all the secondary products fall to pieces because they've been getting thinner and thinner, less and less dense, the space between their atoms greater. Or else: they do not fall to pieces, because the very same thing has been happening to the consumers of them. These people too are now ghosts—ghosts of the beings they originally were. But no one notices.

A fanciful analogy, no doubt; but then, writers think in fanciful, displaced images. And indeed I perceive that here is the germ of a story: *Down the Mine*.

Maybe it won't write itself as easily as it otherwise might, since now I know the meaning of the story in advance. But I hope that I can allow the organic story to over-ride this pre-programmed meaning. (The most interesting of Van Vogt's stories, to me, is "Process". It is about a potent yet stupid super-forest, with a forest-consciousness of violent instincts. Periodically an impervious starship lands and steals riches from the forest by goading it to quarry uranium to pile around the intruding starship as a bomb. This short story is a perfect analogy for the process of artistic creation in one writer at least—with the masterful consciousness plunging, well-armoured, into the tangled, hostile unconscious to extract necessary wealth. I also believe, though I may be wrong, that it is a completely unconscious metaphor on Van Vogt's part.)

Next week, or the week after, or in a year's time when it has gelled, I really must write *Down the Mine*. Then the story might show me what the real analogy to the present writer's dilemma is.

I still haven't written a story called "Down the Mine"; but here is one of the stories which spilled out like lava, and became the starting point for a novel, *Deathhunter* . . .

A Cage for Death

Ralph Hewitson's Thanatoscope was the ultimate product of that strange man's obsession with death. Thanatology is, of course, the study of dying, and Hewitson's machine was intended to enable us to see, and ideally to "trap," Death itself. Or himself. Ralph Hewitson always took it very personally that he or anyone else should have to die.

No doubt all of us go through this stage of horror and affront when we are children. Then we file the trauma away in the back of our mind. We lock it up in the mental lumber room, and it creeps out again only in our last days. Sometimes it remains as offensive as ever, but increasingly nowadays—thanks to the Thanatology Foundation's centers across the land and the re-interpretation of dying as an altered state of consciousness—it is transfigured into a friend, an intrinsic part of oneself, the keystone of the arch of life.

Hewitson, however, kept intact the old animist vision of some invisible thief of life. His Thanatoscope—his deathwatch device—was to be the tripwire camera, *and cage*, that surprised Death himself.

True, some scientific testing of death has been conducted in the centers in addition to the psychological studies and therapies—but only in the sense of weighing the body before and after death to see whether any tiny weight loss occurs, as of a departing soul, or using aura photography to try to record this departure on film. None of these fringe investigators have ever tried to demonstrate the converse occurrence: the *arrival* of Death as an active force.

Hewitson was a tall, black-haired man with a slight permanent stoop as if he never trusted doorways to be quite high enough to let him through.

"I wonder whether Death's doorway will let me pass when my time comes," he said to me one day, darkly humorous. "Or will I get stuck in it? Halfway in, halfway out? You know, I've been thinking that zombies could simply be people who get stuck in that door. Their conscious mind has gone through, but the automatic mind gets left on our side of it, running the body mechanically."

"You mean the autonomic nervous system, don't you, Ralph?"

"Do I? Do I?"

I'd come to the Sixth Street Thanatology Center only three months earlier from Neo-Theology College after majoring in Death-of-God counseling, and it was something of a shock for me to find someone who—if he plainly didn't believe in God—nevertheless firmly espoused the doctrine of death incarnate. But I had taken a liking to his black jokes, which seasoned his obsession with a dash of pepper.

No doubt this was the way he performed in his own counseling of the dying—he made death seem something of a farce, a Marx brothers' comedy. That approach could probably work wonders with some people. I've met them. They hate to be contemplative about their demise. They think that it's sanctimonious. Whereas with other people who are still scared—well, a joke could be a fine nerve tonic.

Of course, to Ralph deep down this was no joking matter.

I was being given a guided tour of his machine up in his office on the fourth floor of the center. It was a pleasant, sunny room with a gilt-framed medieval *Dance of Death* on one wall and, by contrast, on another a large color photograph of the Taj Mahal. The machine, which took up most of the spare floor space, was the "excluded middle" between horror and blissful peace. Ralph had, however, included it: a way not of greeting death with alarm or with joy but of damned well capturing him.

There was a waterbed-cum-bier, implanted with medisensors, set within a delicately filigreed Faraday cage, which could block out any kind of electromagnetic radiation or isolate any radiation arising within it. Enclosing this cage were polarizable glass walls that could be rendered opaque—turned into an infinite internal mirror. Various tiny cameras and mirrors were mounted within on silver rods, and outside the glass walls were fluorescent screens, an electron scanner, and a kind of hooded periscope. Also within were small, highly sensitive (to one part in a billion) chemical sniffers alert to the pheromone of death, the complex chemical released in minute traces by the dying body, that we sometimes call corpse sweat. This chemical is akin to the sexual attractor pheromones released by humans and all other creatures, and personally I think it is a normal evolutionary by-product: a warning signal to others in the vicinity.

Most deaths in ancient times would have been violent, in one way or another, and spelled trouble. Hewitson, of course, thought differently. He had the notion of this molecule as an attractor signal, too. It was something that Death would smell and descend on like a mating moth. The death orgasm couldn't happen until Death had been called. This accounts for certain overly protracted deaths; the bodies of such people simply couldn't produce enough of the pheromone.

True to form, Hewitson had managed to get tiny amounts of this corpse sweat synthesized, and he had built a number of prototype death traps designed to release quantities of it and to snap shut on whatever vectored in upon the molecule—with no success. So he concluded that a dying body actually needed to be there.

Despite his qualms at taking life—which he regarded as sacrificing to Death—Hewitson had equipped his second-generation traps with dying animals. But again with no result. Whereupon, he conceived the idea that the deaths of animals and the deaths of people may be different in essence. (He became interested in the Catholic doctrine that animals have no souls and are automatic objects.)

Incorporated in his perfected machine as well, then, were tiny pheromone taps with the stored drops of the chemical isolated by vacuum and mini-Faraday cages.

His idea was to imitate death: to hypnotize oneself into a deathlike trance, then turn the taps on.

"Do you want me to lie down in there?" I asked him. "Is that what all this is leading up to?"

"And then I release the nonexistent whiff of cyanide?" he suggested with a chuckle. "Oh, no, Jonathan, nothing like that. But of course you can try it out for size and comfort if you like. This'll be a pretty famous bed soon. Much more famous than your historic beds where Good Queen Bess or Lincoln or Shakespeare slept. Go ahead. I'm not proprietorial."

"Well, thanks, but no thanks."

"I wonder whether I *should* equip it with cyanide gas or something similar. Then I not only catch Death, but kill him, too. After all, if you can legitimately shoot someone you catch burglarizing your apartment—well, Death's a mass murderer by comparison. The biggest criminal."

I couldn't tell whether he was joking or being serious.

"I wonder in that case whether I'd be killing Death in general, or just the personal death of whoever was in the machine."

"A whole lot of people die every second, Ralph. They die simultaneously. Even if this Death of yours skipped about at the speed of light—"

"Okay, I see your point. I suppose death could be general *and* particular, though." He hemmed and hawed awhile. "If I killed the particular death—if I zapped the bullet with this person's own special name on it, right out of the way, swatted it, squashed it, vaporized it—would this person," and his hand drifted over the imaginary contours of his subject volunteer, as sensously as a fantasizing soldier stuck in a jungle hundreds of kilometers from a brothel, "would this person *live forever*? Would I have perfected an immortality treatment? Rich irony, Jonathan, for the Thanatology Foundation thus to defeat its own purpose!" His voice hushed, mock-conspiratorially. "Don't breathe a word of this to anyone. Your Neo-Theology College would be up in arms."

"I guess it's a way of persuading people to volunteer," I joked in turn. "Roll up, roll up! Come into Hewitson's Death Cage and he'll make thee immortal with a hiss . . . of cyanide gas. Oh, but you're forgetting something, Ralph. You'd kill the subject that way, before you nailed his death. Baby and the bathwater, Ralph. Baby and the bathwater!"

"Ah . . ." Ralph looked crestfallen.

But this was all just horsing around. "You're going to try it out yourself, then?" I asked, more seriously. "But by just simulating death? By pretending? I take it that'll be with the Swami's help?"

The Swami is our pet name for our Indian counselor, Mr. Ananda. Ananda has delved deeper into the oceanic unity state of death insertion than anyone else I have ever met. (An oceanic state, on the one hand, but he also compares entry into it to a space capsule leaving the familiar earth behind and entering into orbit high above where all minor details are erased, up on the edge of the endless sea of death space.) Ananda has used deep meditation and self-hypnosis techniques, of Indian origin, to plumb this way station into nothingness—sometimes accompanying the dying down, or up there, in deep rapport with them —before returning to full life to report on it. Needless to say, Mr. Ananda has never met Death—Mr. D—on his journeys.

"I've been taking lessons," Ralph nodded. "Admittedly I haven't spent years at it as he has. But I think I can turn the trick. I think so. When I get down deep enough, my own theta-thanatos brain waves will start the pheromones of death dripping."

"When's all this going to happen?"

"Next Tuesday. I'll need a few observers. Ananda has volunteered, though he thinks my motives are—well, you understand. But he's cleared a space in his schedule."

"I can spare the time, too, Ralph."

"Good man. Now look down here—"

He showed me how the periscope, the optic fiber, and the mirrors let the outside observer see around the whole inside of the cage even when the glass walls are mirror opaqued. As I gazed through the hooded periscope into the pearly-lit interior, the empty bier reduplicated itself perhaps a dozen times in all directions before losing itself in a thickening golden fog while the filigree network of the Faraday cage overlapped and overlapped itself within the mirrors.

Tuesday came. Besides Hewitson and the Swami and me, there was also present in his office Dr. Mary Ann Sczepanski, our foundation medic, looking lovely in tight silver pigtails, her *de rigueur* white coat carving her flanks in ivory marble.

Here, then, was the mousetrap with the big cheese—Hewitson—soon to be laid out in it, synthetically Gorgonzola-scented with death (though it wouldn't be an odor that any of us could pick up consciously), a trap of the nonlethal variety.

"It is a far, far better thing I do now," Ralph grinned, hamming it up a little—to Swami Ananda's evident disapproval—as, clad in a thin linen smock, he wriggled through the door of the Faraday cage, careful not to buckle any of the surrounding thin wires. He stretched himself out on the water bier.

I shut the door and locked it with Ralph's golden key, as per instructions. The key chain I slipped round my own neck. Then I turned on the current to the cage, at very low power. It hummed faintly.

The glass walls descended and locked together, still in their see-through mode. Air recycling *on*.

"You look like Snow White," shouted Mary Ann, checking his vital signs on the readouts. "But where's the poisoned apple?"

Hearing her, Ralph nodded ironically in the direction of Mr. Ananda. Then Ralph composed himself as Ananda began loudly to intone a monotonous tape-loop refrain in Sanskrit, which Ralph took up—I suppose—in duet, though I couldn't hear his voice.

Soon Ralph raised his hand, and I opaqued the glass walls.

When I peered in through the periscope, he was lying utterly still, looking suitably blanched and corpselike in the pearly inner light. He lay beside his mirrored self, which lay beside another mirrored self. Toe to toe with yet others. Each in their gilded cage, the bars of which grew thicker as the bodies proliferated further. It was quite easy to lose the center of focus and get lost. At this moment Ralph's machine seemed more like a device for cloning corpses.

The descent into the death trance took the best part of an hour. Mary Ann monitored Ralph's vital signs dutifully the whole time. The sun shone in through the window upon what seemed like a great marble block, a white kaaba, a mausoleum. A bedraggled pigeon strutted to and fro for a while on the window ledge. Distant street sounds drifted up, and a few times the whirring of copters beat down. Otherwise it was very quiet.

Mr. Ananda peered at the brain-wave screens. He tapped one with a slim brown finger and impeccably manicured nail. "Here's the beginning of the theta-thanatos rhythms."

I hugged the periscope hood around my head and heard only the Swami's voice. "The other rhythms have flattened out now. It'll take four or five minutes more before the theta-thanatos is is full enough to switch on the pheromone drip." But I wasn't about to pull away. I had no intention of missing anything—not that I believed there would be anything (and a videotape was running, anyway). But I'm like that. Set me on a hilltop and tell me to count shooting stars and I'll watch all night, for a friend.

"Ah . . . Pheromone drip *on* now," Mr. Ananda announced.

I sniffed reflexively, even though I'd have smelled nothing whether the experiment had been enclosed in glass or not.

I watched the point of the needle, near Ralph's bare calf, waiting—at Mary Ann's command—to plunge a massive dose of stimulants into him should the need arise. I kept my hand on the button that would multiply the power fed into the Faraday cage fiftyfold.

What I saw then didn't record on the videotape—as if the tape couldn't register light of the wavelength I saw, as if it came from a different spectrum entirely! But my eyes saw it—I swear it.

A red (except that it wasn't "red") thing appeared abruptly, perching on Ralph's chest. It was like a bat; it was like a giant moth; it was like an angel on a Christmas tree illuminated by firelight. It flickered, strobelike. It seemed to dance in and out of existence. It had big glassy eyes and a tiny sharp beak. It had scalpel claws on its veil-like wings—if they were wings—like the spurs that are fastened on fighting cocks. (I realized that I was seeing only what my eyes and brain *could* see, not necessarily what was actually there.)

"Theta finale!" sang the Swami, who couldn't see any of this. "Stimulants, Mary Ann."

"I already have! The signs show—"

I squeezed my button, too, at the same time. It wasn't needed. Whatever Ralph had set up to trigger the powering up of the cage had already done its job. The cage crackled with fiftyfold insulation.

The needle had slid into Ralph's calf. He jerked, like one of Galvani's frogs.

He sat upright on the water bier, his eyes wide open.

The red thing leaped from him, flickering, phasing in, phasing out (but more in than out). It hit the side of the cage and seemed to pass through the electrified filigree. And the glass walls, too. But, no, it passed through, yet not into the room we were in. It passed through into one of the reflected doubles of the cage, actually into it, leaving no "original" behind in the real cage. I realized, as I hadn't earlier, that there had been only "one" of it all along, from the moment of its first appearance. No reflections. No duplicates. Many reflections of Ralph, but none of it. How could something I could see with my eyes not possess a reflection in a mirror? Perhaps it had to do with its own indivisible essence.

The red moth beat from one phantom cage to the next, circling outward from the real Ralph Hewitson. But as it got farther away, the golden bars thickened. Now it was flying into a wall of increasingly thick syrup. It could get no farther out through the reflections.

Ralph, sitting upright and following it with his gaze, grabbed the air with both hands. The air above the real water bier was, of course, empty. The thing—Death—wasn't there. But all the hands of all his reflections grabbed in unison in all the mirror cages. He seemed to know exactly what he was doing.

Death flapped frantically around the circuit, from one cage to the next, to evade his hands. But it was all one cage to Ralph.

He caught it. He caught it! In a cage thrice removed from the original, his reflections's hands closed on it and held it tightly. His own hands—and those of all the other reflections of him—were empty. But not that pair. Not those. They held the red thing. The bat-moth. Death.

Death slashed at his hands with its wing claws and gouged with its beak. Blood ran down the hands and wrists of that one reflection. The real Ralph cried out in pain. Yet his hands showed no trace of wounds. Only the hands of the one mirror image that held the creature were flayed, but he felt the pain. He continued to wrestle with the creature. Face distorted, he held on: two empty hands cupped in midair, sinews standing out. And however much it hurt him, however much flesh it tore from his phantom fingers, his finger bones still held it securely out in the reflection.

"What's happening?" Mary Ann called. "He's overreacting to the stimulant! What's happening, Jon?"

"He's fighting Death," I cried. "He's caught Death, and he's fighting it!"

Just then Ralph turned to face me—toward where he knew I must be. "Depolarize! Transluce the glass!" he shouted.

I tore myself from the periscope hood, found the switch, and hit it. Immediately all of us could see through the cage. And of course all of the reflection worlds had disappeared.

But Ralph still wrestled—with thin air! His fingers still clutched. Ah, I could see what he was doing, though to the others it must have seemed an insane pantomime. He was tearing Death free so that he could hold it on one clenched hand—to throw it far away from? No, he'd never give up his hold on Death now that he'd succeeded. He held that one imprisoning hand aloft in a kind of open-fisted salute, grinning through his agony, baring his teeth.

"Cut the current!" he ordered harshly.

I squeezed the bulb. The crackling hiss faded away.

"Unlock the cage, Jonathan!" Even in his pain he refused to abbreviate my name.

I hesitated briefly. Was I, in effect, letting Death out into the world? But with the current no longer flowing, I suppose a mesh of wires could be no obstacle.

Ralph saw my hesitation. "You fool, I've got hold of him!" he shouted in my face from the other side of the wires—which he could have burst through by main force, but even *in extremis* he had no wish to damage any part of his invention. "Anyway, he isn't *here*. Not in this 'here.' He's still in the reflection—and I've got him tight there!"

Had he? Had he really? Or was the pain so deeply etched into his torn nerves and scoured finger bones that he only thought he had? Was he only feeling the ongoing fight in the way that an amputee still feels intense pain from a severed phantom limb? As he continued to clutch the air and bite his lip, I couldn't believe that. The reflections had gone away, wherever reflections go when they're off duty, but his reflected hand was still clutching Death out there, mimicking the shape and stance of his real hand here.

I tore the key from my neck, snapping the chain in my haste. I jabbed it at the lock a few times before I got it in and turned it.

I pulled the door open. Ralph crawled out and stood, his clenched empty hand at arm's length, triumph and torment on his face.

Three days have gone by now. Ralph hasn't slept a wink. I doubt that he could let go now if he wanted to. His hand and Death are too intermixed: claws trapped in bones, bones binding wings. His hand remains bent like that of the worst victim of arthritis, unable to flex, yet to all other appearances a perfectly unblemished hand.

"Hysterical cramp" is what Dr. Sczepanski diagnoses about his hand. She doesn't believe what I saw. Neither does Swami Ananda. They know there's no such thing as Death, and the videotape only shows Ralph alone in the cage, then suddenly jerking erect and scrabbling at the empty air.

I'm alone with him now in the office. It's night. Many deaths occur at three o'clock in the morning. That's the dead point between night and day, the hour of despair, the low point of the body rhythms. Right now it's one-thirty. Ralph sits slumped in his chair, kept awake by pain, his clenched hand resting on his desk.

"You saw, Jonathan."

"I saw. Yes."

Mary Ann believes that I autohypnotized myself by staring through that periscope into the reduplicating mirror room too long. My attention drifted away into the mirrors. I was virtually in a state of sensory deprivation. I was hallucinating freely and grandiosely when Ralph jerked upright and began his phantom fight. I was seeing a mote in my own eye. I gave it unreal life— just as Ralph, torn out of deepest trance, blood pounding through his heart, saw that blood personalized in midair as the rooster, the bat, the moth of death.

"You believe me now, Jonathan."

"Believe? I *know*."

So Ralph sits before me, holding Death at arm's length— though for how long? When Death at last escapes from him, does it wing elsewhere, or does it come directly here? Homing in, to perch on the real hand whose mirror image holds it at bay, captive in the realm of reflections?

"It feels as if my bones are coming apart," Ralph groans. But maybe they aren't at all. "This hand's still solid. Oh, my too, too solid flesh! But I can't *see* them: the other bones. I only feel.

God, what I feel!'
 "Let him go. Open your hand."
 "I can't, Jonathan. I can't."
 It's a quarter to two. Outside, the city is as still as a sepulcher. Silent night: Ralph is too weary to scream.
 Together, we wait.

POLITICAL

IAN WATSON

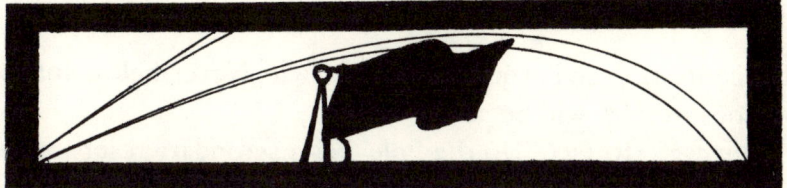

My first real experience of Socialism was in Tanzania; and Julius Nyerere remains for me a hero of integrity. Subsequently the social offensiveness of Thatcher's Britain, and the nuclear threat to Humanity (not to mention to everything else on our planet, which might possibly be the only abode of life in this galaxy), a threat made worse by a new Cold War, forced me into active politics...

Up the Pole

This column is meant to concern itself with matters science-fictional. Maybe, therefore, a more suitable title for the current column would be 'Up the Pohl'—rather than 'Pole,' as in the pole up which I am driven by various events that occur outside of the charmed circle of science-fictiondom, events such as dogmatic monetarism and inequality and the new Cold War. ("What have *they* got to do with SF?")

Maybe, indeed, the proper title should be 'Up the Poll'? Since this is where I am aimed, at the moment of writing: towards the County Council elections, in which I am standing* as a member of the Labour Party to try to do something to halt the wreckage of this country by ill-conceived economic dogmas, savagely applied. (In this rural area where I live, it is a Tory safe seat that

---

*Have you noticed that in Britain candidates stand for office; but in America they run?

I'm contesting, so I'm quite unlikely to win. Nevertheless, for the curious, results will be added below.)

But wait. In fact, 'Up the Pole' has a secondary resonance at this moment, in the wake of the Solidarity events in Poland. In SF terms, this title perhaps sounds a plea to supply duplicators to Poland—as indeed happened at the most recent British Eastercon in Leeds, prior to which fans were exhorted by fanzine fliers to stop reading this rubbish and *do* something . . .

Yet actually, *Finnegans Wake*-like, all these different connotations for the spoken, audible phrase (as opposed to the written-down, defined phrase) cohere and intermingle pungently in my mind, as though designed for each other not by a mere accident of homophony but rather by historical necessity and metaphorical cross-infection—something which James Joyce favoured in words.

Up the Pole. Up the Poll. Up the Pohl. All these connect up. (Though, in the last case, 'Pohl' is merely synecdoche—which is not an American city, of course, but the rhetorical use of the part for the whole.)

At this year's Eastercon, where I was Guest of Honour, a panel discussion was held on the theme: 'Should SF support causes?' In my GoH speech, during which I expressed the need for a political commitment by SF fans to ensure that there *would* be a future about which, and in which, to read SF, I had already made the point that, commitment notwithstanding, overt propaganda and art do not make very happy bedfellows; so this was not for me the point at issue. And it seemed to me that the panel was shaping up as yet another lively, stimulating, useless debate without any practical consequences whatever—when the prime cause today is undoubtedly to ensure the survival of life on Earth; or at least civilization.

So I proposed on impulse that the audience should vote on a proposal to call on the British government to abolish nuclear weapons unilaterally.

And the roof blew off.

Interesting, indeed, it was to hear Author X portentously accuse me from the floor of bringing GoH status into disrepute by dragging politics into SF. And noteworthy it was to hear American Mrs. Y declare in fury that I ought to walk out in disgust at this insult, and that speaking as an American she wanted the filthy weapons removed. Illuminating it was, too, to hear Author Z agree absolutely that Britain is an occupied country, under the thumb of a foreign (American) army of occupation, and insist that we musn't do anything about this because we would be punished. What's more, if we acted in this way, we would Sever Our Historic Ties With The British Commonwealth! (What price that sovereignty, upon which these ties depend, if we are run behind the scenes by an army of occupation?)

Many of the audience supported the motion, a much smaller number disagreed—and a large number were passionately against there being any such motion at all because we would thereby be polluting the precious bodily fluids of SF. The beer which we sup in harmony at the bar, toasting our beloved genre, whether we are left wing, right wing or have no wings at all, would thus turn foul and sour. An additional objection, voiced by quite a few people, was that we should not draw attention to ourselves by making a political statement (which isn't actually a *party* political statement, but simply one in favour of sanity, and of the future of civilized life on Earth) *when we are science fiction fans*. Because people laugh at SF. SF is regarded as a joke. So we don't want the media to laugh at The Cause, by associating ourselves with it.

And this, in a sense, answered the question posed for the panel, in a peculiar and distressing way—at least from the point of view of some of the audience. If SF supports causes, those causes are thereby diminished; so said several voices.

Tom Disch, present as American Guest of Honour, remarked to me afterwards that this was for him the saddening and surprising feature of the discussion from the floor. The heartening aspect, for him, was the articulacy and cogency of almost everyone who spoke from the floor. You wouldn't get this at an American SF convention if the same thing occurred, said he. Yet at the same time no one in America would feel ashamed to be identified or presented in the media as an SF person. SF people in America can demand and expect public respect. The image of SF is a positive one, not a negative derisory one. No one is worried about drawing attention to themselves. Thus, paradoxically, even though the level of debate at this British convention seemed to him far beyond that at an American convention, nevertheless a significant proportion of the audience—cogent and articulate though they were—at the same time displayed what he could only identify as a deep sense of insecurity, a guilty defensiveness about the subject they love.

And this, frankly, drives me up the pole.

Black Power—in its widest sense, of dignity and pride—wasn't possible until people were proud of being black, and insisted publicly on their dignity. Nor (varying the focus of the pride) were Gay Liberation; nor Women's Liberation. Some SF people obviously need to learn how to be proud of being SF people, and to insist on respect, and to demonstrate they they are capable of making informed statements, *as* SF people, about the world at large. (Lord knows, they're technically better informed than the majority of people, and their horizons are larger!)

True, the media in Britain will continue to play up the Fancy Dress aspect of SF—but might not the reason for that be that insufficiently intelligent things are being said, and said repeatedly, to the media? Defensively, the SF fan or organizer can always make jokes about gafiation, crudzines et al, to the visiting journalists; and ham it up. (Yet, on the other hand, John Baxter was present at Leeds recording material for a BBC programme on SF, and he was *delighted* at the new political dimension in evidence.)

True also, many 'responsible' political messages in America—associated with support for space research—have deeply capitalist, free enterprise, America-first associations. But at least they're saying it. And they're being listened to. As is Harlan Ellison, when he campaigns for the Equal Rights Amendment. Showman that he is, he means it, and gets heard. And whatever we think of the Trekkies, by applying pressure they got a shuttle named *Enterprise*.

(But of course Harlan Ellison would be horrified should I associate the term SF with him. How he inveighs against the 'true believers'—lunkheads, all of them. Personally I regard this as a pity; and I made the point on my election leaflet of describing myself as a writer of science fiction, and not—diplomatically—merely as an 'author'. I'm not worried that the cause of the Labour Party might be diminished by a 'science fiction writer' standing in an election. On the contrary.)

If SF people become known for speaking sense (as well as for having fun) they will be listened to... after a while. SF imagery is now deeply rooted in British society; the coinage is in circulation all over. Who shall maintain the standard of that currency, and fight against its debasement, but those from whom it is being mined (to revert to the metaphor of my previous column)?

Another curious feature of the wrath stirred up at Leeds, against 'dragging politics into SF,' was the fact that under the auspices of the Convention some overtly political activity had *already* occurred in the hotel before the nuclear weapons vote—namely the 'Dupers for Poland' auction held to raise money to provide duplicating equipment for the Polish free trade union. This, somehow, was an innocently 'unpolitical' affair—whilst a resolution to save all our lives through nuclear disarmament seemed to many to be militantly political. Paradoxical, indeed!

Now, why should 'Dupers for Poland' be innocent and unexceptionable activity, whilst opposition to nuclear weapons is so disruptive?

Could it just be that, *whatever* the inherent merits and 'just cause' of Solidarity, it is a cause which has been strenuously supported in the Western media *to a large extent as part of the rhetoric of the new Cold War*, and has been duly programmed into the minds of everyone as something self-evidently good, and in a sense *anti-political*—'political' equating with Communist hegemony and State control? Support for the Poles is an article of faith, because by implicit definition this defends freedom and strikes at the tyrannical Russian bear which is so self-evidently poised to gobble up everywhere (despite the USSR's obvious, and reiterated, reluctance to do anything of the sort—unless goaded unendurably). And why, pray, do we have nuclear weapons, and American weapons stationed on our soil, *not* under our control, and permitted by *no* British law, Act of Parliament or anything else? Why, because the bear must be resisted, even if Britain and all its people have to be sacrificed in the process—in a war that might conveniently be fought in Europe, with Britain as Airstrip One, the floating aircraft carrier and launch pad. Poland, good; anti-nukes, subversive... as Napoleon Pig might have put it. But they are actually part of the same equation, in so far as the Polish situation has been used and manipulated—*whatever* the case for Solidarity. Yet we do not realise it.

I would suggest that many people at the Leeds Convention who attended the Dupers auction were engaging in political activity already, but unconsciously so. A huge amount of media activity has normalised Poland as a brave and obvious cause—which no doubt it is for the Poles. A similar media blitz has *not* been directed at American nuclear weapons on our soil, or at Britain's nuclear submarine pretensions. Thus, when asked to act with regard to Dupers for Poland, no one batted an eyelid.

Yet when asked to act against the expensive schemes for the destruction of civilization promoted by the Establishment, immediately many in the audience felt with instinctive annoyance that it was not the right way to behave. Because it was political. The moral of all this would seem to be that, whether one wishes it or not, one is operating on political premises even when those premises happen to be an SF Con hotel; but in some cases unconsciously so, because of attitudes that have been imprinted. And surely it is better to be conscious than unconscious (or dead)?

Let us consider, in passing, another unconscious attitude which seems on the surface to be merely escapist fun, yet which may actually be intimately bound up with the nuclear weapons threat. I refer to the love of heroic fantasy—in its various permutations from novels through role-playing games to fancy dress hijinks with broadswords and axes. Don Wollheim remarked to me at Leeds that it seemed to him, alas, than an increasing number of fans are mentally equipping themselves thus for Life After The Bomb, in the new primitive world of tribal warfare, conquest, barbarian rituals, rape and mayhem—in a neo-primitive society of 'heroes.' These fans are training themselves for the new life style, after civilization has folded up; and they believe that they will be better equipped to survive and even enjoy themselves—*because* they have trained in the heroic fantasy arena. For them, fantasy will transmute into reality, and the Golden Age of yore will be succeeded by an even more luminous age: the Plutonium Age. And this is an utterly crazy fantasy, of survival, sick at heart. In its acceptance of a nuclear holocaust, this too is covertly political.

Speaking of sickness, I saw a pregnant sheep in Banbury a few weeks ago, attempting to give birth in the back of a van. A vet, up to his shoulder in her birth canal, was trying to extricate the contents of her womb. Which stank. From ten yards downwind, how it stank, with the stench of foetal death and rot. That would be the smell of the holocaust. And of the survivors. Who would not romp around in golden breast-plate, with broadswords slapping against their mighty thighs. But who would stink. And starve. And kill and injure, and be injured, meanly and lingeringly, not nobly.

Coincidentally, not long after I watched the misery of this sheep, BBC-TV was showing *Bread or Blood*, an adaptation of W. H. Hudson's *A Shepherd's Life*, in which the shepherd similarly, though more swiftly, delivered a lamb and then by the same method his wife, of a son. The TV film was intensely, shall we say, 'earthy'; though it couldn't convey the smell, or the droppings tumbling out of loosened bowels. But this all puts me in mind of another sort of 'pole': namely, the greasy pole of traditional rural fairs. If you could climb the greasy pole, you got the piglet. Once upon a time.

Once upon a time, too, in the Hudson tales of circa 1830 the countryfolk rioted for two shillings wage to feed themselves. So they were sentenced to death or transportation as evil criminals.

Today, going round the rural villages canvassing for the election—and driving in short space from some fairly wretched council houses to stone mansions with paddocks full of ponies—I hear the poor described as evil criminals again, because they are unemployed. And a few people in those Council houses are still going to vote Conservative. They are going to vote for their own impoverishment. Because they *know* from the media that unions and Lefties are evil.

Just so, quite a few people at Leeds knew that it was not proper behaviour to oppose nuclear weapons at an SF convention. Or they rationalised this feeling by arguing about procedure—always a convenient way out of embarrassing situations.

Because they have been told for many years that politics is something we can do without. We can do without it in local government; we can do without it at SF conventions. Politics is something which spoils: rugby tours, or cricket tours, or England's green and pleasant land and the chance of all pulling together to get us out of our present crisis (politically created, of course), or which spoils the gentle art of getting on together (some on top, many underneath), or which spoils Art, or Science Fiction. . . .

But these people are already leading political lives, unaware, even at an SF convention. And it is highly convenient to the Cold Warriors in power that they should refuse to acknowledge the fact. And abstain. And try to keep politics out of SF.

Election Results (Helmdon Division of Northamptonshire):
Tattersall (Conservative): 1860
Watson (Labour): 927

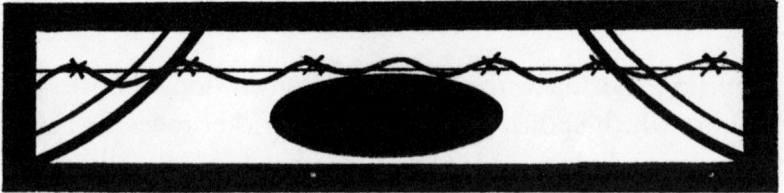

As I mentioned earlier, "Shrines and Ratholes" was written for a high-circulation, glossy French magazine at the behest of its editor, Jean-François Bizot. After I'd written the piece, total silence ensued, despite several letters from me *en français*. Early in 1984 a French fan sent me a copy of *Actuel* dating from the previous summer with my piece in pride of place, leading off Alberto Moravia, William Styron, Richard Brautigan and others on the theme of earthly hells and paradises. My words had been edited very creatively, and I was tagged as an Irish author. Maybe, without revealing himself, Monsieur Bizot had been lurking in Paris's new Irish restaurant on the night when I visited it? (See *April in Paris*.) He certainly hasn't revealed himself since. But at least my basic message was correctly conveyed . . .

Shrines and Ratholes (part II)

I guess the ideal rathole to describe would be a bug-infested brothel in El Salvador or somewhere else exotic (exotic, so long as you don't have to live there yourself!). But thanks to the world financial crisis, the savageries of our mad British monetarist government, and the way publishing—particularly in the USA —is being run by corporate accountants who couldn't care a piss for art, I've been an economic prisoner in my home island for what seems an eternity.

So I nominate for worst rathole my cursed idea for a brief

idyllic holiday last summer with wife and daughter and our three cats (quite a Noah's Ark) on a narrow boat on the South Oxford Canal, and the specific location of the rathole Upper Heyford village in Oxfordshire.

Of course in the context of waterways a 'rathole' ought to be quite a sentimental thing. Here in England we're reared on the picnics and escapades of Ratty and Mole in the classic children's tale *The Wind in the Willows*. So, abandoning the overdraft, the mortgage, days chained to the typewriter, and exclaiming "La chair est triste, hélas, et j'ai lu tous les livres (or even perhaps: j'ai écrit tous les livres); fuir là-bas, fuir!" away we fled to be caressed by the douce brise humide, on a rural canal, where ratholes are the homes of happy little furry animals.

Hélas, we did not get too far as regards 'fuir' but the 'là-bas' bit was true enough. Canal boats (steered by me) blunder about like bemused elephants; Victorian locks are bloody exhausting to crank by hand, and the very first lock was the deepest on the whole canal, a descent into a dripping stone abyss out of Dante by way of Gustave Doré. Surviving this first ordeal with the help of cans of strong beer, we then got drowned from the sky by one of many lashing thunderstorms; though the arctic gales did dry us out quickly afterwards. Meanwhile, of our three cats, two went catatonic with culture shock; while the third leaped ashore while we were choking down our lunch and killed 23 mice in an orgy of murder, leaving corpses littered along the towpath, finally becoming so excited that he tumbled off the boat into the canal; whereupon he did not so much learn to swim, as to launch himself out of the water like a Trident missile, racing back inside the boat to splatter the whole interior with litres of canal water.

Mooring near Upper Heyford, nerves too frayed to try another lock that day, we were of course directly under the flight-path for take-off from Upper Heyford US Air Force base—rubbing home one basic fact about much of the idyllic English landscape which was never known to Rat and Mole when they played around in boats hereabouts: namely that behind every second cow there lurks a radar dome, a microwave transmitter, an airbase—and soon, soon, we can look forward to cruise missile mobile control centres and launch trucks too, ambling through country lanes.

This was Upper Heyford, so here it was F-111s which hurled themselves thunderously overhead every few minutes, at an altitude of 200 feet or so, preparing for the Third World War, while the US and British governments crank up the Cold War in preparation.

Every year at the 'Promenade Concerts' held in the Albert Hall, London, they finish the concert series by singing William Blake's poem *Jerusalem*: ". . . and we will build Jerusalem, in England's green and pleasant land!" But the land is pockmarked with the ratholes of the next war, pockmarked with transplanted enclaves of military America where the US army of occupation eat their burgers and play 10-pin bowling, in between jockeying their jets. (Army of occupation? Is that accurate? Well, what will happen if a future British socialist government tries to carry out its promise to expel all US military bases? How long will that government survive, before the country is destabilised?)

Walk up the lane from the canal, through Upper Heyford village, and you arrive at a Peace Camp outside the airbase gates, of women living in battered little caravans and under plastic sheets on a tiny patch of bridlepath. (Just as at Greenham Common, where 40,000 peace women recently encircled another camp, hand in hand, and where peace women blockade the entrances by tying themselves together in spiders' webs of knitting wool.) Of course, the local councils try to expel them and take them to court; while Margaret Thatcher inveighs against the decline of family life, with mothers quitting their homes and husbands to demonstrate for survival.

Just beyond the Upper Heyford peace camp, behind the wire, commences a slice of Texas or Alabama—and of course the peace camp is a dirty, cold, unhygienic rathole, with its denizens looking like female tramps, while the US base is very neat and prosperous and domestic, God-fearing and elegant. But I know which is the real rathole. It's the foreign warbase in the green and pleasant land, where Rat and Mole and Toad of Toad Hall used to wander and where Rat once exclaimed, "Believe me, my young friend, there is *nothing*—absolutely nothing—half so much worth doing as simply messing about in boats."

Actually, exhausted by lock gates and soaked to the skin, I don't quite agree with Rat's sentiment, but what really put paid to the proposed idyll was the thunder of the F-111s, presaging the thunder of the H-bomb.

Fuir, là-bas! Hélas, I only escaped to reality.

Anger is one response; but comedy is also a weapon...

The President's Not for Turning

"They're cutting our funding by fifty per cent," Sam Dexter announced to a conference room full of worried faces. He chopped his hand emphatically down, as if dividing an apple in half with a cleaver. "There's too much public spending on science. That's the new policy. As you all know. So here it comes: chop, chop. Frankly, I'm surprised we survived *this* long. I believe I'm not overly boastful if I say that I—"

"Have defended us, like a wolf her cubs." Dr. Marion Kurtz completed the sentence for him, not exactly as Sam would have completed it, but satisfyingly enough to his ego, none the less.

"So what do we do now?" asked Dr. Xerxes Ritsos. "Send up half a satellite? Send it half way up?"

"Perform bio-engineering with a single helix?" asked Dr. Kurtz. Others were calling out too.

"Okay, there are a lot of competing interests in this room: space science, social science, biology, theoretical physics. Obviously you can run fifty per cent of the programmes, and axe the rest. "*But*," and Sam raised his hand to stem the swelling murmurous tide, "that might be the neat administrator's answer. But it isn't mine. I will *not* have this Foundation fight each other tooth and claw for the half of the beefsteak that's left. I'm not a specialist, myself, so I've no special axe to grind. All of you are equally precious to me, and to the Foundation. The work of the whole damn lot of you, and your departments—whether they contain fifty people, or just two—counts equally, in my view. I will not have any discussion of who to kick in the teeth, to save the rest of you. Sure, I could play it that way. It's what the Government expects. But I won't. The whole point of this Foundation is its interacting, *synergistic* structure."

Mark Bernstein, of Economic Forecasting, stood up—rather than merely raising his hand, as many others were.

"That's a very idealistic pitch, Sam. I'm sure we all love you for it. But the economic war's arrived on our home front. Shouldn't we get on with the business of *triage?*"

"What's *triage?*" demanded Dr. Ritsos, suspicious that a powerful tool was being brought out of hiding, which he didn't know about.

"French word. It means 'sorting.' Specifically, it means rationally sorting the wounded into those who can survive without attention, those whom medical aid will save, and those who are just going to have to be put on one side, to die. In the absence of enough bandages, or money, or whatever."

"*No,*" said Sam. "That's just my point. This Government is playing Divide and Conquer. And what I say is, we all survive together. Tell me, Mark, what is your honest assessment of the new economic policies?"

Mark smiled wanly.

"Well, they're borrowed from Britain. So we have a working example over there. The result: the collapse of industry, and nearly seven million people unemployed. The virtual destruction of a functioning country—not by the red beast, Socialism, but by a Conservative administration. It's a punishment mentality, really. 'You'll all take your medicine, and may it poison you.' It spells the death of initiative, and hope, and research."

"And?"

"And perhaps the same'll happen here."

"Perhaps?" cried Marion Kurtz sarcastically. "It's happening right now. Fundamental research is *essential* to the future." She glanced at Paul de Leuw, from the tiny Theoretical Mathematics division. "Even if it seems quite cooky. Or, let's say, marginal."

Paul rewarded her with a faint grin.

"You mustn't cut back on funding fundamental research because of an economic dogma about belt-tightening," she went on. "I mean, I'm relatively okay, I guess. Genetic technology is a boom business. But I agree with Sam. On principle, I must defend the sort of games that Paul plays, with geometry or topology or whatever it is."

"You needn't defend them to the death," said Xerxes Ritsos. "As you said, *you're* not dying. So you can afford to be generous. But me, I'd never sacrifice one antenna from the new space probe—for a new concept of infinity, or the seventh dimension!"

"My work may have space travel applications," said Paul mildly.

"Oh sure. *Hyperspace* travel applications. You find some kind of space that's 'higher' than ordinary space. You pop into the eighteenth dimension, and out again five minutes later at the nearest star. How close are you to a breakthrough?" Ritsos allowed himself to sneer.

"Well, I hadn't been meaning to bring this up at a crisis meeting. But actually, I think it may be possible—I mean, it isn't explicitly ruled out mathematically, in which case it may only need a hell of a lot of energy to stress the underlying topological structure of space-time for a few micro-seconds—that's to say, the space-time matrix—"

"What you do mean is, zilch."

"No..." Paul waved his hands, but there was no stick of chalk in them, and no blackboard near.

"So what would this achieve? Instant travel from the Earth to Mars?"

Paul frowned.

"We *might* be able to build a field—some day—that would change left into right. I mean, we could put a glove in the field and it would come out reversed—with the thumb pointing the other way."

"Great for thumbing rides in trucks, eh? I guess some of us are going to need rides, real soon."

Paul persevered.

"By rotating it through a higher dimension, you see. Or else we could rotate a mouse, and it would have its heart on the other side, and its patches reversed left-to-right."

"Neat. Very neat. Just what the world always wanted: a mouse-reverser. Didn't somebody once say, 'Build a better mouse-reverser, and the world will beat a path to your door'? I foresee guaranteed sales to the Army. Reverse all the infantry left to right and the enemy will shoot them neatly in the heart—and miss."

Everyone laughed—except for Sam Dexter, and MacDonald Carr, from Geophysics, who was fiddling with his hands, turning them over, fitting one on top of the other.

"I don't understand what you're talking about," said Carr angrily.

"Sorry, Mac. It's quite simple, really."

Paul tore a sheet of paper from a notepad, pulled out a pair of pocket scissors and snipped the paper into the shape of a hand. He smoothed it flat on the table.

"We'll call this crittur 'Mr. Left Hand.' Suppose his world is completely flat. Suppose it only has two dimensions: length and breadth. But no height. Well, Mr. Left Hand can move around his world okay, so long as he doesn't meet any obstacles." Paul demonstrated this by sticking a pencil in front of the piece of paper. "Because obviously he can't climb over them. But there's no way he can make himself into a right hand. Except," and Paul flipped the paper hand over, "by moving through a third dimension: height. Now he's Mr. Right Hand. But *we* already live in a three-dimensional world. You've got that scar on your left cheek, Mac. Could it ever become a scar on your right cheek? No way—unless you were turned through a higher, fourth dimension."

"Fascinating," said Carr. "Now could we please get on with the business—of survival?"

"Wouldn't it be really *cool*, though—" murmured Bernstein. But he shut up.

"What would be really cool?" Sam pressed him.

"Oh, I was just thinking about economic policy speeches by our beloved leaders. In particular, the President's 'Not For Turning' speech last month in Syracuse. He borrowed the phrase from the British Prime Minister, of course. She used it when everyone was begging her to do an economic U-turn, and inject money into industry and research and public works. 'The Lady's not for turning,' she said. She borrowed it from a play called *The Lady's Not For Burning*. I was just thinking how it would be cool if we could turn the President and his policies right about face, by yanking him through Paul's higher dimension..."

Again, everyone laughed. Except for Sam Dexter.

"Could we?" he said. "Could we? If you say it's possible to create this 'field' for a few micro-seconds... Could we," and he looked only mildly embarrassed, "possibly change a right-wing mouse—or politician—into a left-wing, liberal mouse? Or politician."

"You'd have to be careful with that sort of thing," called out Ritsos. "The Pope walks into your field—and emerges as the Antichrist! Heh, heh. But first, *catch your mouse*."

Sam pursed his lips.

"Oh, I think that would be possible. A Presidential visit isn't exactly out of the question. We command a certain amount of respect. It could even be seen as a trade-off. *We* swallow our medicine. *He* comes and pats us on the back."

"But, Sam," protested Lara Davis, of Oceanography, "this is just fiddling while Rome burns. It's worse than that! You're seriously suggesting that Paul eats up *more* of everyone's funds —to build a, what, a mouse-reversing machine?"

"A higher-dimension oscillator," said Paul, crisply.

"Call it what you will! It's an absurd joke. Is that the *real* idea: to show what madness politicians can force us into? You mean: if they're going to make nonsense of our legitimate research, we might as well be inventing a mouse reverser? You want to set this crackpot project up, then leak it to the Media? As a sort of psychological warfare—is that it?"

Sam quieted her with a practised gesture.

"Whatever I'm up to, Lara, please remember that fifty per cent budget translates *either* into half of us working for one year —or all of us working for six months. Which, as the wise Dr. Johnson once remarked, *à propos* a man condemned to be hanged, is a thought which should concentrate our minds wonderfully. Paul, I want to see a reversed mouse within six weeks. Everyone else: you'll offer all the help and facilities you can. But we'll keep this under wraps. Understand? *Totally* under wraps. Only department heads are to know what's really going on. Only the people in this room."

The meeting broke up in some turmoil.

Eight weeks later, Sam Dexter and all the department heads gathered in a large, fluorescent-lit chamber in the sub-basement, into which cables—as fat as pythons—snaked, feeding equipment bristling with mirrors and lenses which looked rather like the glass skeleton of some dinosaur attempting to eat its own tail. Or like a set of interlocking geometrical theorems arranged as a crystal mobile.

"The Museum of Modern Art are going to love this," said Bernstein ironically.

In the center of the array stood an open-top perspex box with a small white rat sniffing and pawing. It was a white rat—but the whole left-hand side of its body had been painted black. So maybe it could be better described as a black-and-white rat ...

Paul hoisted the rat out by its tail, mumbling soothing apologies to it, and conveyed it to one of Psychology's best mazes, on a nearby bench. A video display unit flashed up the trained rat's choices of left or right turns, till it reached its reward: a chunk of stinking gorgonzola cheese. Paul hastily retrieved the rat before it could spoil its appetite, and dumped it back into the perspex box.

"I see you've converted a mouse into a rat already," remarked Ritsos.

"Uh? Oh. Rats remember mazes better," said Paul. "Okay. Stand back beyond the white line. Ready? Here goes."

All the mirrors and lenses seemed to flash at once, full of momentary images of rats, too fleeting to focus on. Something tugged briefly at the spectators' guts. There was a sensation of sea sickness, of butterflies in the stomach. Then it was all over.

Inside the perspex box a puzzled rat was still sniffing at the pong of gorgonzola in the air, whiskers bristling. Its whole right-hand side was black.

Triumphantly, Paul hoisted the rat and rushed it to the maze.

Its choices were the exact opposite of its earlier choices. Try as it might, it got nowhere near the cheese.

Sam smiled grimly.

"Now for the Big Cheese," he said, rubbing his hands. "We'll describe this to the White House as a mock-up for, oh, a particle beam weapon satellite detector—based on new mathematical principles. No, wait a minute, I've got a better idea: a super-image intensifier, so you can spy on what's happening a thousand miles below you by capturing single photons of light. Think of a name for it."

"How about Project Gorgonzola?" suggested Bernstein with a gleam in his eye.

"I *like* it."

Secret Service agents had swarmed all over the building, then stationed themselves at doorways and by coffee machines prior to the Presidential visit, that morning.

As Sam led the Presidential entourage down to the sub-basement, he decided that he had orchestrated the flying visit rather well. The department heads, wreathed in smiles, had been servilely supportive of all the President's statements about spending cutbacks.

Some ten heads of department followed in the wake of Sam and Paul and the President, and his aides and agents.

The apparatus had been successfully rejigged to allow a much larger space at the center of focus of the dimension-rotation field.

"If you'll step over here, Sir," said Sam to the President, "we have a full-scale model of a device which can revolutionize remote geological surveillance over poor-weather terrain—even with permanent overcast—if it was put into orbit a thousand miles up . . ."

The President smiled appreciatively.

"A lot of you fellows, all over this great country, are showing me their goodies. But you know, we've only got so much cake to share out—and the *dough* for that cake comes from the taxpayers—"

Sam wasn't sure whether the President was making an awful pun, or simply betraying his ignorance of cookery.

Then the President caught up with what Sam had said.

"*Surveillance*, did you say? From orbit? Do you mean it can see through clouds?"

"Certainly. It gathers up the little bitty bit of light reflected through the clouds off the ground, or through dense jungle cover—"

"It can see through jungle from a thousand miles up?" The President smiled at the naïveté of scientists. "This thing could be, uh, adapted to photograph troop movements in dense jungle?"

"You could take somebody's photo close-up at midnight in the middle of the Guatemalan jungle," admitted Sam. "I mean, if you wanted to. Step over here, Sir. I'll show you."

There was a brief, confusing flash, a shimmering of images, a tug at the guts of all present in the laboratory. But even as the Secret Service agents started forward, it was obvious that no harm had been done. The President still stood scrutinising the apparatus.

He turned.

To Sam's eye, he was only subtly altered—and his suit jacket now buttoned on the opposite side. One of the more perceptive aides blinked, rubbed his eyes, shook his head—then quickly gave up wondering about the moment of strangeness which had just touched him, since the President was evidently the same man as a moment ago.

The President himself knitted his brows in a frown. He touched a suit button. He peered at the faces of his aides. He looked about to ask a question, but stopped himself in time. He noted the Air Force officer with the nuclear Go-codes chained to his wrist, and nodded to himself—ruefully, it seemed.

"Okay, fellas, let's go," said the President. "It's time to make the big speech."

*

"What are you mumbling about, Paul? You ought to be delighted."

"I just thought of another solution to the equation, Sam." Spying a blackboard, he wandered over to it and started chalking. "There's a false infinity here, so I kind of ignored it. But it collapses back into a finite solution if you introduce this lambda *here* . . ."

Paul wrote a new equation, humming to himself like a refrigerator.

"So what does it add up to?" asked Carr impatiently.

"Oh, just another interpretation. You see, instead of merely rotating our subject through a higher dimension, so that he's reversed left to right, *conceivably* you could say that there's a whole mirror-image universe next door to ours—where everything is much the same, but different in value—and the rotating really involves swapping our subject here, with the mirror image of our subject over there. They'd mass the same, so you wouldn't be subtracting any matter, or adding it."

"Rubbish," said Xerxes Ritsos. "If everything's different in value, it would have to be an anti-matter universe. So anything brought over here would annihilate. I didn't notice the President exploding."

"No, it isn't a question of the charges on particles," Paul insisted, tapping the blackboard. "It's—"

"But look," Carr cut in. "The events in your mirror universe would need to be *exactly* the same as the events over here. Right?"

"No, no. They wouldn't have to correspond exactly. I mean, obviously the President would have been visiting us, in the mirror universe—but for a different reason. And the apparatus in this room would have had a different purpose, even though it looked roughly the same."

"Nonsense!" snorted Carr.

The three men went on arguing, till Sam called a halt.

"*I* say we should go upstairs and open some champagne. Let's get all the gang together. I imagine we can afford champagne now."

The celebration that followed developed into a full-scale party in Sam Dexter's office.

At the height of the party, Marion Kurtz switched on the wall TV set.

The President appeared, standing at a podium in Pasadena. His reversed face peered at the audience. Nearby him, sat the Secretary of State.

"Boo!" shouted Xerxes Ritsos, tipsily.

Others started up a slow hand clap.

"Shut up, you guys! called out Sam Dexter. "Let's hear how much money he's pumping into research."

The room fell silent. Marion turned the volume up.

". . . prepared a speech, but I'm not gonna read it, fellow citizens. I'm gonna speak about something much more vital—our sexuality."

"Holy heck," said Lara Davis, softly.

"I thought we'd got our world all sorted out, as regards the population problem—and all the macho aggression stuff—under my leadership. But here I can see another bunch of you all sitting, acting out the same old reactionary caveman roles."

A buzz of bemusement and outrage rose from the TV audience. The row of Secret Service agents, trained to pay no attention to what was going on behind them, leaned forward alertly, hands moving closer to their inside pockets.

"It must just be this area," the President went on. "I've been noting the warning signs since about noon, and they've only gotten worse since. So I'm gonna speak out with a warning that I know's gonna be heard all over this great country.

"The days when men were men, and women were women, are gone *for good*. I'm saying this as your elected President: the first gay President of this land, and certainly not the last.

"As you oughta all be well aware, all my cabinet are Gays too.

"But just in case a few old-fashioned souls have forgotten this simple fact, I'm gonna remind you all graphically right now."

The President turned from the podium, wearing a shy smile on his face. Crooking his finger, he beckoned coyly to the Secretary of State—who was on his feet, in any case, with a look of appal on his face which might, just might, have been mistaken for an expression of wondering love.

"There's no hate possible," said the President, "in a world where all men love each other."

Stepping over, he kissed the Secretary of State lustily on the lips.

The Secretary of State's automatic reflex was to punch the President in the pit of the stomach.

The babel of outrage from the audience intensified as the President doubled up. Hastily the agents drew their guns, pointing them this way and that, as one person leapt up, then another.

Now the President was on his knees, bowing and unbending like a Moslem at prayer.

The Secretary stared at what he had just done, then at his fist, non-plussed.

"Gee, Sir, I'm . . . well, I'm . . . Well, I mean . . ."

Painfully, the President pulled himself up and stood erect.

"You're *straight*, Mr. Secretary," gasped the Presidential voice. "I've been suspecting this. You aren't gay at all! You ain't like the rest of us. You've never made love to a man in your life. You're sacked!"

The Secretary of State recoiled.

"You *can't* be the President!" he shouted back. "No way are you him. You look twisted about. As soon as you got here, I thought you looked a bit twisted. You're a double. You've been switched. You've been substituted for the President! To make us think the President has gone mad. Maybe so they can sneak in a nuclear attack!"

"I am the elected President of the United States," said the President, more firmly. "And I'm gay, and I'm proud of it."

Sam Dexter strode to the TV set and cut the sound. He faced the silent little crowd.

After swearing briefly, he said, "I don't think any of us need to be a hot-shot futurologist to predict what's going to happen now. Pretty soon people are going to start asking *where* precisely the President got switched. We should be so lucky if it takes them ten minutes to come up with the right answer."

MacDonald Carr grabbed Paul by the lapel.

"Okay, smartass, you got us into this!"

"Couldn't we come clean right now and offer to switch the President back?" asked Marion, intervening.

"Oh, sure," said Mark Bernstein. "It's just the twenty years in jail *afterwards*, that I'm thinking about."

"I mean," said Marion, "this could demonstrate to the whole country the desperate straits that respectable scientists are being reduced to."

Bernstein sighed. "Do you really think they would ever believe a hundred per cent that it *was* the real President—even if our dimensional friend here did rotate the man back out of wherever he is right now?"

"Mark has a point there," said Paul.

"Right," said Sam Dexter. "They couldn't trust it." He cocked his head. "Sorry—I thought I heard a siren . . . No, it's too soon. Right. As I was saying. Now, we're supposed to be a roomful of crack brains. We're supposed to be able to think nimbly—and I'll remind you once again: together we stand, divided we fall. So: no recriminations. The one remaining question seems to me to be this: Paul, how many people could pack into the center of focus of the dimension field, if we all stand really close together?"

"I guess . . . thirty, maybe."

"I thought so. All of us. That's about the only way we can escape some pretty long jail sentences for conspiracy. You'll rotate us out of here. I want two things quickly. I want a remote control to switch the field on. And I want something to disable the apparatus—fuse it, melt it down—as soon as it's been used. But without hurting our gay doubles from the other America, who'll be taking our place. That way, nobody can switch us back again, to stand trial."

"You want us all to transfer over into a *gay* America?" cried Xerxes Ritsos.

"It sounds like a more peaceful place than here. Whatever else it is! Surely we can all fit in. We can pass. We arrive forewarned. And if we all stick together, we can act, er, normal—in private. We'll survive."

"And what about our poor old doubles?" asked Marion.

"We have to apply the principle of *triage*," said Mark crisply. "We shall escape. They'll have to look after themselves. Though perhaps," he added as a mellow afterthought, "we could leave them a note or something, explaining."

Half an hour later, all the heads of department were crammed into a white circle on the floor of the sub-basement. They held tightly to each other, like sardines, so that no one would fall out.

Paul de Leuw held a small radio transmitter clear of the mass of shoulders, his finger poised.

"I *can* hear sirens now," said Sam. "Just faintly, outside. So they must be really screaming. They're coming."

"Okay, everyone?" called Paul.

"Yes, yes, get on with it!"

"Okay . . . *go*."

There was a brief flash of light . . .

But unfortunately, they had all forgotten that the real President had arrived in the alternative America a few hours before them.
The people on the other side were waiting.
They were not appreciative.

HYPOTHETICAL

IAN WATSON

Something is rotten in the State of Denmark, alias the SF publishing scene, which simultaneously develops anorexia nervosa and elephantiasis . . .

Hype Hype Hoorah!

In a recent issue of 'Vector' my eye was caught by a handsome full-page advertisement by Pan Books for *Lord Valentine's Castle*.

How pleasant, in these straitened days, that a publisher is paying for a full page in 'Vector'! One's joy turns to ashes, though, when one learns that Pan Books were spending the majority of their SF advertising budget on promoting this one book. And very little on promoting anybody else.

In a way, this ad is a collector's item. After explaining that Bob Silverberg has made a fortune from writing, and how a frantic publishers' auction took place as soon as he had scribbled the idea for this book on the back of an envelope, and how the opening sentence subsequently came to him like the lines of *Kubla Khan* to Coleridge—lucky for him that California is far from Porlock!—the ad then presents some quotes hailing this book as a magnificent Behemoth, et cetera. (Funnily, this particular quote is from the supposedly left wing Labour Party newspaper *Tribune*, who regularly leave their political acumen at home whenever it comes to reviewing SF; *Lord Valentine's Castle*, of course, is a book in praise of the Divine Right of Kings.)

Yes indeed, it is the Day of the Behemoth—and the lesser animals get trampled.

And it is the day of hype... which can indeed be hilariously funny, if one has a black sense of comedy.

Essential to the best grand hype is an array of ecstatic pre-publication quotes from one's authorial peers, destined for the cover of the brand new book; and thus publishers are currently turning authors—whose specialty is supposed to be freshness, sincerity and originality in thought and utterance—into a new breed of hectic copywriters, determined to persuade you, with glowing fervour, that this book washes whiter.

At which point I might toss out a proposal for the Non-Book of the Year: namely, *The Book of Hype*, which will gather within its pages all the best examples of this species from the book covers of the last five years. There will also be a Do-It-Yourself section, with multiple choice lists of suitable syntactic structures, comparisons and superlatives—to save authors some trouble, yet not to offend the publishers who may also issue their own books, or may do so in future. Really, this proposal should save authors quite a bit of time, and rescue them from being forced to think like copywriters every few weeks; and probably no one would notice the difference.

This could even become something of a game, instead of what it is now becoming: an embarrassment, and a periodic degradation of a creative artist's brain. (In the good old days, this is what *critics* were for.) 'Hey, how did you rate Fred's new book?' 'Gee, I tossed the dice and came up with a sixteen, an eighty-four and seventy-niner.' Those possessing word processors could simply slot in a tape of *The Book of Hype* with instructions to print out a randomised letter of appreciation.

For it *is* getting embarassing, as one's author-peers grope for new and decorative, heartfelt metaphors and similes to describe the overwhelming readerly experience they have just undergone, staying up two nights running to finish the book, shocked and exalted, slavering with frustrated appetite for the sequel.

Pocket/Timescape did all authors in this fix a service recently, and laid a foundation stone for *The Book of Hype* by distributing *The Pocket Fanzine* with a range of exemplar letters from authors in it, which I cannot, alas, quote "in whole or in part in any form." I think I might mention, however, that statistically the lead metaphor seems to be shaping up as that of a *tapestry*—lots of gleaming threads, pulled tight . . .

Actually, it *is* getting difficult to come up with fresh metaphors for science-fictional achievements—and for the field itself; as I realized in the bar at a recent convention, faced—just five minutes away—by a panel discussion boldly entitled "The Edges of SF", and wondering what on earth these were. Joe Nicholas, newly returned from Australia, happened to mention that the population level down under is pegged by the limited availability of fresh water. (Or was it the amount of beer they could brew?) Whereupon I remembered the old Rand Corporation plan, now funded by the Saudis, for towing Antarctic icebergs northwards; and the image sprang forth, fully formed, of genre-SF as a great big iceberg carved from the Gernsback Glacier being towed through the equatorial mainstream, and melting at the edges . . .

Yet this metaphor was quite overtaken by another panelist who proposed that in a couple of hundred years time, or less, the immortal science-fictioneers of today, playing variations upon their song-book of themes, may well be regarded as exactly akin to medieval French court poets, and will attract as little attention as those poets do today—for the book itself as an artefact will be obsolete.

In the Darwinian struggle for survival of this panel, the emblem of medieval court poetry quite trounced that of the melting iceberg—though I still retain a soft spot for the latter . . . At a subsequent convention, once more hunting for the elusive Snark of an appropriate metaphor—in this case for the nomination-worthy, Best Anthology-worthy, consensus type of short story—I stumbled upon Jellied Pig's Head. (For Günter Grass wrote a witty and grotesque poem of this title which while nominally a sleeves-rolled-up-to-the-elbows paean to Grass's beloved art of cookery, is also a fine biting satire on the recipe for writing a politically correct poem.)

In these circumstances, and notwithstanding the ruthless Darwinian combat of new metaphors—tapestries wrapping up icebergs, as in the game of Stone, Scissors, Paper; with medieval court poets leaping aboard, to be drowned in a pan of simmering pig's head; now a parable takes shape to round off this column. For new Behemoths are rearing up on the horizon, while the banners of hype unfurl.

Lo, here comes *Majipoor 2*—and how can we possibly wait, cries an anguishedly hyping authoress, for the second volume of *The Saga of Pliocene Exile*? And now it transpires that *The Snow Queen* is actually part of a trilogy. And, et cetera . . .

Let us entitle this parable:

Of Ground, and Ocean, and Sky

Ocean, Ground and Sky met together one day, to discuss the recent upheavals.

"New masterpieces are arising all along the boundaries of the old," declared Ground, shaking with anticipation. "Other books are going under. We three should get up an expedition to be present at the eruption of the next new work."

"Shall we take gifts with us?" asked Sky. "Such as gold, and incense—that sort of thing?"

Ocean shook his wavy head.

"No, I imagine there'll be plenty of gold and incense."

"We ought to take something, though—if only as a peace offering," said Sky. "There are such grindings and rumblings when a new fiction bursts forth. All the fault lines of the other writers tremble."

"When the engine of the imagination turns over," observed Ground, "there is always much screeching and vibration. Yet without this disturbance there would be no fresh deposits of the Imaginary on the planet's surface. The older peaks would wear down after a while. Everything would go flat."

"Will this new arrival be a novel?" asked Sky innocently.

Ground did his best to explain to her.

"It isn't as cut and dried as that, my dear Sky. Novel, novella, novelette, short story—the one category thrusts up into the next by a natural process of evolution. The Himalaya of the novel, with its sparkling crown of lucite, grows up almost of its own accord out of the foothill of the novelette—quite rapidly, too, in some cases. I imagine we will see a novelette born, or even a short story. But this will grow and grow, volcanically, with much steam and smoke, within a few weeks . . ."

Ground hesitated.

"And yet?" prompted Sky.

"And yet it *may* be a whole novel all at once—or even the Pelion piled on Ossa, of a trilogy. A whole range of mountains may emerge instantly from underground."

"What shape will it take?" asked Sky. She was busily sculpting her clouds into castles.

Ground pondered for a while.

"It will be full of strata of relationships. These will fold over and under each other, cunningly."

"And what will the scenery be like?"

"Ah, there will be plenty of surface beauty for your eye. There will be exciting gorges and pitfalls, too. Adventurous crevasses and ledges to cling to. And perhaps some long meanders. Yet the folds underneath will change the meaning of what lies on the surface—for those who look beneath the surface. Though, for those who don't look too deeply, the surface will be colourful enough."

A gale of petulance blew down from Sky.

"It isn't my fault that I can't see all the complicated folds under the surface!"

"Ah, but in *this* case everybody will want it to be known that they have seen beneath the surface. So there will be a convenient network of caves, with an easily navigable subterranean river."

"Excellent," said Ocean. "The story will flow easily, then."

"This won't be too *dense* a product of the imagination," continued Ground. "Massive, but not dense. Rule One of Tectonic Success: he that rises to the surface must be twenty-five per cent lighter than the others."

"When shall we set out?" asked Sky, excitedly. Her hair blew out in long streamers.

"Right now," said Ground. And slowly he revolved himself on his axis, to bring himself closer to the source of the new eruption.

Ocean launched himself along a powerful current.

Sky blew in the appropriate direction.

The three friends passed by a number of older mountains, still massive, though now gone cold inside. They also passed an aborted volcano, whose initial gush of lava had solidified in its throat after the first eruption—though substantial puffs of steam still issued from vents around its sides. And they passed many hills and lesser mountains, still actively thrusting themselves upwards—though already these were being jostled by the new disturbance.

"There! I can see it!" called out Sky—since she could see further than Ocean or Ground, although Ground felt all the deep vibrations. "The earth's splitting open!"

Ground groaned in sympathy.

And from out of the hot bowels of the imagination there flowed a new hill. The surrounding hills and mountains all nodded to it, since it most definitely broke new ground. It expanded their territory.

"It's a novelette," said Ocean.

"Wait," cautioned Ground. "It's still growing. It's going to be a novel."

Presently, Sky brushed across the new peak.

"Why, it's a hundred thousand words high already! A moment ago it was only ten."

Ocean reared up on a high wave.

"Fine exciting terrain, there."

"Good deep caves beneath," commented Ground. "Simple but convincing. Only a few of them are empty air pockets."

"It's . . . stopped."

"No, it hasn't—there's a sequel!"

Beside the first mountain there rapidly arose an even higher peak.

"Two hundred thousand words high, that one," marvelled Sky. She was quite out of breath at its height.

"But it's the same shape as the first one," objected Ocean. "It's just bigger, that's all."

"Going for the trilogy, now!" shouted Ground.

The third and highest mountain reared up and up, till it reached the very fringes of space. And this mountain looked quite different at first glance, but actually it was a mirror image of the second mountain.

Nevertheless, incense arose from fumaroles all around, and a rain of gold filled a hollow between the two latest peaks, brimful.

But even as Ocean and Sky were politely applauding the new trilogy, Ground cried out. More seismic shocks had reached him.

"Another eruption? So soon? Surely the engine of the imagination will seize up with the heat!"

Even so, another eruption was already taking place, not far away.

Another novelette appeared from nowhere and swiftly swelled into a novel of splendid girth, shouldering the new trilogy range aside.

Ground sensed disaster. Just in time he warned Ocean and Sky.

And a few moments later the whole crust of the world lifted off its roots, turned over and thumped back down again. Young mountains, foothills and even mature ranges tumbled. Catastrophic oscillations shook the land. Before very long, there was only one vast plain of debris.

Sky loomed over this flattened plain, searching in vain for signs of activity. Ground settled himself beneath it, patiently to await the advent of some future geological epoch. And Ocean flowed away. He felt bitterly cold. For a long time there was an ice age.

Needless to say—though quite unexpectedly—within a few months I found myself starting to write my own trilogy: *The Book of the River*; *The Book of the Stars*; *The Book of Being*. Or rather, the trilogy began to write itself—suddenly one day when my heroine gave birth to herself, and when I mapped her world and wrote down all the place names within ten minutes. But meanwhile, still kicking against the pricks, and with the year of George Orwell due soon, I decided to see how Philip K. Dick might have tackled *Nineteen Eighty-Four* . . .

The Real Winston

"For pity's sake, O'Brien," cried Winston, "what do you want me to say?"

O'Brien's hand hovered by the control lever of the pain machine. Desperately Winston searched for words, but he had no idea which were the right words.

"You admire unfacts, Winston."

"No, I mean yes. Yes."

"You want the false version of reality to be the real one."

"Yes, yes," bleated Winston. He sweated copiously. "You know that."

"I know *you*." O'Brien adjusted his spectacles pedantically. "I've watched you for a long while. Your rectification of misquotes in *The Times* was almost masterly. Alas, you lacked that final vital ingredient: belief-unbelief." The word and its opposite rolled off O'Brien's tongue as one single concept. "Consequently your work remained a virtuoso exercise, a game. Which is more treasonable than incompetence." O'Brien's voice softened. He smiled a weary, almost loving smile. "I'm afraid, Winston, you were no metaphysician. But if we're ever to beat the Enemy, you must become one."

"Become one . . . of the Enemy? But I thought I *had*—"

O'Brien's hand twitched slightly. Winston felt as though his whole body was being torn asunder, twisted out of shape forever.

"So I'm being tortured," he gasped, "because my work was *almost* masterly?"

Again Winston's body flooded with searing agony, worse than before.

"That was stupid, Winston. This isn't a punishment. Far from it! I'm taking trouble with you, because you're worth taking trouble with. You do appreciate that?"

"Yes. I mean—"

"You mean yes. You *aren't* stupid, are you?"

"How do I know what I am, any more?"

"Oh, but you do."

For a bried instant Winston's frame was torn by pain; but this time the respite from agony came so quickly that paradoxically it felt as though O'Brien had flooded him with balm and bliss instead.

Winston craned his neck against the restraints. Was there a second, concealed lever which pulsed pleasure into him? He couldn't see, and for a few moments he was totally confused. Agony? Ecstasy? Which? Pain and pleasure had changed places. He no longer knew which was which. And in those moments he felt as if some barrier in his mind had almost fallen, and insight almost had illuminated him. He stared up at O'Brien's fatherly face, feeling an awful sense of love.

"Ah." O'Brien beamed down upon Winston like a friendly summer sun. "Excellent!"

Sun... father... father, son. Even words had lost their meaning; the revelation had receded.

O'Brien spoke in a patient, schoolmasterly style.

"In Russia," he said, "they use the tool of the dialectic to combat the Enemy. There they have developed the antithesis of the thesis, the negation of the negation. And in America they have perfected Doubletalk. Whereas in east Asia they cope with the problem by means of disciplines rooted in Zen. Simultaneously: to exist, and *not* to exist. To be *and* not-to-be." O'Brien permitted himself an indulgent chuckle. "But you, Winston, are our latterday Hamlet. 'To be or not to be,' eh? One or the other. You aren't unique in this. This form of thinking has its own roots deep in European rationalism—in the idea that there is one fixed reality founded on the evidence of our senses and historical records."

Winston hoped fervently that O'Brien might carry on lecturing him for another two minutes, *five* minutes. He even hoped that O'Brien might be about to pull out of the bag the mental conjuring trick required to save him from further pain. But if the trick was simple, why then all the pain?

Winston closed his eyes, concentrating on the fact that for a few moments he honestly hadn't known whether O'Brien had hurt him or pleasured him, whether O'Brien was his father or the sun in the sky, the source of light. He felt he was very close to some magic formula which could free him from this torture seat, when O'Brien rapped out sharply, as if reading his mind exactly:

"There *is* no magic formula, Winston! No simple Credo you can recite. Even now you're trying to fool me, by fooling yourself."

Hastily Winston opened his eyes. Yet O'Brien did not look angry. Rather, he seemed benign, serene, as he gestured to the black-uniformed guards.

"Room 101," he said casually.

"What *is* in Room 101, O'Brien?"

"You know what is in Room 101, Winston. Everyone knows. In Room 101 we keep the worst thing in the world."

The guards released Winston's bonds.

Months earlier, Winston had commenced keeping a diary. This in itself was not specifically forbidden. Several of his fellow workers at MiniReal, the Ministry of Reality, jotted private memos to themselves about the day's news broadcasts. They were able, thus, once or twice a week to skip 'voluntary' evening attendance at their local Truth League building for updating on current events.

Admittedly, wall posters everywhere within MiniReal proclaimed, REMEMBER! RELY ON YOUR MEMORIES! Yet to Winston's knowledge nobody had yet been liquidated for scribbling a few notes to assist their work of reality rectification the next day.

Of course, it was always possible that such memos to oneself might themselves alter overnight. That was why the taking of notes was frowned on during Truth League lectures; but one's memory provided a check on the veracity of written memos.

Winston himself had never made notes; had prided himself on not doing so. It would never be Winston Smith who introduced an unfact into his work through lazy reliance on the written word. As a result certain of his colleagues regarded him as a prig. Yet all the while, in one compartment of his mind, he regarded the work he carried out with such zeal as essentially farcical: the equivalent of knitting a garment by day, which hidden fingers would unpluck during the night. Winston never quite understood this paradox about himself until the evening when he began his diary. He'd thought that perhaps he was simply terrified of scrutiny by the Truth Police.

But of course there was *the dream*, too . . .

He dreamt the dream once a month or so. He would be walking down a leafy lane lanced by golden sunlight. The whole world was at peace, and just around the next bend or the one after waited someone who would tell him the truth. Not merely any run of the mill, common or garden truth, but Absolute Truth, eternal verity which would answer all his questions forever. Sometimes he believed that the person waiting would be a man: a man with an unflinching granite aspect. At other times it would be a beautiful woman. Maybe the man was Winston himself, Winston transfigured; though who the woman was, he had no idea, unless she was the Goddess of Truth.

In order to reach the end of that lane he had to recite a long poem, about peace and joy, order and beauty. At some stage he always jumbled the words. Without intending to, he altered them; and woke up frustrated.

So, one bitter evening in April, after trudging back home to Verity Mansions through the wind-blown gritty streets, alone in his shabby flat Winston had started to write down the forbidden unfacts which he had been rectifying at MiniReal that day—as though by doing so, by recording those unfacts permanently, he might reach the end of that lane at last.

April 4th, 1984, he wrote. To help him concentrate he tapped out a cigarette from a packet marked SOOTH CIGARETTES. This was harsh tobacco, rough on the throat, though the best that the beleaguered state could provide. Printed on the side of the packet was the standard reality warning, such as could be seen on hoardings all over London:

TRUTH IS EVIL
RECORDS ARE FALSEHOOD
REALITY IS FANTASY

Winston inhaled, and coughed. Suddenly words flooded from

his inkpencil:
> *April 4th, 1984. This morning at the Two Minutes Truth they showed clips of a treason trial in Russia. The criminal had a raggy beard and looked like a mad prophet. He worked for the Russian Recdep, their rectification department, and he abused his trust. He wrote a samizdat, a private news sheet full of unfacts which he called* The Chronicle of Current Affairs. *How we all cheered when they shot him! TruPol might get me too & shoot me but I dont care. Peace order beauty joy, thats the only way to reach the end of the lane.*
>
> *So here goes. The first job I had today was a big one, the sort I pride myself on, nothing routine, something responsible. Of course Tillotson in the next cubicle might have been working on the same story as me, maybe dozens of us were all working on it, but that didnt matter.*
>
> times 4 apr 84 sov-premier speech malquoted rectify
>
> *I never told anyone I have an almost photographic memory. I dialled the front page of* The Times *on the telescreen and read "in Moscow yesterday Soviet Premier Kutuzov announced that the USSR is to reduce its nuclear arsenal unilaterally by 30 per cent. Said Kutuzov, 'Our planet may be the only home of intelligent life in the whole universe. What criminal folly to imperil it! By switching arms spending into genuine space research I'm sure we can reach the stars.' (Full text on page 7.) His speech was hailed in London, New York, Peking..."*
>
> *Unfacts! Unfacts! Its the same every day at MiniTrue. Except for sundays but then its twice as bad on monday mornings with two days unfacts piled up. Its been like this for years. Our memories arent tampered with, but history changes—the history of a hundred years ago, the history of yesterday—and we have to change it back. Sometimes Christ was never crucified and we have to crucify him again in the history books. Some-*

times Hitler was never born and the holocaust never happened. Myself, of course, I specialize in contemporary unfacts.

Its one damn thing after another, it takes most of the resources of the world, which is why the cigarettes are so foul and the food so tasteless. If we let up, we wouldnt be free human beings, we would be characters in a fiction.

How does it happen? How? How?

If the Inner Party knew, surely theyd have put a stop to it. Maybe the real question isnt how, but who? Or what?

If all unfacts were really facts, could I reach the end of the golden lane where the golden age of truth begins? If I write down the unfacts, will that make them stronger, more enduring?

At this point his inkpencil dried up, and Winston had sat staring at the wall till the lights went out, as an economy measure, at twenty-two hours.

The next evening, with a new inkpencil, he continued:

April 5th, 1984. The proles live in a golden fantasy, they believe the unfacts that keep on appearing in the newspapers even though the printers print the truth. They believe them in spite of all the power cuts and the missile crisis and the Verity coffee. But we cant stop printing newspapers and books. WE CANT! That would be to give up entirely, to lose our roots in the past even if its only yesterday, to lose ourselves forever. And not all the news is changed, only some.

I dont believe in God, I dont believe Gods doing this because if he was, if he existed at all, it would make nonsense of being human, nonsense of free will. Maybe theres no actual cause, maybe thats the answer. Its an absence of cause, of cause & effect, like a creeping sickness, an epidemic.

Everyone in the Party is fighting back, but its a grinding wearying job. I see the future as a big foot stamping false events on the face of time, and that face, a human face with its mouth wide open, is biting back

Till the lights went out, Winston wrote down the unfacts he had rectified that day.

O'Brien was the man's name, and he was a member of the Inner Party. Winston had seen him often enough at a distance in the labyrinthine corridors of MiniReal, but on April the 9th O'Brien turned up just before the Two Minutes Truth and stayed right through it.

Winston had left his work reluctantly to attend the Truth, resenting the interruption. According to that morning's *Times*, Iran had declared peace on all her neighbours several weeks earlier, in violation of reality, and Winston had been ransacking his memories of recent Middle Eastern affairs when the buzzer sounded for the Truth.

Whilst everyone was settling in their seats in the assembly room, he still brooded about battles on the Khorramshar front, bombings of oil refineries, sabotage of supertankers. This was a ticklish assignment, and bound to end off upstairs in committee. The main trouble was that the Iranian fanatics accepted the false news much of the time, one of the reasons for the war being the Russian-backed Iraqi intervention aimed at imposing reality upon the Iranian government... This whole business was a nest of tangled snakes!

Trumpets sounded from the telescreen, and the Truth began; but not before O'Brien had slipped into a nearby seat.

A feverish euphoria soon gripped Winston, mounting to ecstasy, an almost sexual delirium, as the announcer's voice proclaimed the plain truth: of hijackings, minor massacres, missile tests, natural calamities. However, at the climax a little voice seemed to whisper inside Winston's head, 'Are these events any truer than the unfacts? *Need* they be any truer?'

Just at this point he noticed O'Brien observing him. O'Brien alone seemed remote from the ecstasy of the Truth. The man sat like granite. And Winston understood: O'Brien was the man waiting at the end of the lane, the man that Winston could become!

After the Truth Winston felt wrung-out emotionally. Yet now he saw an ingenious way to rectify the Iranian situation. It was as if somehow those two minutes had rewired the frayed strands of logic and feeling in his mind. He even whistled as he walked back along the corridor.

A body brushed past, knocking him softly. For a moment a girl's face came very close to his, her dark hair swirling against his cheek. It was that girl from Unpersec, the Unperson Section! Unpersec's job was to scan all history books and edit back into existence persons who had vanished from the texts: persons such as Torquemada, Adolf Hitler, Heinrich Himmler. Obviously this was a vital job, yet it was common knowledge that Unpersec was staffed by people of low moral calibre: sadists, perverts and drug addicts who alone could edit such persons back into existence with equanimity. Momentarily the girl stared into Winston's eyes as if to plumb the depths of his own depravity. She winked, then hastened on ahead whistling a parody of Winston's tune.

Winston felt befouled. He wanted to shear her long hair off, wash the greasy red lipstick from her mouth, then strip her roughly and scrub her all over in a cold bath with gritty carbolic soap and pumice stone.

It was a week later that the same girl sat down opposite Winston at a table in the canteen. No one else was at the table yet, so this must have been a deliberate choice, however casual it seemed.

A fat woman wheeled a trolley past, collecting greasy plates, cracked tea mugs, empty gin glasses, humming a tuneless refrain to herself. Probably she was a TruPol officer; and Winston had no doubt that several of his colleagues eating in this very room supplemented their ration coupons by acting as informers for TruPol . . .

When the skivvy woman was safely past, and before anybody else could join them, the girl apparently was seized by a coughing fit. She leaned right across the table. Her head lowered, she whispered, "I love you—spiritually. I fantasize about you. You're the most unreal person I know!"

Incredibly, three weeks later the two of them were sitting together demurely holding hands in a clearing amidst young elm trees and hazel bushes—at the end of a golden lane.

Julia had found this country hide-out on one of her outings with the Junior Truth League. She had whispered the route to Winston amidst a dense crowd milling around the foot of Verity Column, whipped up by a rumour that some truth saboteurs had been caught.

The hide-out seemed a paradise—and Julia was not a pervert or sadist or whore at all. She only pretended to be. Actually, she was sweet and pure and simple.

With a laugh she dismissed her work in Unpersec. "Oh, it's all such nonsense! Who cares if those filthy people existed or not? We just have to cram our little heads with Hitler and the Marquis de Sade in case they disappear overnight, that's all."

"If they did disappear," Winston said cautiously, "this wouldn't be the real world any more."

"Poo to that! Then the whole world could be just like this: a golden dream."

"And it wouldn't be true. We're the guardians of evil, you and I, Julia. That's what is really meant by the slogan 'Truth is Evil'. If all the evil truths get washed away, then we're lost. We'd have lost ourselves. Ah yes indeed, we're the guardians of evil."

"Really? I'm afraid that's way over my head. Look, Winny, if there was a great flood that washed every book and document away, we could start out again all clean and simple. Wouldn't that be nice?" She shrugged. "Since that isn't going to happen, who cares?"

"There's a flood all right, Julia. It's a flood of unfacts. Don't you ever wonder how it happens?"

"Of course I don't. That's boring. It's just a fact of life like the weather."

"I think maybe there's a secret organisation—which is tampering with reality. Its members are savants with superhuman powers, using tools we can't comprehend."

Julia yawned and stretched her limbs in the sun. "Maybe the moon's made of green cheese, dear."

What *if*, wondered Winston, there really was such an organisation: one composed of supremely wise sages possessing extraordinary powers, operating out of a secret headquarters somewhere remote such as the Himalayas? If the Inner Party knew this, why didn't they atom-bomb the Himalayas or the Andes or wherever? Maybe they had tried, and failed.

What if these savants were more-than-men: a secret race who would one day supplant the human race? With a guilty thrill Winston contemplated this notion. Perhaps, perhaps he had himself already taken one small step towards joining this superhuman band. And perhaps one of this band, operating undercover, was none other than O'Brien!

Winston told Julia about his diary, his own humble chronicle of utopian unfacts. She seemed not to see the point of it, beyond murmuring, "What an unreal fellow you are, to be sure!" Soon she drifted off to sleep in the drowsy sunshine. Presently he slept too.

Later, after waking and tidying twigs from their clothes, Julia and Winston kissed each other chastely on the cheek before retracing their steps.

It was two months later, and they had started meeting in a rented back room in a prole district of the city. There Julia would wash off her lipstick, tie her hair up in a tight bun and occasionally permit Winston to kiss her upon those cleansed lips. "My unreal lover," she would whisper, giving the word its ancient, modest sense, "my fantasy friend. You are Abelard and I am Heloise. You're the Prince and I'm Snow White, though my hair is dark."

"Snow White slept in a coffin, Julia. That's where we're bound, too, on the day that TruPol finds out."

"Yes," she would sigh.

That particular evening Winston told Julia how O'Brien had stopped him in a corridor at MiniTrue. At last. At long last.

"I've been observing your work on *The Times*, Smith," O'Brien had said, loudly so that anyone could overhear. "With approval, I might add. It so happens that I chair a committee concerned with micro-untruths."

"With—?"

"Ah, but you wouldn't know about those, would you? Micro-untruths is our technical term for seemingly petty, trivial falsifications—as opposed to unfacts, which are gross distortions of major events. We believe that the force behind Untruth is stalemated—though not beaten—by our efforts. Now it is trying a different and more subtle ploy, namely the forgery of very minor banal details. This may seem mere pawn play, yet *en masse* it could link up into a deadly attack. I thought you might care to be co-opted on to my committee? Perhaps you would be so kind as to call at my flat one evening to discuss it?"

"I'd be delighted."

Excitedly Winston related this encounter to Julia; for obviously O'Brien's words concealed a very different message indeed.

Julia nodded, and yawned.

A lone spider was dangling down from the ceiling, as if aiming for her open mouth.

"Ugh!" cried Winston, and threw his shoe at it.

A week later Winston and Julia worked up their courage to call on O'Brien in his Inner Party flat. A servant ushered them in: a little man with beetling brows, who might have been a deaf mute for all the noise he made.

The couple stood waiting across the shag-pile carpet from O'Brien's desk, while the man continued dictating top-level memoranda. As soon as the servant had left, however, O'Brien looked up.

"Shall you say it, or shall I?"

"I'll say it," said Winston. "I believe Untruths are caused by a secret society of savants who have evolved beyond the human race. I believe you're an agent of this society, risking your life at MiniReal for the sake of a future utopia when the human race will have forgotten all its tragedies and villainies, forgotten all our history, forgotten Auschwitz and Genghis Khan and the Inquisition. I want to help this society. I love Untruth."

"So do I," added Julia, though less firmly.

"And what would you do to help this, er, society?"

"Anything!"

"Would you be prepared to obliterate Shakespeare and Dante and Homer? Shakespeare for his tragedies, Dante for his Hell, Homer for his wars?"

"Yes!"

O'Brien asked several questions in like vein, to all of which Winston answered 'yes' enthusiastically, with Julia nodding along.

"Very well," said O'Brien at length. "There *is* a society of supermen who are behind the amelioration of the news and history."

"Amelio . . . ?"

"The bettering, Julia. Aiming at a bettering of reality itself—a world without war, cruelty or intolerance, without futility or tragedy. These supermen work from a distance to change the texture of the world, using meditation and mind-trance. Events themselves they cannot alter, but the record of events they *can*."

"Yet people still remember, and set the record straight," said Winston. "Is that because the society won't allow itself to tamper with people's minds directly? Otherwise people would cease to be people, cease to be free?"

O'Brien nodded gravely. "You yourself will never meet any of these supermen personally. Nor will I. Neither you nor I can betray them, nor even prove the fact of their existence."

"Because they hide in the Himalayas?"

"Don't ask." O'Brien spread his hands expressively. "You mustn't ask, nor may I answer. But some day—perhaps tomorrow, perhaps in ten years time—you will receive a message to commit some act of sabotage inside MiniReal. Afterwards, possibly—just possibly—the society may be able to spirit you away to safety."

"In the Andes or the Himalayas." It wasn't a question.

"In the Andes," O'Brien echoed him, ironically, "or the Himalayas. And now you must both go."

"Will we talk together again?" asked Julia.

O'Brien regarded her thoughtfully.

"Only . . . only at the end of the golden lane!" exclaimed Winston in a rush.

"Only," agreed O'Brien, "at the end of the golden lane."

When they were arrested subsequently, Winston discovered what he had known all along in the core of his being: namely that the golden lane was one of the floodlit corridors deep in the basements of TruPol . . .

Room 101 seemed to him the deepest chamber yet, as though the whole world weighed down on it, compressing even the air. The room was bare, but for a heavy metal chair and a table with something bulky hidden under a cloth upon it.

To Winston, strapped immobile in that seat, O'Brien said, "The worst thing in the world varies from person to person. Sometimes it is death by impalement on a stake through the anus. Sometimes it is death by burial alive. Occasionally it is something trivial, not even fatal. In your case, Winston, the worst thing . . ." And O'Brien whipped away the cloth.

Sick at heart, ice in his bowels, Winston mumbled helplessly, "Spiders . . . No, you can't do that to me, O'Brien, you can't. Can't, can't."

"Observe the construction of this box. It fits over your head thus. When I pull up this plate, the contents of the box will crawl all over you. Some will enter your nostrils; others will make their way into your ears. They're overcrowded in the box. They're in a bad mood. They're hungry. They'll spin webs. They'll sting and wrap. To them, your head is one big fly."

Winston heard a distant screaming. It was himself.

"One word of advice, Winston. Don't think too hard. Thinking won't save you."

Don't think? How could he possibly think anything? He had to stop the spiders. He had to *put something* between him and them. Something. Someone.

"Don't do it to me!" he heard himself begging. "Do it to Julia! Not me! Julia!"

"You'll have to do better than that," remarked O'Brien sadly as the box was lifted over Winston's head.

"What do you want? Anything! Tell me!"

"Our Enemy is subtle." O'Brien's voice sounded very far away now. Much closer to Winston's ears was a soft, gentle sound of infinitely many legs all moving. "Thought and science have failed to combat the Enemy. Our Enemy hides from us, masquerading perfectly. Perhaps the Enemy is ourselves, without our knowing it. Perhaps it is our own minds acting in concert, dreaming unfacts into existence, eating holes in human history..."

Words bleated inside Winston's brain. To be or not to be! But there is no fixed reality! To be *and* not-to-be!

Spiders. He was a big fat fly. Suppose the spiders didn't know that? What if *he* didn't know it? What if the spiders thought he was something else? What if *he* thought so?

I'm not a *fly*! I'm not a *man*! I'm a spider too! A very big spider that no other spider would dare mess around with!

Winston felt hairs twitching all over him. He felt his limbs tip-tapping—how many limbs, four, six, eight? He honestly didn't know. His spinneret unwound silk from his bowels, his mandibles clicked.

He heard another click too—and he realized that the box over his head had not been opened. It had been closed. Forever.

When the box with its squirming cargo was removed, O'Brien stroked Winston's brow. Tears trickled from Winston's eyes. For he knew now that he did not merely love the worst thing in the world. He *was* it, himself.

It was the lonely hour of fifteen-thirty, at the Chestnut Tree café, and Winston's glass of Verity gin had just been replenished by the silent waiter.

These days Winston was serving on O'Brien's committee for the detection and rectification of micro-untruths. So important was this work that Winston had been relieved of his previous task of correcting *The Times*. Yet the new work could be carried on wherever he chose, requiring as it did a different sort of vigilance. Everywhere now—on public posters, cigarette packets, tax forms, betting slips, beer labels—Winston was on the watch for micro-untruths. These could crop up anywhere; and did. Now that Winston looked back, he was terrified to think in retrospect how the whole fabric of human reality was being nibbled by moths, making tiny holes all over the place, whilst he had blithely assumed that major circumstances such as the arms race or Hitler were the whole of it.

Winston would have to detect all those moth holes, even if he couldn't catch the moths themselves; and spin little webs to repair them.

A shadow fell across his table. He looked up.

A woman with long dark hair, wearing red lipstick. Julia. And at once he could see that in some indefinable way she had changed.

She licked those scarlet lips. "I'm evil," she murmured. "Evil through and through. Just yesterday I was in Unpersec busily restoring Gilles de Rais to the history books. Gilles was Joan of Arc's man at arms. And a sodomist and sadist. He tortured little boys in his castle dungeons. He was the real Bluebeard. I enjoyed restoring him. Because I'm evil, and evil is good because it's true . . ."

Winston nodded. It was quite safe for them to meet now, yet he had no real wish to talk to her; he had too much on his mind. Still, he felt bound to offer her a glass of gin.

Fortunately she declined the offer, and soon left the café without a backward glance.

Feeling peckish, Winston consulted the printed menu card. Food at the Chestnut Tree was rather better than your average processed soy. Not much; but somewhat. The spaghetti bolognaise was Winston's favourite.

The printed price caught his eye. It was cheap, far too cheap! Surely it had cost more last week. Chestnut Tree café prices would have burnt a hole in the pocket of the Winston who had once corrected *The Times*. With inflation, there was no way the price could have gone down.

Hastily he consulted other prices on the list. Others seemed to have gone down too, though few as dramatically as the spaghetti. Trembling, he called the waiter over and pointed a quivering finger at the list.

"Are these the *true* prices?"

The waiter peered at the tarriff. He scratched his head uncertainly."

"Fetch the manager at once!" Winston ordered.

As Winston sat waiting, his trembling calmed. He began to feel full of resolute purpose and granite dedication. A real human being had to be harsh. For now the enemy of reality was everywhere. Winston both knew this, and did not know it; such was the nature of belief-unbelief.

Somewhere in the distance, a clock began to chime sixteen.

IAN WATSON

Most science fiction isn't written in English . . .

April in Paris

This April my French publishers Calmann-Lévy flew me over to Paris for the "Salon du Livre" book fair, and to do a string of interviews about *Le Monde Divin*. (Which, I hasten to add, is the French edition of my novel *God's World*, not a theological newspaper . . .)

So, economic prisoner of the recession and Thatcherism for the last few eternities, with one bound I broke the chains attaching me to my typewriter and drove to Birmingham airport.

Something else broke, too, on the way there, namely whatever cable connects up the clock which counts the miles. If you're ever driving along a deserted road alone on a dark morning, and hear a sudden raging squawk like the Night Stalker leaping on you, fear no evil; that's probably all it is, the clock clocking off . . .

From Birmingham Airport to Charles de Gaulle; along half a kilometre of switchback moving walkways through tunnels and glass tubes to the taxi rank; and off to my hotel, near the Opera. Then out for the first major event: lunch with my French editor, in a Lyon specialty restaurant. Which, it goes without saying, is quite a different kettle of *poissons* from a Lyons corner house. A couple of bottles of wine later, packed with deliciously sauced *jambon* and buttered spinach—though I sternly declined the veal on grounds of cruelty (*my* pig lived and died happily, as I could tell by the taste)—it was round the corner to the offices of Calmann-Lévy. Their building, with a huge brassbound door down an arched courtyard, quite resembles Gollancz in its creaky antiquity, though it is rather vaster and even more of a veteran. For here trod Baudelaire, clutching his newly-minted *Fleurs du Mal*; and Flaubert, bearing *Madame Bovary* . . .

Surrealism commenced with the first big interview, scheduled to take place at 'X', a mysterious rendevous. Off I was driven to a road junction in the great spread of the Tuileries Gardens with no obvious buildings near, only an access tunnel leading deeply and steeply down into what looked like a subterranean carpark, the sort where you just *know* from a hundred TV movies that a car engine will suddenly rev, there'll be a screech of tyres and it's bullet time.

But actually this was the entrance to the underground stronghold of the post-telecom people, buried far and wide beneath the surface of the gardens; and the TV director who was orchestrating my interview wanted a futuristic setting for the recording. So we all descended further by lift into measureless concrete and electronic caverns and found a hall which suitably resembled the bridge of a starship, which was then floodlit in green and red and orange, for me to pose Saganesquely (Carl, not Françoise) while I answered questions about the malady of heroic fantasy, and about SF metaphysics and economics.

Perhaps even lower down in the bowels of Paris beneath my telecom starship, were nuclear bunkers? If there were, no one seemed particularly interested. "What's that?" I was asked the next day, about my CND badge. And it turned out that people hadn't even heard of the women of Greenham Common, though they are big news in Japan, America and Germany; and the French were aware of recent anti-missile demonstrations in

Germany. But not in England. How peculiar.

After the TV recording, it was off to the "Salon du Livre", held in a stone and wrought-iron palace the size of Paddington Station (but far more beautiful) just off the Champs Elysées. About 450 French publishers had stands there, with lawns of green carpet in between; and *Le Figaro* commented the next morning that the French publishing industry was certainly *behaving* as if all was well with the world, whatever the harsh reality was. Certainly the champagne flowed freely enough at the *Magazine Littéraire* cocktail party and the Calmann-Lévy soirée later on. In between these two pleasant bibulous, bibliophilic events I squeezed in an interview or two, and was whisked outside for a walk around with a photographer—whose son had gone to study engineering in Lancashire and, *horreur*, declared that he was going to settle in Blackburn forever. Her stand at the "Salon" was hung with her photographs of Nabokov, Barthes, Borges and other writers; and she posed me in various locations around the Champs Elysées standing on plinths and caressing stone dolphins. Ah, magnifique. Perhaps I can become a fashion model if the world stops reading books.

Back to the soirée, where author Philippe Curval—*Brave Old World* (Alison & Busby), a lovely book—was very keen to try out Paris's recently opened Irish restaurant.

What, an *Irish* restaurant? In Paris? Visit Paris to visit an Irish restaurant? The mind boggles. But at this point I recollected that *The Observer* had devoted two sprightly columns to this brave new venture, a couple of weeks earlier. The fact that in Moreton Pinkney, deep in the empty quarter of Northamptonshire, I happened to have read a long critique of the new Irish restaurant in Paris struck Philippe as equally bizarre; so obviously we had to go there, all piling into the car of Marianne Lecomte.

And oh my gosh, was it *good*. The *assiette de fruits de mer*, piled with smoked and raw oysters, smoked and cooked salmon,

Dublin Bay prawns. The beef and pepper stew . . .

There seems to be a lot about food in this column, even unto the newly-minted *Fleurs du Mal* (which was quite unintentional, I assure you). And even so I've left out the Savoy-style restaurant, and my trip under my own steam to a vast crowded low-cost eating hall walled with many large mirrors (not forgetting the enormous painting of a stone stairway in a chateau garden with implausibly big roses or perhaps camellias) where the waiters out of Toulouse-Lautrec did all the correct things like scribbling the bill on the paper tablecloth, and where a beautiful young Englishman out of *Brideshead Revisited* at the next table was trying to talk his older French *amie* into putting up the finance for an erotic movie. The place was wine-stained, crumb-scattered and elbow-jostling, but the *truite aux amandes* was almost as good as anywhere else. But I promise that I'm not, this time round, auditioning to be a cook. It's just that SF events in France automatically become gastronomic events too; and there's quite a difference between this and staggering out of a British con hotel for a gut-blaster Vindaloo curry.

Bon appetit! La vie est bonne . . .

But how is life, in harsh economic reality, for French science fiction writers?

Well, there are problems.

The first problem of course is that the world SF market is dominated by books written in English; and if we in Britain are frequently and generally the poor relations of American science fiction—economically speaking—the French are the poor relations of all us Anglo-Saxons. Where can their books be sold? Belgium, Luxembourg, a bit of Switzerland, Quebec. How can they get translated? It isn't easy. There are a handful of exceptions, but on the whole British publishers can't afford to pay a translator for a French SF book, and US publishers haven't got anyone who can read French—should they even care. Patrice

Duvic sold a story to *Omni* a few years back, but by writing it in English; and there's a whole world of sweat between writing a short story in English, and writing a whole novel, if indeed anyone could contemplate such a mad project.

Add on to the problem of the dominance of English language SF, other problems which crop up in Anglo-Saxonia too. First of all, rubbish sells a lot better in France than good stuff. Conan books go like a bomb, as do space operas from Fleuve Noir—many of these hacked out by good French SF writers in between doing more serious books.

Then, the good French SF writers are not very popular or well-known in their country, they say . . .

I digress. Actually, the print runs of the French equivalent of hardbacks (expensive trade paperbacks) are quite a lot bigger than equivalent UK printruns and the numbers generally sold would gladden the heart of a British publisher; but even so, I have a theory about this, which brings us back to cookery. Several times I've heard British publishers complain that we Brits will not fork out the price of a hardback book when we would be quite willing to pay the same sum for a meal in a good restaurant. But perhaps we Brits at heart are just gluttons, not gourmets—how else to explain the popularity of Berni Inns? Whereas in France a meal is also an intellectual event, and a good meal is seen as of equivalent importance to a good book (at least among readers); this, due to a unification of sensibility between belly and brain, a recognition that the mouth which eats also utters intellectual discourse. To translate the British publishers' complaint into Newspeak: 'Britreaders unbellyfeel Ingbooks'.

Anyway—end of digression—the best French SF authors don't feel that they're all that popular in their native land; and while it was slightly gratifying (of course) it was also rather horrifying to be told that *I'm* rather better known in France than they are.

But then, in our own fair land, are not Messrs. Watson and (oh well, I'd better not add any more names, out of respect for my colleagues' feelings), Messrs. Watson and others less well known than . . . about 50 American SF writers?

Which, in this study of hierarchies, leads on to the interesting question: in America, which outsider, which alien, is better known as an SF writer than *American* SF writers?

Maybe Borges could come to our aid here by inventing (as in his tale "Tlön, Uqbar, Orbis Tertius") the works of an imaginary major SF seer—who would obviously not be Kilgore Trout—who would gradually supplant all the native authors, thrusting them into second place in public esteem . . .

Or perhaps here we have an analogical proof of the existence of God; a rebuttal—in the SF dimension—of Gödel's disproof of self-validation within any enclosed system. For there seems to exist, in the SF world, a category of supreme beings, greater than whom are no others. The hill of skiffy has an actual, non-infinite summit. Olympus, USA.

But hark, I have just thought of one candidate.

Arthur Clarke. Oh dear, I did not intend in this column to prove by remorseless logic that Arthur Clarke is God . . .

What's special about Arthur Clarke, incidentally? Well, he doesn't have a nationality in any narrow sense of the word. He has transcended himself. He's unidentifiable (like certain phenomena in his Mysterious World). He's a world-citizen. (Please stop reading this, Arthur, if you are. This is no good for your moral character, modesty etc.) He's, um, a man of the world. As it were.

Whereas the French are imprisoned by their language and nationality, and so are we Brits on the whole (though I myself tried to mutate into a Japanese for several years). Whilst the Americans, on the other hand, know for certain that their own country *is* the world. Which is just as trapping for them, even though it equips one with the illusion of Super Powers: general cultural edge-of-the-future perceptiveness and whatnot.

And maybe, just maybe, science fiction has run slam-bang into a cul-de-sac not merely because of malign commercial forces encouraging unoriginality and drivel, but because in absolute objective terms (economically and global-culturally) American SF *is* the zenith, but in America SF discourse has begun to recycle itself in a closed circuit—by contrast with the brave initiatives not so long ago, of Delany, Zelazny, Le Guin etc.—precisely because there is nowhere else mentally to go. Meanwhile, too—and let's not underestimate the effect on consciousness—history is repeating itself malignly, with a second Cold War, a second Depression, a second mini-Vietnam in Central America, a second-rate actor in the White House.

We're all looking out eagerly for the book that is truly *other*. (We even keep on trying to write it, too!) Unfortunately, what seems to be other often turns out five minutes later to be more of the same. (I mean, *is* Gene Wolfe's *Book of the New Sun* entirely an enormous breakthrough in discourse ... or is it a sword and sorcery novel without a plot written by someone supremely literate?)

If SF is to break out of its current mental logjam, somehow we've got to become *other*, *autre*; and I don't just mean migrate into the mainstream. We've got to become somebody else; and in my next column I hope to explore a bit further the notion of becoming somebody else.

HORTICULTURAL

IAN WATSON

I never did finish exploring how to become someone else. But never mind. In an alternative universe, I am a market gardener . . .

Some Cultural Notes and Pest Control

It occurs to me that running through my life as a writer is a strong horticultural theme. Years ago I used to collect cacti and succulents avidly; and actually my first four paid publications were columns in the pages of *Amateur Gardening* and *Popular Gardening*, written when I was fourteen or fifteen. At the moment I'm looking at the only one I still have a copy of: "Growing the Sacred Cactus," *Amateur Gardening*, 19th September 1959. This was about the peyotl cactus, producer of mescaline (which reminds me of another dawning interest). There were earlier articles as well, about the Cochineal Cactus, *Nopalea cochinilifera*, the Crown of Thorns, *Euphorbia splendens*, and 'living stones', of the Lithops clan.

Given the resources, I would gladly have grown orchids too, and bonsai. As it was, though, I stuck to succulents and cacti. I was even thinking of specializing—in Stapelias, that intriguing species which produce flowers that look and smell like rotting flesh, to attract the blowflies which fertilise them.

But then I gave up.

Yet did I really? When I was putting together my recent collection *Sunstroke & Other Stories*, it occurred to me that maybe I had never stopped at all, but instead had set out to breed my own species, by verbal rather than genetic engineering. There in the book were my queens of the night and bitter aloes, my crown of thorns, my fly traps and pitcher plants, my bonsai of the mind. More than a few had spikes or trapdoors or sticky tendrils, or otherwise played tricks; for such are the kinds of plants I would have grown.

Then again, I've written a novel called *The Gardens of Delight*; and here I am sitting in Moreton Pinkney while the Autumn rain pours down, with the silver cup for best front flower garden still on our mantelpiece for the second year. (Richard Cowper tells me that *he* won the cup for best vegetables; but, say I undaunted, we are self-sufficient in double asters and floribunda roses!)

Yes, the chilly October rainfall. And I can see black soil again in the garden, now that a lot of succumbing plants have been hauled out and trucked to the tip in our garden-refuse wagon of a car. The dahlias are still busy, the Rudbeckias have flowered incredibly all Summer long and are still at it; and the fire-thorn Pyracantha is covered with bright red berries. But otherwise it's pretty well over for the year. The lawn has been raked, and spiked, and just awaits a top-dressing. The houseplants are all in from the tubs, and the downstairs windows are curtained not with net and Draylon but with chlorophytum and geranium, yucca and ivy and begonia. There's a huge Crassula, the Tree of Happiness, on my desk, managing to look remarkably like a bonsai forest. The first chapter of a new SF novel lies on one side of it, and on the other side are letters about the correct thickness of tug-of-war ropes, and the Inter-Village Quiz sponsored by Avon cosmetics; as I'm secretary of the village hall.

Outside, the farmers are transhumancing their sheep down Weston Lane, to pastures new.

Transhumance: I never knew this word till the other night at the village hall, when we held a quiz to select the Moreton Pinkney team for the Avon quiz. Neither did anyone else but the question master, a teacher from the grammar school in Towcester who drinks in the Red Lion and who had tackled the setting of the questions with gleeful relish. Baffled farmers stared in amaze as he revealed the true name of what they are up to: seasonal movement of livestock.

What do I see from my windows? Out there, between the ironstone-walled vegetable allotments, with the Old Fire Station tucked away in them (from the days when a cart and horses trundled forth to quench any blazes); and the Scottish baronial gates of the Manor House on the other side? It's lively. There are non-stop events: teams of penny-farthing bicycles, vintage cars heading for rallies, tractors towing bales of hay, combine harvesters, flour lorries, scrap metal lorries, low flying war-planes screaming just above the trees, the local millionaire's helicopter, autogyros and hot air balloons wandering from the Silverstone racing circuit (we can hear the engines revving up like faint thunder ten miles away), local riders astride their horses, racers from the Towcester race course being exercised, packs of (apparently) Vietnamese bicyclists, car loads of Japanese tourists, parties of ramblers in stout gear, herds of cows, cats, squirrels, geese, a pony and trap, the Hunt off to annoy the farmers. (Not quite all at once.)

This is the 'village of pigs and paupers' of the 19th century—at which time it had five pubs, now reduced to one. Since then it has upmarketed a bit. Here lives the aged president of the Bronte Society, with his library in the old stone forge on the lower green; here lives an ex-librarian from Camden, ex-member of the Communist Party, Jewish atheist who married a black man—along with her nuclear physicist sister. Here lives an ex-rally driver and after-dinner raconteur; and a USAF ground controller currently with bright red eyes due to a collision between US metabolism and ale. Here lives a Canadian spy; why else did he say he was going on a course in cryptography before being sent to Mongolia? Here live those who sell sheep-shearing clippers, and motorcycles, and rubber bits for cars; and who are likely to be off to Moscow or Melbourne at a moment's notice. In the largest house in the village, The Grange, lives the local taxi driver. There's no policeman within miles, so the local pub stays open till... but I'd better not divulge that, save to say that now I know why people in the radio soap opera *The Archers* only drink half pints, which I always thought a bit soppy; it's the only way to stay conscious long enough.

And here we garden. And natter over the hedge. And weed, till there are no weeds left; and zap the pests and parasites—which unfortunately, as regards the lawn, has to include worms, since worms are mole-food. (This confession quite distressed the Vicar, who cited Darwin's early treatise on earthworms. Of the Vicar, incidentally, it is written in the *Northampton Independent*, this county's version of *Country Life*, that his old sprawling vicarage "has become an incubus" for him. Being interested in erotic demonology, I must seek more details.)

Weed. And deadhead. And zap parasites. Or the garden of delight will not flourish.

Being a great believer in sermons in stones, and tongues in trees (and duly mindful of the quip about Wordsworth that he found those sermons in stones, which he himself had put there), at this point I feel moved to a few remarks about other kinds of parasites and weeds: namely, literary ones.

After I gave up growing cacti, for a while I became an academic, of the Eng. Lit. variety. So naturally I wrote criticism. Here are some products of that period: 'Nothing else to live but sins: Jean Genet's Africa', *Transition*, Kampala 1967; 'E.M. Forster: Whimsy and Beyond', *The Rising Generation*, Tokyo 1969; 'Elias Canetti: the One and the Many', *Chicago Review* 1969; 'For Love or Money: Shakespeare's *Merchant of Venice*,' Japan Women's University theatre programme 1969 . . .

Perhaps these titles, though actual, read a little like parody? Such as we might find in one of those university novels which feed new solipsistic grist back into the academic mill?

But, then, criticism is itself parody. It is a travesty of the original words in new and condensed form: Campbell's Rhetoric Soup. It is parasitical on original creativity, something secondary. It imitates the creative act, as weeds imitate the seedlings they grow beside (in an effort to strangle them).

No harm, of course, in writing reviews and criticism as an amateur ('out of love': love of the subject). But there is a whole parasitical sub-worlds, in love with itself, of the middlemen of art—academics, critics, pundits, personalities, those who sit on committees for the arts—which actually harms art; and which drains resources therefrom.

This came home to me strikingly at a one-day conference I attended at the London Institute of Contemporary Arts in March this year, entitled "Focus on Fiction," supposedly designed to enquire into the health of the contemporary novel, high and low, genre and literary.

I shall pass over the morning's activities, commencing with a dowager empress opening address by Marghanita Laski—who took it upon herself in passing, by a kind of parenthetical imperial fiat, to exclude pornography from the ranks of fictional art high or low; later a puzzled questioner said, "But when I was reading *The White Hotel*, I suddenly realized that a lot of it *was* pornography, and that was why it worked so powerfully . . .

I shall likewise pass over the succeeding college tutorial circa 1955, concerning the Grand Tradition, a further exercise in rampant twee, further establishing the sense of *haut* snobbery and sophisticated social nicety.

I will not allude to the slights, both implicit and overt, suffered by the invited representatives of the Romance genre; though I almost felt inclined to rush out at once and buy a few Mills and Boon books out of solidarity. And I will pass directly to the nub of the matter: the afternoon Writers' Forum, supposedly a panel discussion in which various authors would present their own points of view, and expound their reasons for choosing a particular literary form, to be followed by questions from the audience.

On the panel were Salman Rushdie, representing the 'art' novel, Jessica Mann for thrillers, Jeffrey Archer for best-sellers, Roberta Leigh for romance, and myself as skiffyman.

So we five authors duly presented ourselves, each clutching a crumpled page of notes about something that we particularly wanted to say.

And they changed the format. With one bound, we were chained. Hey Presto, Frank Delaney, literary lion tamer extraordinary, was brought on stage to interview us all as *specimens* of authors. While the critics were allowed any amount of time to flute on, and hold forth whither so ever they wished, the authors were not even permitted their promised ten minutes of free speech, but instead must have their words rigorously controlled by standard questions. The authors—the producers of the primary product without which the whole conference, and criticism itself, couldn't have existed—were to be kept locked in cages, exhibited, put through their paces, then dismissed. Each with their page of notes—about things of desperate import to the authors themselves, as authors—still clutched unused, or crumpled up in sheer frustration.

When it came to my turn to be interrogated, I asked if I might make a comment on the format; and pointed out that the assumptions implicit in this format, and implicit in the rest of the conference too, so far—of the supremacy of the secondary mediators of culture, over the primary producers—in fact vitiated the whole supposed purpose of such a conference. Salman Rushdie promptly inveighed, likewise. And Roberta Leigh, too, who had been lured along (till then, under false pretences), because she actually had something original to say about Romance, from the point of view of a practitioner of that genre. The circus animals rebelled. And at least the audience enjoyed the fray.

Alas, this episode is all too symptomatic of something rotten in the State of Creativity. The ivy thrives, but not the tree.

Consider a piece in *The Observer* (13 June 1982) entitled "The Critic as Undertaker", by Peter Conrad. It's a survey of the first batch in a new Contemporary Writers series of books, from Methuen; assorted critics holding forth on Saul Bellow, John Fowles, Joe Orton, Thomas Pynchon *et cetera*. The preferred metaphor of almost all the critics turns out to be that of an autopsy conducted on the authors and their *oeuvre*; plus a reckoning up of what they have 'bequeathed' us in their literary testaments. In the general background Roland Barthes conducts the funeral service, proclaiming the death of the author, negated by his text, which makes possible the birth of the critical reader. And attempts are made, in the case of authors who haven't yet literally flaked it, to diagnose fatal symptoms: thus John Fowles is detected to be 'falling off'.

A shared metaphor cropping up simultaneously so many times can only unmask the actual vested interests of such critics, who really have little in common with creators yet who are competing in the same ecological niche, for the same slice of the cake of life, the cultural slice—and for the icing upon it.

Consider, finally, the Arts Council's advertisement for Writers' Bursaries 1982/83: "It is emphasized that writers of nonfiction works of literary merit, including those books *which are in any way a support to literature*, are eligible." (My emphasis.) This is a bit of a new departure. So public tax money may now be spent on funding those people who are in any way a support to literature—rather than on supporting the creation of literature itself! What is this but a charter for parasites?

One does not of course doubt the probity of the Arts Council, who administer the national largesse for the arts. Did not the out-going Director, Sir Roy Shaw, deny that he had "been offering prominent people in public life large sums of money to become directors of a new private leisure complex in London," and then change his mind and admit it? (*The Observer*, Pendennis column, 14 March 1982.) But as to their concept of supporting the arts by supporting people who support the arts in any way, ho ho hum. Someone has got their priorities seriously mixed up; though is that really surprising when one considers how many members of the supporters club are knit together by mutual obligations, sponsored conferences and the rest of the circuit of metropolitan supportativeness? (Oh dear, the football team have got no boots—but the supporters club is doing fine.)

Not only do authors have to put up with being at the wrong end of the publishing process, financially. Not only do they have to put up with the engulfing and axing of the publishing industry by corporate conglomerates practising bottomline economics. Not only do they have to put up with the wholesale warping of the profession of literature by media hype, best-sellerdom, film tie-ins, ooks (artificial books), and the rest of the phony circus. (And all the while sweat and brood and work like hell to conceive and bring their works into the world.) But they have to put up with parasites waxing strong on their bodily and cerebral juices.

Little can be done by most authors to make themselves into powers within publishing. Damn all can be done to persuade Gulf Oil that they owe a duty to that micron of their empire which spans, say, original SF anthologies.

But the sub-world of parasites is closer at hand, elbowing authors in the very same socio-economic niche.

Gardeners: zap that weevil. Authors: squash a parasite today.

And on the subject of weeding . . .

The Culling

HOPE AND CHARITY were playing the Culling Game with the other younger village children. A dozen youngsters spun like human tops in the street, humming loudly to themselves. Their arms were flung out, with one index finger pointing. The other hand was a fist, a counterbalance. A little club. Around and around they spun, in a trance.

Several mothers watched from the doorways of the little wooden houses. A brisk early November wind blew the last torn-off leaves along the street, where straits of mud were widening every Winter between the crumbling islands of old asphalt. A couple of teenage boys were pulling a small cart loaded with split logs down from that part of the woodland which the villagers of Harmony were allowed to thin out this year.

Polly, at her door, hummed too.

'What a good, *good* game,' she thought. Angelic chords flooded her head, magnifying the thought, touching her very pleasure centers till she rocked from side to side in near delight.

All of a sudden the children stopped stock still. They stared in the direction of their pointing fingers. Four fingers—including that belonging to Charity, her sister—were aimed directly at Hope. Eight other fingers pointed at someone else or nobody.

The children hesitated for a moment, since Hope was hardly a unanimous choice. Then they began to chant, slowly at first then picking up speed:

"Cull her! Cull her! Cull her!"

As their voices rose in pitch, the words sounded more like: "Kill her! Kill her!"

Hope fled to her mother Polly. But Polly was coasting up a crescendo of joy just at that moment. She pushed the six-year-old away from her quite roughly.

But the moment was spoiled. The climax was lost. Polly remembered that she loved her daughter. She remembered that only four fingers had been pointing, after all. She remembered that this was only a game, a mock prelude to the real thing, due to happen on Midwinter Day.

She folded her daughter in her arms, hugging and consoling her.

"There, there. You won't be 'It.' I won't let you be!"

The *Gloria* in her mind became a harsh, keening wail.

"I won't let you be!"

Her head ached fiercely, and she thought of the red and golden beauty of the sunset in the West, instead. Blood ran down the sky: the blood-letting of the day . . .

"No! It's beautiful, beautiful!"

Quickly the pain eased, and the discords ceased their dinning. As Polly stared into the sunset, evensong hymned its praises, only slightly out of tune.

"Home time! I'll cook you something nice."

Polly drew her daughter inside their neat little cabin.

"Where does the music really come from, Mummy?" asked Hope, not for the first time.

"I've told you—from the Aliens."

"But what *are* aliens?"

"They're people from another star in the sky. They came to Earth to help us. To stop us poisoning our lovely world, and eating all the food, and cutting all the trees, and breeding like flies. And being out of tune."

"But do they look like you and me?"

"How should I know? I've never seen any aliens. I've never heard tell of anyone who has. We hear their songs in our heads, that's all. They hurt us when we do the wrong thing, and when we do the right thing it sounds... too lovely for words. Maybe the aliens can't speak and can only sing, so this is the only way they can tell us."

"It's horrid when I do something wrong. Like when I ran to you. I'm sorry, Mummy."

"Maybe it's us who cause them pain when we do wrong, and we hear their pain, rather than that they mean to punish us. But it comes to the same thing. So we all have to live in harmony, don't we?"

"Well, it's our home," said Hope, not understanding. "Where else could we live? Harmony is our home."

Polly smiled, and ruffled her daughter's head.

Did the beasts of the field hear this music too? Did the singing birds hear it? Who could say?

But they *should* hear it. For the Earth was clean again. The Earth was lovely—restored, renewed. The Earth itself sang. A joyful cry sounded softly, as though far away, then repeated itself much louder, closer by.

"People used to live in cities," Polly struggled to explain. "Big stone places, with not a blade of grass or a rabbit running about. We live quite near what's left of one of them. Over the hill there." The thought of the city, even in ruins, scraped across her mind like a fingernail on slate. "People destroyed it as much as they could before they fled. It isn't a nice place. But it'll be countryside again, one day."

She shouldn't even be thinking of the city! If the other villagers could hear the caterwauling in her head, she herself would be culled, come Midwinter . . .

How would little Hope and Charity fare without her?

But she no longer cared. The idea of the Culling was a ravishing *obbligato*; wonderful sounds warbled in her head. This particular song only gathered force every five years, but it never failed to come. For people went on making love—and of course bore children as a result—even though by the fourth and fifth year their heads ached with the harsh displeasure of the shrieking as they tumbled between the sheets.

But after the Culling love would be a soaring melody for the next year or three . . .

"Where's Daddy?"

"I don't know, darling. Donald went off for the day."

"He should be here!"

"I know. Let's not think about Daddy, while he's away."

Donald was sitting underground, in a man-made cave once known as a subway station. It was the last station on the line out of the abandoned city. A single torch, powered by an ancient long-life battery, illuminated the little group of malcontents: Sam and Carmen, Alice and Tate.

Their heads all hurt with the echo of being in here: a *boom, boom, boom* which ought to have driven them back up the rusty escalator before they ever reached bottom.

"You were wrong, Don." Tate held his head in pain at the drumming migraine. "It isn't damped out by being underground."

"Maybe it is *a little*."

"How can a fellow *think*?" They had to shout at each other.

"You can still think," said Carmen. "So can I." She was their liaison person with two surviving groups of malcontents to the north of the former city. "Now, some villages believe that aliens have done this." She kept her sentences short so that she could finish them, and they could understand them. "But the people in Purity believe that the Earth has done it. The Earth Herself. Great Gaea sings us these songs. Is it possible? Can a whole world come alive, to sing songs? Okay, the Earth *is* alive. In a sense. The ecology is a living network. But it isn't intelligent."

"So the aliens must have done it," Tate groaned.

"*We* . . . are the only hope. Us little groups. We're the only hope, of regaining . . . what we could have been." This was too complex a thought. It shrieked its wrongness.

Donald picked up the torch and stared along the railway tracks, trying to guide his own thoughts along their straight line. But the tracks disappeared into the darkness of the tunnel. From dimness into utter blackness.

He spoke with an effort.

"I found an old boo-book." He stuttered over the word. "About whales—you know, whales in the sea. The book had lots of lovely pictures in it, so I could look through it without being hurt. And because whales spell harmony with nature, I could r-r-read some of the words. It said that whales sing. They can sing all around the world. From sea to sea. People used to know that. But we were kill-kill . . . we were *culling* them." This word soared jubilantly, like a single bugle call attempting to reverse a chaotic rout. It would be so easy and rewarding to follow the bugle, back into line. But he persisted. "Did the whales learn how to sing to us, from all around the world, inside our heads? Not aliens at all—but the whales in our own oceans?"

He quit thinking for a while, till the screech in his head subsided. But he had passed his idea on.

"If the secret's in the seas—in all the deep seas," asked Tate, "how can we ever prove it?"

"S-s-somebody must go down to the sea," Donald forced himself to say. "Somebody must persuade the good fisher folk to sail out. Far out. Somebody must try—no, not to talk to the whales—but to sing to them. To make music at them. *Our* music, not theirs." He fingered the flute at his hip. "We've played their songs for too long."

Tate laughed dismissively.

"One man, playing solo flute out at sea?"

"It might prove something," said Alice. "Anything's worth trying. Will you go, Don?"

Donald nodded.

They all embraced, in farewell, for it would be increasingly dangerous to meet and exchange impure thoughts as the weeks rolled on towards Midwinter. Above all, they must survive. They agreed to meet in the New Year, when Donald could report back —if he survived.

Then they climbed up the rusty metal staircase, out of the booming tomb into the fading light. The sun had just set, and the twilit ruins—overgrown though they were—were harsh on the ear. But the tree-clad hills beckoned vibrantly and lovingly.

Donald pulled his flute out of its sheath, and set it across his lips. As soon as he began to blow the long song of the evening hills, weight and pain lifted from him. His steps lightened. Though it would be dark long before he arrived home, the journey would seem timeless. He copied the pure tones in his head, and each tone that he blew seemed to be sustained indefinitely. He inserted whistle-stops—harmonics. He pranced along.

By the time he arrived in Harmony, he was almost too enchanted—too saturated with the vibrations of the universe—to remember for what jangling reason he had gone to the ruined city in the first place.

When he climbed between the sheets with Polly, bursting with this pent-up joy, she rejected his embraces, though.

Of course. It was long past the time for sexual embraces of any loving sort. His head beat like a demon drum.

"Sleep," urged Polly. "Sleep." She crooned a kind of lullaby, from deep inside her brain.

Donald wept. And ached to weep.

Little Hope and Charity both ran round the blanket screen that divided the house in half at night and began to batter little fists against Donald's bare chest.

"The sea," he mumbled to himself. "The sea."

Taking up his flute, he blew the lullaby along with Polly till the children went back to bed, comforted. And by then he half believed in the lullaby himself.

There was work to do, to prepare for Winter. Whenever, gritting his teeth, Donald thought of his promise to walk down to the sea—a hundred and fifty miles distant—it was far sweeter to put off going and perform some tuneful task instead.

Yet the villagers of Harmony were beginning to whisper among themselves about the impending Festival of Culling; and whenever they did so, they glanced in his direction.

He played his flute enchantingly to them, but it seemed to make no difference, as though the songs they heard in their heads and the songs that he played were subtly different, exposing him as a false player who should be cast out of the orchestra of their lives. (He was a very good flautist, in these days when few amateurs dared play a note for fear of it being so much less than the song in all their heads.)

Horseplay began to spread from the younger children to the older children, from the adolescents to the young adults; and frequently Donald was the butt of it, for no very obvious reason.

Finally, after the first snow had fallen, he set off secretly one morning with a pack on his back and the flute at his side.

*

The decision caused a foul cacophony in his head, but he walked on, thinking resolutely of other things: such as the black lacework artistry of bare trees, or the adagio of the rolling hills, or the grace-notes of pockets of snow counterpointing the fleecy backs of sheep. He played to these.

This was a long, hard journey, but he played for his supper in the villages along the route, passing himself off as a holy fool. The children were all playing the Culling Game by now more vigorously, with sharp sticks and string nooses as well as with voice and finger. They dogged Donald's heels, teasing and jeering. Yet the theme was still merely being stated; the climax was a few weeks off. Donald received bread and meat and shelter, and his playing must not have seemed too much out of tune, since his food was neither poisoned nor was his bed riven with a knife.

Along the route, too, he made contact with a few other malcontents—by a sort of mutual recognition. He spent two days resting up in the isolated hut belonging to one old bearded dissident called Michael.

Michael was a shepherd, an occupation which kept him from having to mix with other people too often. Even so, he lived in fear of his life during the coming Culling. For once long ago he had been a scientist of some kind, and even though he ached to think wrong thoughts, think them he still did.

Michael claimed to belong to a vague organization which he called 'the Network.' The Network were positive that people of the previous age were responsible for the songs. According to them, the songs were a weapon of war or of mass control, run by some sentient computer which had run amuck, independent of its builders.

"But it *can't* be a human weapon," argued Donald. "Humans could never have built anything that listens to people's thoughts, and sorts out which are good and bad, and rewards or punishes."

"Couldn't we just? Thought is an electromagnetic field. If you have a machine that's big enough and sensitive enough, able to carry out billions of operations per second, and if you use the Earth's magnetic field as its listening dish—"

"I can't believe in such a thing."

"It's a damn sight easier to believe in than telepathic whales—when there were never any telepathic whales before! If the whales feared us so much, and had the power, why didn't they just make us all kill each other?"

"Maybe it was against their ethics—their sense of harmony? So they just made us wreck our technology. And culled us down to size. Now they're trying to guide us, to live naturally. So they think! If only I can show them what they've really done to us—"

"But they must know that already."

"If I can plead . . . I'll promise that we'll never harm them again."

"Do this to a fellow, and you'd *never* dare let him get up again."

"We can be partners, now that we've learnt our lesson. Them in the sea, us on land."

"Lord, it hurts my head to think about it! Look, Don, this is a human machine: a machine for spying on our thoughts and correcting them. It's a social engineering super-computer that ran amuck. I think the Chinese or the Russians built it. But it clobbered them too, or else they'd be here today running the show."

Donald shook his head. His skull was a bell, his brain was the clapper of the bell.

"There was a mutant whale born," he said firmly. "A changed super-whale. That was because of all the poisons we poured into the seas. And through it, every singing whale joins in. It'll have had mutant children too, by now—dozens of them."

"You're forgetting the channel capacity of this thing, Don. It has to be a machine. And the machine doesn't want us to find it. It doesn't even want us to *think* about finding it. But there's a way. The Network's working on a way. Will you let me try to hypnotise you?"

"Hypnotise me?"

"Well, we can't build another machine to jam the first machine—that's for sure. We don't know how to, any longer. But if we use our own minds as a weapon... If we can learn to act on command, without thinking of what we're doing... If we can hypnotise all our children, even if it takes a hundred years, when the command's given we'll go and get that machine!"

"So long as you can swim down to the bottom of the sea!"

Donald left Michael's hut, sick at the stupid notions of the Network. Probably it was ninety per cent talk, indulged in by a dozen people at most. Or else Michael wouldn't have told the secret. What sort of plan was it, anyway? People already acted on command. People were already hypnotised by the songs, like snakes dancing to a flute.

Besides, he didn't believe in the machine any more than he believed in the aliens, or in Mother Earth giving voice.

It had to be something natural, and mighty, that had somehow changed. Mutated.

He played himself away from the shepherd's hut, and continued on his journey.

It snowed; and he struggled through. It thawed; and he waded through. It froze; and he slid through. Not unexpectedly he heard no more hint of a Network. Indeed, as he came nearer to the coast he encountered hardly any malcontents at all—then none whatever. The people in this part of the land seemed more simple-minded, as though they had reverted—or been plunged —far deeper into the human past, when a more elementary kind of language made it impossible even to conceive certain thoughts.

Finally he arrived in sight of the sea, whipped to a froth by gales.

The good fisher folk had all beached their boats long since. Donald walked from shingle cottage to shingle cottage, playing his flute, and the folk came out to mutter and prod him a little and caper round him like performing bears. They prodded him as though they were weighing up a sacrifice, which had just delivered itself voluntarily to them to ensure that shoals of fish filled their nets next Spring.

Still, they behaved quite respectfully and even indulgently towards him after the initial prodding and prancing. The victim should be honoured—till the moment of the sacrifice arrived. They pressed fish upon him: salted fish, dried fish, fish stew. No doubt they saw him as some sort of mythic figure.

Also, in this part of the country music was no longer a human art at all. No sea chanties were sung; no bagpipes wailed; no tin whistles blew. The competition in their heads was much too daunting. The most that the fisher folk produced by way of music was a monotonous, murmuring hum that rose and fell like the waves. They hummed in the way that other people chew tobacco. The fisher folk were a people of few and simple words, and much inner music; but Donald could almost hear, by sympathetic vibration, the exact drift of their thoughts. Perhaps this prodigy that he was, this willing victim, ought to be culled out at sea rather than on the shore, to make full use of his magic? Donald played upon this sentiment.

The Herring family gave him shelter, and the best bed. From the grunted conversation which punctuated their humming, Donald gathered that they had lost a son at sea quite recently and so, alas, felt little personal urge to cull themselves. As the Midwinter Festival loomed, there was a hollow in their lives. But now they adopted Donald, to fill this hollow up. They took him to their bosom on behalf of the whole fishing village. So now they hummed to their gutting knives, as they sharpened them, and to their bludgeons as they hefted them. Donald watched, praying—to he knew not what—that the weather would improve.

At last, on Midwinter Day, the sea calmed, *sostenuto*. It lay flat. The breeze from the south was only the gentlest of murmurs.

After the Festival lunch, Donald put his flute across his lips and led the Herring family down to the beach, to their boat, playing the Song of Culling. By now this was the only dominant joyful theme running through everyone's mind, yearning upwards in a long crescendo towards the evening's climax.

The Herrings pushed the boat out and scrambled on board. Donald stood playing in the bow as the *Saucy Sue* sailed far out, through the day into dusk.

Presently the stars shone down like ice crystals. The night was clear. No land was in sight. Donald played and played: an angrily plaintive summoning serenade. It was the first time he had played anything that was really of his own. The Herrings stared at him calmly, in the starlight, realizing that he was setting himself apart from them. Gently, the black sea began to swell.

And something swelled beneath the swell of water: something that was giant and ancient, something mountainous that displaced the sea.

A single absurdly small eye regarded Donald from somewhere in the flank of the mountain: an eye that was in the process of devolving back into that fortress of flesh, which saw far more clearly by means of sound.

Quivering with joy, the Herring family turned their knives and clubs towards Donald.

Donald projected his thoughts so fiercely at the mountain of flesh wallowing alongside that he felt that his eyes would pop out. Through the caterwauling in his brain, he cried out silently:

'You. Do you—? Do you do this to us? To our world?

'We were once the lords of creation. And perhaps that was the whole trouble. But surely we didn't deserve all this? To become mere harps played by hidden hands?

'At least show me that it is you! At least give me a sign! Let me die, knowing!'

The *Saucy Sue* drifted ever closer to the mountain as the Herring family advanced slowly on Donald, humming like beehives.

Donald made a great leap from the gunwale, out on to the flank of the mountain. A moment later, by what feat of scrabbling and scrambling he never knew, he lay sprawled on top of the beast. His head gonged with his rebellion. The Herrings stood slack-jawed and dumbfounded, staring stupidly across a growing chasm of black water as the beast now moved away from the boat. Waves sloshed Donald's ankles. Soon the *Saucy Sue* vanished into the night; Donald was alone with the stars and the sea and the beast, and the grinding discords in his head.

The beast picked up speed but it did not submerge. Gradually the raucous riot in Donald's brain was replaced by sweeter, haunting tones: long whistling harmonies and soft low cries, echoing and overlapping.

Presently he made out several other moving humps in the water. Three. Five. Seven. A small flotilla converged and proceeded together. Shivering convulsively, his hands locked to the beast's back like suckers, Donald scanned the stars. The Plough pointed their course: towards land.

Eventually the land loomed blackly—but little flickers of light burned here and there: bonfires along the beaches.

Donald could hardly think of anything but of the love songs of mournful delight coursing through his mind. These salved the pains of exposure.

The flotilla rushed towards the shore. Were the beasts going to cull themselves too, upon the rocks, upon the pebbles? In that case, all was lost. They too were slaves of the music that ruled the human race.

But the beasts knew the shelves and shallows of the unseen sea floor far better than any human being. When it seemed that they surely had no other choice than to dash themselves aground, the flotilla stopped.

The nine beasts floated lazily, watching with their little eyes. People were dancing on the beach, round a bonfire where several bodies burned, still recognizable as bodies as they sprawled in the flames.

Then in unison all of the beasts—including Donald's own mount—submerged, casting him adrift in the cold water. Like great worms turning, back to the deeps they were gone.

With arms and legs of ice, Donald somehow struck out towards the beach where the bonfire beckoned with its heat.

Somehow he waded ashore.

A band of fisher folk—the very same folk he had sailed away from earlier in the day—turned to greet him, holding nooses and clubs and bloody knives. Ecstasy sang in their heads, and his.

As they walked towards him with the tools of the Culling held out, a thin Moon rose up over the sea horizon; and they all paused.

For no longer was it Midwinter Day. It was the first minute of the New Year.

The song in their heads changed key. It announced a new theme: the celebration of the cleansed world.

Promptly the good fisher folk slung their ropes over their shoulders and tucked their long knives back into their belts. Instead of butchering Donald-from-the-Deep, they raised a hearty cheer.

Donald staggered to the bonfire and collapsed by it, beneath the burning bodies, to dry off and warm his bones.

Although his clothes and his limbs dried presently, his face did not dry. Though the song of New Year moonlight enchanted him and the fisher folk, his eyes still wept upon the sand tears that were as salty as the ocean.

In her neat home a hundred and fifty miles away, Polly woke up at this moment. She began to hope for Donald's return, and then to long for it. He would come; she could almost hear his footsteps, and his flute.

Beyond the blanket-screen little Hope and Charity both lay dead, to Polly's surprise as much as theirs. As soon as Donald came back, a new little one could be conceived. Once again lovemaking would sing like a harp string.

As the thin moonlight touched her cheek through the window Polly also wept, for the harmony and beauty of it all. For the world had turned in its orbit towards Spring. The year had turned, and the five-year cycle too.

Polly turned upon her side, and before very long she was sung to sleep by an inner lullaby from far away.

IMMORTAL

IAN WATSON

As dessert to this miscellaneous bill of fare, here's a tale set in the Egyptian desert where I once rode a camel, though not for very long. Here's a story which, to my surprise, turned itself into a blank verse drama. But then, surprises are what writing is all about . . .

The Pharaoh and the Mademoiselle

A river of aether flowed from God's empty skull to his feet, then back again. Its route took it along the left side of the spine, through the pelvis, down the narrow valley between the legs. The river was in two layers. The upper one journeyed towards the feet; the lower layer returned in the opposite direction. So we built a boat of carved bone to ply back and forth. Hull and steering oars rested in the understream; linen sails flew in the upper. Judicious use of sails and oars propelled the boat from skull to heel, from heel to skull.

We built the vessel because Ho and Emtep were boatmen, and what else could they do but sail? Even though our world was only the length of all seventy of us lying head to toe.

Yet the opening of the river to navigation seemed to broaden our horizons. In the old days when God's dead body occupied most of the space in our world, life was much tighter.

That was before we snipped and burrowed and dug and sawed, converting God's substance to other uses. We made tunnels then caverns then quite emptied him out. We mined him, accumulating wealth in the process. What we didn't need we tossed into the stream, which dissolved loose soft substances. Of course all this activity took a long while—more than sixty million turnings of the sand-glass of Ote the Timekeeper.

The boat would not dissolve. It was sawed from God's shoulder-blade, which was hard. Besides, Otem the Priest had laid a binding spell upon the vessel by carving God's name on the hull. (That was before Otem took a revulsion against the boat and began to loathe it.)

Let me list our wealth; for was I not Tep the Treasurer?

We gained many things from God. From his scalp: hair to braid into rope. From his jaw: the ivory of a false tooth together with the gold wire holding it. From up his rectum we extracted cedar oil and honey; from inside his head other oils and balms. Body fats, wax, carbon, black paste, oil of turpentine, bitumen, mercury: all these things from his flesh, and many more.

Sheets of leather lay upon his shoulders. Rugs of gazelle skin hid God's ulcer scars. From his wrappings we gained cotton and saffron cloth and linen.

When we first became aware of our existence, we were all enmeshed in that linen and could hardly move. It took unmeasurable time to bite and claw our way free. And cut; fortunately some of us clutched sharp tools in our hands.

We also obtained glass, lapis lazuli, and silex; gold and silver and copper; jewels and rare iron.

From God's chest and belly we excavated straw and wadding and salts. We threw most of the straw and wadding into the river. God was spacious to live in after that.

We disposed of most of God's flesh likewise, but we left the muscles of one arm and thigh intact. On the arm we grew the little mushrooms which glowed with so bright a light. Whenever we felt hungry, which was very seldom, we ate some mushroom. We absorbed it into our faces. Its light entered us, letting us see clearly into the deepest nook.

On the thigh we nurtured a few beetles and mosquito eggs and puppae which—just as seldom—we ate. We cut the wings off the two adult mosquitoes of each generation which we allowed to mature. We hamstrung the beetles by breaking their legs.

We drank by bathing in the aether stream.

But enough of this bragging of our wealth! I did not let it obsess me merely because I was the Treasurer. (In the way that Ho and Emtep were obsessed by the need for a boat to sail.)

God's name was Hotemtep. We knew this because his name was carved on every one of us. According to Otem we were supposed to serve the God after his death. It seemed to me that Hotemtep served us instead; we were his maggots.

We were all black of body. All of us, with the exception of Em the Musician, had the same face—which must have been the face of the God Hotemtep, though his own huge countenance had been burned away by an excess of caustic unguents. Our eyes were small, close-set; our cheekbones prominent; our noses thin and long and slightly hooked. Our jaws were strong and powerful. Our lips were thick. Our ears protruded.

As for Em, her countenance was a smooth blank. Maybe the God forgot to give her a face before he died. Maybe a musician did not need a face, since her character was manifest in her music. She had ears, and experienced no difficulty in hearing her way around our world.

I loved Em in her scanty lutist's costume. I loved her music, which was voice enough. On my abacus I tallied her golden notes. On her lute she plucked the tally of our treasure. To me her facelessness suggested wax craving the impress of my own face: my nose, my lips, the orbits of my eyes, my tongue. But of course *my* face was just like anyone else's.

We people weren't meant to recognize each other by our faces. What distinguished us was the cut of our clothes and the kind of implements we bore, announcing our function: the stonemason's mallet, the weaver's bobbin, the smith's hammer.

But we learned to put our tools down. We discovered how to detach them from our hands. So to avoid confusion we adopted personal names, which we took from the lexicon of Hotemtep's own name as inscribed upon us. Priest Otem said that since each of us was only part of Hotemtep it was fitting that we should each bear only part of his name.

When I met someone I announced who I was. "I am Tep," I said. In reply he or she announced their name. Consequently our sense of being different individuals was reinforced.

When we saw each other's faces with our own selves reflected so many times over, surely we were meant to reflect that we were all the same—that we were all parts of another, who was dead and torn apart by us. Instead we felt that we were all unique.

We grew apart and altered. We found love and hate. We learned rage and laughter. We smiled and frowned. We helped one another; sometimes we conspired or argued or deceived. Generally we had work to keep us occupied, but we also had leisure. Leisure gives the opportunity to cultivate oneself. That's because in leisure you find yourself to be a mystery, a taunt, a hollow demanding to be filled.

Otem, as Priest, was our source of secret knowledge. He it was who first taught us to read God's name. Even so, his knowledge was limited—as became obvious.

One time a number of us were sitting perched on the phalange bones of Hotemtep's right hand. I was there, and Otem, and Te the Mason and Carpenter Hote, and Em with her lute, and Timekeeper Ote forever turning his sand-glass, recording within him the number of turns since time began.

Otem announced that our world was a wooden box.

"Beyond the box is the land of *life*. But not immediately. The land of life is too far away for us to reach, unless we first die like the God."

"How can we die?" I asked. "What is dying?"

Otem frowned.

"*We've* no idea," said Timekeeper Ote, "and neither have you."

"It is the long sleep," said Otem.

"What is sleep?" asked Ote.

Otem made no reply.

But if sleep and dying were a puzzle, we certainly knew what a box was! Carpenter Hote had built boxes to store treasure in. And Hote was fast becoming a humourist.

"If our world's a box," he said, "it has two sides."

"No, boxes have six sides," said Te.

"Aha! I mean an inside—and an outside."

"If the land of life isn't immediately outside the box," I asked Otem, "then what is?"

"Another box," replied Otem. "A bigger wooden box enclosing the first box."

"And beyond that?"

'A third box, and maybe a fourth box."

"Oh yes? And beyond?"

"A box made of stone not wood."

"I see. After which, we find a still bigger stone box?"

"Made of granite, the hardest stone of all."

Te tapped out a rhythm with a chisel on God's finger-bone. He matched the strummings of Em's lute, and this made me feel a surge of resentment at him, which I named *jealousy*.

"Hmm," he said. "Even the hardest stone can be split by lighting a fire against it then quenching the fire suddenly with moisture—and repeating the process many times. I know that because I'm a mason. Silex struck on stone will make a spark. The spark will inflame wadding soaked in oil; be thankful we saved some wadding. And if the idea of moisture is inside me, then so is moisture itself. I could spill it from my eyes, *weeping*. I could spit it from my lips, in *contempt* at the granite."

Otem seemed put out by this display of knowledge to which he wasn't privy. He began lecturing us.

"Our world is a hollow concealed within increasingly hard shells!"

Te spat. A blob of moisture stained God's bone, though it soon dried. This was an example of contempt.

"Beyond the hardest shell is the land of life where the demons dwell!"

"What are demons?" demanded Te.

"Demons are terrible beings. Appalling, abominable, abhorrent. Cruel, vile and wicked. We must not rouse those demons. If we do, we'll be destroyed. Within our hollow here we are safe. Yet every time that boat's prow bumps the wall before turning, a tiny noise travels forth through shell after shell." (This was when Otem first became consumed with hatred of the boat.) "One time a demon might notice. And tear the shells apart!"

"According to you," Te reminded him, "the outer granite shell is ever so hard."

"Demons are strong beyond belief! Hotemtep died so that he could protect us here within; so that he would be a world unto us."

"Then Hotemtep must have been a demon." Te struck a glancing blow with his chisel at the finger-bone, breaking free a flake.

"Hotemtep was a God, you fool! Gods are not demons." And Otem strode off angrily.

I tugged Em by the hand. "Come with me. I'm Tep. I've had

an idea."

We walked together under the femur of God's unfleshed thigh till we reached the pelvic arch by the side of the river.

My idea concerned two things. One was the blob of moisture which Te had produced from out of his mouth. The other was the way we absorbed food into ourselves. Perhaps something could pass between Em and me.

"Lie down, Em." She lay; and I lay down upon her. "I love you," I said.

As I rested on top of Em I felt a swelling and glowing sensation deep down in me, and began to squirm. The hot swelling intensified into a fire—a blaze which must somehow be quenched. Yet the fire didn't hurt; or if so, the hurt was a pleasure.

Em must have felt similarly. She was writhing and tearing at her lute with polished nails, twanging the strings loudly, making wild music.

Of a sudden I felt a boiling release, of part of my own being which was absorbed into Em.

We lay still a while then I helped her to stand. Briefly she cradled her blank face against my shoulder. Softly, as though we might melt into one another.

"I name this *sex*," I said. "It is the finest treasure of our treasury. It is the diamond."

We both went on our way, she to strum about our discovery, I to speak.

Soon many people were enjoying sex together in their leisure time. But now that our world had become so well organised, leisure was on the increase. Sex generally occupied no more than fifteen or twenty turns of the sand-glass; and we discovered that we had to wait several hundred turns before our diamond was sharp and bright again. Thus there was still leisure time to fill—otherwise the dispute between Otem and Te and me (and by extension the boatmen) might have been forgotten.

It certainly wasn't forgotten by Otem, who in his pride didn't know when to leave well alone. Some time later when the boat was tied up to one of God's ribs and Ho and Emtep had just swum ashore, Otem arrived and denounced the boatmen. He accused them of urinating over the side of their boat. This would pollute the aether, said he.

This accusation was a lie. True, some of us had begun to urinate—though seldom. Whenever we did so, our beads of urine were trapped in our robes, there to dry sweetly. But Otem had conceived a loathing for the boat, which suggested the possibility of travel to some place else. So he who had once blessed the vessel now sought a scapegoat in its crew.

"Pissers! Polluters!" he shouted.

Emtep wasn't to be browbeaten. "We did no such thing," he asserted stoutly.

Otem stamped his foot. He pounded his rod of office on the ground.

Emtep wouldn't back down. Emtep clenched and unclenched his fists. Suddenly Otem lashed out with his rod, catching Emtep a violent blow across the shoulder.

Amazingly, Emtep's arm snapped off. His right arm sheared away cleanly and dryly at the shoulder and tumbled, tunic sleeve and all. It lay on the ground with the fist still opening and closing. Many eyes stared from the scar to the arm, from the arm to the Priest's cruel rod.

Then Emtep's partner, Ho, howled and launched himself at Otem. He wrested the rod from the Priest's grasp and beat Otem fiercely with it. Ho's labours on the river had made his muscles mighty. His first blow smashed off Otem's right arm. The second blow, his left arm. A third blow cracked the Priest's head off at the neck. Blow followed blow. Ho belaboured Otem till he had demolished him into a dozen large pieces. Still the boatman wasn't satisfied. He thrashed the pieces of Otem as they lay on the ground, reducing them still further.

Finally Emtep stayed his partner's hand. "Enough. I name this *fury*. You'll wear yourself out."

Discarding the rod, Ho picked up Emtep's severed limb. He was careful how he held it in case the flexing fingers closed blindly on his own hand, trapping it. Ho fitted the top of the arm to Emtep's scar and held the two together for a good few turns, but the arm stayed loose and unjoined. Ho sighed deep in his chest.

"I'm Te," said Te. "A mason joins stones by chipping till two blocks fit perfectly." He flourished his chisel.

"The join is already perfect," said Ho. "Can't you see?"

"Simpler buildings use mud to bind the straw bricks together. Maybe some of God's mud would help?"

Carpenter Hote pushed forward. "I could drive a nail through. But the sharp point might shatter the hard flesh."

"I know mud," said Gardener Hoë. "Spittle may be better."

"Wait," I cried. "We must call for Ep the Nurse, with her salves!"

"Of course!" chorused everyone. Now that I had pointed this out, it was obvious. The situation had simply never arisen before.

Immediately a loud call went out for Ep. In the silence which ensued I was the first to notice the squeaking of many tiny voices. Stooping and cupping a hand to my ear, I stepped among the scattered ruins of the Priest.

"Beware demons!" squealed a toe.

"The land of life," piped a nose.

"Boxes within boxes," muttered an ankle.

All the pieces of the Priest were talking, with a noise in proportion to their size. From ear and shoulder-chunk and elbow, Otem continued to nag and curse and instruct us.

"It seems to me," said I, "that our voice isn't of our lips alone, even though it sounds that way. It is of our whole being. Ho hasn't rid us of Otem—he has multiplied the nuisance."

"Aye, but at least I quietened him! And he can't wander around any more."

If our voice was of our whole being, why couldn't Em speak? I resolved to ask her this. But meanwhile Nurse Ep had arrived bearing her tray of jars. No one had needed these, and Ep had put her tray down long ago and turned her hands to other things; but when the call came, Ep found the tray soon enough.

She assessed Emtep's injury competently then uncapped a jar.

"Sticky honey from the God is what's needed." She smeared the sweet thick ooze upon limb and scar alike then held both together for a while. Soon the honey set, and Emtep was healed.

"Thanks, Ep!" Gleefully Emtep clapped his hands. And we all discussed what to do with the Priest.

Ep said, "If you sort all his parts into the right order, I can fix him together."

Hote said mischievously, "What if we get him in the wrong order, so that his nose grows on his knee?"

"No!" Ho barked out. "I say we should throw his parts in the river like rubbish. The God's name, carved on him, is broken apart. So the aether may dissolve him. We'll be rid of him forever."

Mason Te spoke up, cunningly. "His being might flow through the end of the world."

"And betray our presence?" Emtep asked.

"I don't believe in demons. What would you give, Emtep, to be able to sail that boat of yours through the end of the world into the land of life, to explore?"

"If only . . . but it's impossible!"

"In a boat—quite. In that case we must creep."

"Creep?"

"Aye, creep through the tunnel which Hote and I will bore and drill through the shells of wood and stone. Of course, we'll need assistance."

Hote and Te must have been plotting privately. Never mind! As treasurer I was fully convinced that our time should be used to gain something of value. This scheme would certainly solve the problem of excess leisure.

"That's a good plan," I said. "I support it. We must invest our time and treasure."

"But this might take millions of turns," said Timekeeper Ote.

"So what?" I countered. "It's a bold and excellent plan. And a fine insult to our cringing, bullying Priest."

"What about his parts?" Nurse Ep reminded us.

"I could build a box to store them in," said Hote. "O the Soldier could guard it with his spear."

"We must keep them separate," said Emtep, "otherwise they might join up of their own accord, honey or no honey."

"Let's not forget," said Te, "that Otem taught us to read words. And he told us of the boxes, and the land of life. He might possess more information. He could be valuable. The difference is, now we can control him." The Mason grinned. "How many bits is he broken into?"

I scanned the ground and strummed my abacus. "About seventy, I'd say."

"That's one for each of us. I propose that we all carry a piece of him round with us, in case we need to hear his voice. Emt the Smith can fix loops of God's gold wire to each part. We can hang them from our necks as amulets. If they're a nuisance we can take them off. If he's disobedient we can scorch him or smear foul black paste on him."

"Yes!" cried many voices. So the proposal was adopted.

I hurried to find Em the Musician so that we could enjoy sex together. All the excitement had inflamed me.

*

However, Em was already lying with someone else. I felt jealousy mount in me as I watched them—but then I restrained myself. Blows struck in anger could break an arm off. Blows could smash a person to pieces.

As soon as Em's lover stood up and saw me, he said, "I am Temte the Manservant."

"Is Emep the Maidservant busy, then?" Temte usually lay with Emep.

"Why yes, Treasurer."

"I see. Well, we shall all be busy soon. We're going to burrow out through the end of the world. This will be a great task."

"I'll serve gladly," vowed Temte; and I knew that I had made a loyal friend, where I might rashly have made an enemy.

When he had gone I sank down by Em. "Surely you have a voice," I said.

By way of answer she played music at me, and in my heart I clearly understood the tune to mean: "A voice I will have, when I have lips and a face."

Heedless of the fact that Em had just had sex, I fell upon her lovingly. But gently, lest she break. Or lest I break a part of myself. It was then that I found that woman's sexual diamond can be sharp and bright again immediately; unlike man's. I decided to keep this information to myself, since men outnumbered women by a factor of two and additional sexual opportunity might interfere with our work schedule.

Within a few hundred thousand sand-turns Carpenter Hote and helpers had carved a tunnel all the way through the wall just beyond God's feet. This tunnel was ample enough for two people to crawl along in comfort side by side. It led to a second wooden wall which was similar but distinct—between the two there was a narrow fissure.

I had crawled to inspect the gap, but the tips of my fingers would hardly fit into it. I was wearing the upper right section of Otem's head, including one eye and one protruding ear; so I pressed his eye to the crack.

"Look! Tell me what you see."

Silence.

I bit Otem's ear-lobe harshly. "Look!"

"Ouch!" squeaked the Priest's voice. "I *am* looking. It's very dark between the walls. The crevice is as narrow as can be. That's all. Give up this madness while you're still safe. Plug the tunnel with wax."

"Never! Shut up again." I withdrew; and soon Hote was scraping away at the second wall with his tools.

I met Musician Em. She looked different to my eyes. She stroked her belly, which was swollen. She played music which I found hard to understand. Meanwhile Maidservant Emep approached as if called by the strings of Em's lute.

She too stroked her belly. "I am Emep, and I'm swelling. Something is growing in Em and me."

"Is any other woman swelling?"

"No, just us two."

Emep wore most of Otem's left foot around her neck. I reached and twisted a toe. "What grows in her, Otem?"

"Can a foot see into a belly?"

Em herself wore a shapeless piece of Otem's insides. I didn't know whether this had any feelings but I jabbed a finger into it. "What grows in Em?"

"The energy of your loins, Tep," said that chunk of guts.

Hote and helpers experienced greater difficulty with the second wall. Diffuse aether was flowing into the slight gap between the shells. Just as it's hard to pull a sheet of papyrus loose from the aether river—the papyrus sticks where it floats and feels heavier —so there was a tension across the fissure between the walls. It took effort to shoulder through, and gouge beyond. Otem's various parts mocked our efforts, but we punished them and doubled our exertions, working harder shorter shifts in the tunnel. After several hundred thousand more sand-turns the second wall was fully tunnelled through—disclosing a third wooden wall. By now the tunnel was as long as three of us lying head to toe.

When Hote finally broke through the third wall, many hundreds of thousands of turns later, he uttered a great *Ha!* of triumph. Clustered round the tunnel entrance, we clamoured to know what he saw.

"I behold *stone!*" came the answer.

But his answer was almost drowned by other cries from nearby—cries of shock rather than acclaim. O the Soldier came running.

"Treasurer! Em the Musician and Maidservant Emep—they're splitting."

"What?" Yet my wits did not desert me. "Find Ep the Nurse, O! Tell her to bring honey."

I hurried in the direction of some of those shocked voices; and found Em lying on the ground upon her back. Her lute was cast aside, as if useless to express her predicament. Her legs were spread apart. A broad crack had appeared on her scant skirt and belly.

Even as I watched, this crack yawned much wider—and a glistening green ball rolled out of Em's belly.

The ball unfolded itself; it sprouted a number of legs and staggered erect. The thing was kin to one of our captive beetles, though considerably larger.

I yanked Otem's ear-lobe, directing his eye at the creature.

"What is its name, Otem?"

"Ah, yes," whispered that hated but at times useful voice, "the knowledge comes. *Scarab*: its name is scarab."

O the Soldier trotted up, with Nurse Ep following at slower pace so as not to drop her tray. The scarab jerked its head about and clashed its jaws.

"Slay it with your spear!" I ordered O. And in that moment I named something which was beyond Otem's knowledge. I named the possibility of killing something, of rendering it dead. Otem had been smashed to pieces but he had neither died nor slept.

Immediately I had second thoughts. What if the scarab was something godly or demonish which had entered our lives? Was it wise to kill it impetuously?

"No, no, do not slay," I countermanded. "Capture it. Crack its legs with your spear shaft. Cut off its wings, if any, with your blade. Bind it with rope from God's hair. No, with wire! With golden wire. Drag it to pasture on Hotemtep's thigh. Peg it securely. And O—beware its jaws."

This was done.

"Aren't you clever?" sneered my Otem amulet.

Ep smeared honey into the crack in Em and pressed her together. Then she went away to tend likewise to Emep—for shouts told us that she too had produced a scarab.

After a good many turns Em stood up, took her lute, and played a wailing melody.

Scarcely had the two hamstrung scarabs been pegged on what remained of the God's thigh-flesh, than Carpenter Hote approached.

"My job's almost done. Stone is Mason Te's province. But listen to this, Treasurer. As soon as I began enlarging the hole, my Otem started babbling."

Hote's share of the Priest had been a knee. Out of the hollow of that knee Otem's voice ranted quietly, thus:

"I name the tiny light at the end of blackness, a *star*. I name the blazing brighter golden fire, the *Sun*. Sun and star shine upon the land of life!"

"Did you see any star or Sun, Hote?"

"I only saw stone."

"Is there a lot of resistance from the aether?"

"Yes. Te will have a hard time of it. But it isn't insuperable."

Otem's knee said, "When the final granite shell is pierced, much aether will escape. You will see the Sun by night, the star by day. Or the other way round; I'm not sure."

"What is day?" I asked the knee. "What is night?"

It giggled. "Who cares? A mountain of stone sits on top of all the shells. It's tremendous. No one could ever cut through it."

"Then how do we see the star and the Sun?"

The knee simply resumed its litany. "We'll still be safe from demons, I pray. Unless they hear us scrabbling. Unless they smell the aether that escapes. Beware!"

I hit the knee just below the kneecap, making it jerk. "How do you know about day and night, and Sun and star?"

"When the final wood was pierced the aether shifted, and a veil fell from me; I knew. Beware day and night."

"How can we beware what we don't know?" snarled Hote. Wisely Otem fell silent.

Te and helpers began to drill and scrape to open tiny wounds in the stone. Into these holes he smeared oil which he then set alight with silex sparks—and quenched with cups of spit. As though to escape this punishment by flame and moisture the wounds wriggled deeper into the stone. Hammer and chisel could break off flakes and chunks and even little boulders.

The work was hard and dangerous. One labourer suffered from smoke. Another was charred by flame. A third lost an eye —gouged out when his chisel flew askew; but Nurse Ep was able to fix the eye back with honey. Gardener Hoë had her left foot crushed by a tumbling boulder. Since nothing was actually broken off, Ep couldn't help Hoë. So Hoë limped thereafter, dragging her bad foot behind her.

Timekeeper Ote turned his sand-glass a myriad times, but slowly the tunnel lengthened.

Meanwhile the two scarabs were causing trouble. Their appetites were huge. They devoured all within reach. The once-fat pasture of God's flesh was fast becoming mere scraps and tatters attached to the bone. Though the scarabs were hamstrung they often wrenched their tether-pegs free and squirmed to attack and eat our beetles and mosquitoes. O had to stand guard almost permanently, ready to bludgeon them.

"Theirs is a hunger typical of life," Otem's head-part told me. "Beware of life."

Otem had also claimed that the energy of my loins was what had swollen Musician Em. After the emergence of the scarab from her belly Em avoided sex with me. Emep likewise spurned Temte; and soon other women were following their example. Imagine my astonishment when one time I surprised Em and Emep snuggled away together inside the empty jaw of God. The two women were having sex with each other. Both were using their hands a great deal. Em was plucking music from Emep's body, causing a moaning song to issue from deep inside the Maidservant. Emep was moving her mouth on Em's legs and loins and fingering her, playing her like a flute.

I wondered at first, angrily, whether to beat the two of them apart with Otem's rod. Yet after I had watched for a while I found myself pleasurably excited. Stepping closer and crouching down, I enquired whether I might join them; and if so, in what style?

Emep panted. "So that no scarab is conceived!"

"You might be wise. Their hunger's ravenous. Tell me how."

"Lie upon my behind while we squeeze together," said Emep. "Then lie upon Em's."

I did so. I enjoyed. Up to a point. I don't know for sure if the two women enjoyed, but afterwards Em pressed her blank face gently to mine, rubbing softly against my visage.

Eventually the stone wall was tunnelled right through. Beyond the usual narrow fissure, rose a wall of sparkling granite. Granite was the hardest wall of all to tunnel. Mason Te and helpers (of whom I was one, of course) finally had resort to polishing the granite away by using jewels from our treasury. You crouched in the tunnel with a jewel held full in your fist, sometimes in both fists, depending on size. You leaned your weight forward and scrubbed around and around.

Diamonds were best for the purpose. Amethysts rubbed away too rapidly, staining your hands a prickly mauve. Rubies and sapphires also wore away, more slowly, coating you with sharp dust, deep red, azure. Another myriad of turns passed by.

Why were we striving so? In despair at ever rubbing through the granite, and depressed by the tension of aether in the gaps, I asked myself this question more than once. No doubt we all suffered the same crisis of confidence, but nobody voiced such doubts aloud. The pieces of Otem performed that service for us vociferously enough (if hushedly).

Yet the answer was obvious. The answer had been shown us by the scarabs. Until we could burrow out into the land of life, sex and joy must be unnatural to us.

At long last we had all but tunnelled through. How did we know that our work was nearly at an end? Why, our method had polished the granite to a surface like glass. When that surface became very thin we began to see a hint of what lay beyond through the sparkle-specks embedded in the rock. We polished more gently. We did not lean our weight forward at all. Eventually we could stare through what was virtually a window.

An enormous volume of darkness gloomed beyond. In the darkness several large motionless things loomed. In turn we all took a trip down the tunnel to stare through that window. Even Em went to listen to the echoes of her lute returning from beyond.

When we had all gathered outside again, I asked Oëp the Surveyor, "What do you make of it?" Oëp had the keenest eyesight of us all.

"Hmm. I saw four giant jars, each with the head of a beast as a stopper."

"Are the beasts alive?"

"No."

"And what else?"

"There's a vast wall of rock with a wooden door in it—a door as tall as the God himself. Overhead there's a roof of rock. I didn't see any Sun or star, though."

"Beware, beware!" said part of Otem. "You haven't stuck your head into the chamber yet."

"Then we shall do so," I said. "Mason Te, take hammer and chisel—and smash the window."

"Yes, Treasurer." Te crawled back inside.

A couple of turns later we all heard the window break. Immediately aether streamed past us fiercely into the tunnel. There was a great wind, a turbulence. I heard a scream—and thought that Te was screaming. In fact this was the sound of aether escaping out of the hole he had broken, as he later told us. Right now he shouted back to reassure us—he had nearly been swept over the edge.

Two other events clamoured for attention.

"Look up the river!" howled Boatman Emtep. "Our boat sinks! It sinks!"

O the Soldier roared, "Look to God's thigh! The scarabs are

free!"

I quit the tunnel mouth and ran. So did O and the boatmen and a good many others. When we reached the river side of God's thigh, we were astonished. Most of the aether had drained from the river. The boat no longer floated; it lay grounded on the bottom, tilted over. Ho and Emtep clung to each other and wailed with grief. But more amazing still was the sight of the scarabs. The two creatures were devouring one another.

One scarab's jaws had expanded to gobble the whole body of the other scarab. The victim in turn was consuming its attacker from within. Imagine two bubbles on the aether river merging into a single bubble which then shrinks away. That's how it was. One scarab ate the other; the other ate the one. O had no way to prise them apart with his spearshaft. The mingled mass got smaller—till presently nothing remained of the scarabs but a green stain on God's thigh bone.

Truly this was a time of horrid marvels; for now other voices back at the tunnel were called out, "The star! The star!"

I hastened back there. O followed me, spear at the ready.

People milled around the tunnel entrance, several looking dazed. I saw Surveyor Oëp force his way within and followed him. Soon we were both clinging to the edge of the portal which Te had opened. A granite cliff yawned sheer below, dropping to a plain of dusty stone. Above our heads the precipice continued upward—then there was empty space, then a stone sky.

"Look that way, Treasurer—near where the sky meets the wall."

I did as Oëp showed, craning my neck and tilting my head. A twinkling white light assailed my sight.

"The star, the star," I said stupidly.

Oëp crowded his head against mine. "Whatever it is, it's a long way off."

"Re-mote!" cackled Otem's neck, which Oëp wore.

"We're viewing it through a shaft bored upward at a slant through the stone sky. That shaft must be the length of our world, oh, thirty times over!"

"Just as well it's there," said I. "Is it wide enough to crawl up?"

"Yes. But how do we reach the mouth?"

"No way!" said Otem's neck. "You'll never do it. And you can forget all about the wooden door. Even if you cut your way through that, oh the blockages and barriers beyond! The granite portcullises, the pits as deep as valleys!"

"Shut up," I said. "That star is our signal-lamp. If we hang ropes tied to ropes down this cliff, we can descend. We can walk to the wall. Emt the Smith will make nails to drive into the cracks in the stone. He'll build a ladder of nails all the way up to the sky. Once a few of us reach the mouth of the star-shaft, we can help the others up by pulling. We'll leave by way of the sky-tunnel."

"Folly, folly," said Otem.

The next moments were ones of total terror.

The giant wooden door began to groan and shake. With great grindings and screechings slowly it started to open outward! Blinding light flooded around the edges. From beyond, deafening sounds boomed; voices of thunder! My heart hammered and my limbs quaked.

I nearly became insensible. Somehow I managed to haul myself—and Oëp by the scruff—back to the mouth of the tunnel. Even there, all present were stunned, dazzled, and terrified. Still, I hadn't taken leave of myself—as witness my rescue of Oëp. So I had the wit not to say anything about Priest Otem having been right. What I said was this:

"Listen, everyone: there are giant creatures outside. Spread the word quickly and quietly. After that, be silent. Do *nothing*."

I departed in the direction of God's thigh, with Oëp accompanying me tamely as though my hand was still attached to his neck. Soldier O bravely stayed to guard the tunnel mouth, his spear aimed at the fateful hole we'd cut. I hadn't told him to defend it, but no matter. He stood quite motionless. What else could he do but guard? He was a soldier.

By now Ho and Emtep were sitting disconsolately on the bank. Quickly I advised them to get back on board. Voices chirruped near and far in warning—not as quietly as I would have liked—but soon all fell silent, even including Otem's pieces, though thunderous giants could hardly have heard these.

For hundreds of turns we stayed as we were—doing nothing, saying nothing. All this while, strange fearful noises came intermittently from outside. Vast bumpings and draggings. Godly or demonish speech—perhaps! Who could comprehend such sounds? They made no sense.

Finally the culminating horror occurred.

High up, all around the roof, our world cracked open—screeching in protest. Showers of dust fell and billowed about us. Slowly the whole top of our world was lifted off.

Light drenched down through the dust. Sounds drummed at us.

I let myself be paralysed.

Cast of Demons

HARRY, EARL OF DUNDALK
THEODORE PECK
PROF. DANIEL POULSON, *of the Egyptian Antiquities Service*
MLLE. YVONNE BIZOT
TOM KEEVES, *HARRY's 'man'*
MME. MARIANNE BIZOT, *of the Louvre*
ALI BEY
IBRAHIM, *a cook*
GAMAL, *a servant*

ACT 1

(*Inside a large tent a table is set for dinner. Candles burn brightly. IBRAHIM and GAMAL wait at table; the others sit round it.*)
HARRY: How ill-fated we seemed until today;
   Nothing was going our way.
   All Theodore's dollars doled out for dust.
   How his beef-baron Dad would have fussed.
(*He raises a glass of Perrier water.*)
THEODORE: I'd sure like to know what you think
   Is so damn special—pardon me, Ladies—
   About old Hotemtep's tomb!
HARRY: The new Lord Carnarvon Ted would be
   Paying the check for immortality.
THEODORE: Don't blame me if I have the cash
   And you're a penniless Earl.
   Have you been sneaking gin into that glass?
HARRY: It isn't my country which prohibited
      Alcohol—and created Al Capone.
THEODORE: We repealed the Volstead Act
   Three years ago. I'm no puritan.
HARRY: And a poet is never penniless.
   Riches flourish in his heart.
DANIEL: And a sharp tongue in his head.
(*IBRAHIM carries round a soup tureen, and GAMAL serves from it. Both men wear red tarbushes and white uniforms.*)
HARRY: Dear me. My only desire was to amuse.
YVONNE: Que vous êtes un bel esprit!
TOM:
(*He tears up a bread roll.*)
   What's that mean?
HARRY: It means, Tom,
   That the charming and ravishing Mam'selle

Appreciates my wit.
(Madame Bizot clears her throat.)
YVONNE: You are charming yourself,
Monsieur le Comte!
TOM: Oh ho,
And maybe she's hunting a title.
Wed Byron here; become Countess of Dundalk.
MARIANNE:
(She clears her throat more loudly.)
In answer to your question, Mr. Peck:
Hotemtep's tomb presents a strange enigma
—One which may become as notorious
As any trove of treasure.
THEODORE: There's little enough of that commodity.
A couple of sandals with gold buckles
And a cofferful of earrings
Spilled in the antechamber.
The tomb was robbed, by hasty thieves.
MARIANNE: But absence is revealing in itself.
TOM: As on the *Marie Celeste,* do you mean?
MARIANNE: I refer to the absence of tampering
With the seals on the burial chamber.
The twine was still tied. The wax,
Still stamped intactly with Hotemtep's sigil.
DANIEL: *Ergo,* the robbers did not break in there.
TOM: Ibrahim lad, this soup's boiling hot.
IBRAHIM: It will cool, Effendi, if you look at it.
HARRY: Better boiling hot than bubbling with typhoid!
MARIANNE: And yet inside the inner coffin
We find ruination, total wreckage of the mummy.
Explain that if you can.
THEODORE: I blame that mouse hole.
MARIANNE: Mice?

Mice don't bite through granite!
HARRY: Maybe some malicious enemy of Hotemtep—
Such as his mother-in-law—inserted beetles
Down a readymade hole at the last moment
To feast on his flesh? Dung-beetles.
Scarabs. Or that other kind we found.
MARIANNE: The larder beetle, which feeds on dead flesh.
No beetles could account for such damage.
DANIEL: If Hotemtep's mother-in-law had wished him ill,
She would hardly have fed him to scarabs!
The ancient Egyptians viewed the scarab
As a symbol of eternal life. Deified as Khefri,
The scarab is the God of Life ever renewing
And ever transforming itself, forever reborn
Out of its own substance. You'll recall
We found glyphs for Khefri carved here and there,
Hmm?
YVONNE:
(She claps her hands.)
But we did find a treasure, didn't we?
The little figures.
MARIANNE: The *Ushabti*. Yes indeed.
What a wonderful model of society
Three thousand years ago! The detail
Of their faces, hands and tools: exquisite!
TOM: Their faces? You must be joking.
They're all as alike as Chinamen.
MARIANNE: Well, they *are* made of china; almost.
TOM: They all look the same, is what I mean.
Like Chinamen all look the same.
MARIANNE: But of course! That's because
They're all modelled on dead Hotemtep.
As well as being an entourage to serve him

>   In the afterlife, they are different aspects
>   Of his spirit. As a collection they're unique.
> TOM: Box of toy soldiers, I'd say.
> DANIEL: Only one
>   Is a soldier.
> THEODORE: Exactly *how* unique?
> DANIEL: Madame Bizot isn't exaggerating.
>   They're exemplary. In my view this alone
>   Redeems the whole expedition. That's to say,
>   Our efforts were worthwhile. All your, um,
>   Generosity.
> THEODORE: You're kidding.
> DANIEL: I assure you,
>   To a true Egyptologist these Ushabti
>   Are as much treasure as any golden thrones.
> MARIANNE: Oh absolutely.
> YVONNE: I feel I could be
>   A little girl again, and play with them
>   In my nursery.
> HARRY: You are eternal girl, Mam'selle,
>   Fille éternelle! You will never age,
>   Never lose—how would Ted phrase it?—
>   Your peachiness.
> DANIEL: No touching!
> HARRY: My dear Sir,
>   I'm well aware we're at the dinner table.
> DANIEL: No touching the Ushabti unnecessarily.
>   No playing with them, that's to say.
> HARRY: Are they as fragile as all that?
> DANIEL: One of them got smashed to pieces
>   And strung round the necks of the others
>   With gold wire.
> MARIANNE: Another enigma!

>   One which opens a strange perspective
>   Into the conscience of Old Egypt.
> HARRY: The consciousness.
> MARIANNE: Same thing.
> HARRY: Not since psychoanalysis. I must glance
>   At this new *Autobiography* of Freud's
>   Some time, to see if he understands himself.
>   Not that I care much for analysis—
>   We murder to dissect—but I might find
>   The prompting for a poem.
> MARIANNE: The Ushabti
>   Deserve to be staged in a worthy setting.
>   A tableau. A special exhibit.
>   They should be posed all together
>   In a miniature reconstruction of ancient life,
>   Not just lined up in any old glass case.
>   Not these little marvels.
> DANIEL: Hrumph.
> HARRY: Ah, now there's poetry for you.
>   How could the mother of such charm and beauty
>   Not have poetry in her soul?
> THEODORE: I get it:
>   A sort of tableau vivant.
> MARIANNE: Tableau *mort*.
>   But you understand me. Failing the Louvre,
>   Which could certainly do our Ushabti justice . . .
> (*DANIEL POULSON shakes his head violently.*)
>   The local museum might serve the purpose.
>   Somehow I feel the figures should stay
>   Near the tomb where we found them.
>   Twenty kilometres is no great distance.
> DANIEL:
> (***Brightening,** he glances sidelong at THEODORE PECK.*)

>   If only our local museum had more space.
>   Such as a new gallery.
> THEODORE: I'll endow one.
> ALI BEY: Your generosity is exceptional.
> THEODORE: Yeah, well.
> HARRY: Speaking of damage, did you notice
>   How one of the Ushabti had lost its face?
>   The lute-player. How poetically appropriate
>   If it could wear a new face: namely that
>   Of Theodore Peck of Chicago, U.S.A.,
>   Discoverer, patron of Egyptology.
>   Ah, but I'm forgetting: the lute-player
>   Would be female. In which case
>   Only one face could serve as a model
>   Of eternal beauty and artistry.
> (*Plucking paper and pencil from his pocket, HARRY starts sketching YVONNE's face.*)
> TOM: Ladies and Gentlemen, I pronounce the soup
>   Drinkable.

CURTAIN

* * *

ACT 2

(*Six months later; where desert sands meet tomb-pocked cliffs. A full moon shines bright. Holding HARRY's fingers lightly, YVONNE peers closely into his proffered palm as though reading his fortune; or her own. Actually HARRY is showing her something tiny.*)
YVONNE: This is most mischievous of you, Harry.
  But I'm flattered.

HARRY: Oh, I was always
   As handy at this kind of thing
   As a sailor carving scrimshaws.
   My fingers are rather subtle—
   In a number of ways I could mention.
YVONNE: I'm sure they are. Oh God, Harry,
   I've been bored. How could it take so long
   To erect one wretched gallery?
   It was all right for you, lucky fellow,
   You went hunting lions in the Sudan.
HARRY: Need I add that all that time
   Your face burned in my mind.
   Night after night in my tent
   I worked at this face from memory.
YVONNE: Truly, a remarkable likeness!
   In fact, it's *me*. I feel strange—
   As though now magically you control
   Part of me.
HARRY: Hmm. Now I only need
   To fix this face on the little Ushabti
   With tiny pins and strong glue.
   I brought tools with me: a jeweller's drill
   And such. The join will be imperceptible.
   Do you know where your mother keeps her keys?
YVONNE: You are like Monsieur Raffles,
   The gentleman cracksman! Whose crimes
   Were never pinned at his door.
   But won't this one be noticed immediately?
HARRY: Well, yes. Of course—by your mother
   And Dan Poulson and Ali Bey and Ted Peck.
   But they'll all keep quiet as mice.
   Just imagine the scandal there'd be
   Supposing one of them cried foul

At tomorrow's opening ceremony
Before all those distinguished guests.
Such as the Director General of Antiquities,
The Queen of the Belgians, the Maharajah
Of Jaipur, the correspondents of *The Times*
And *Le Monde* and a *Zeitung* or two.
What dishonour. What disrepute.
And all observed by photographers
Eagerly popping off their flash bulbs.
Note how our beef millionaire insisted
No photos of the Ushabti should be released
For earlier publication—so that they
Should positively burst upon a moderately
Astonished world. I'll wager you
Our little lute-player captures the imagination.
She'll be the most pictured. The enigma!
The beauty! Then who'll dare denounce her?
YVONNE: Newsmen might remark on the fact
   That I bear her a striking resemblance.
HARRY: The Egyptians believed in reincarnation!
   You always felt strangely drawn
   To an ancient destiny here by the Nile!
   Hmm, perhaps that's a touch extravagant.
   Why not just act surprised? If newsmen notice,
   Protest! Then let them convert you
   Oh so reluctantly.
YVONNE: I'm sure Maman
   Won't be so reticent in private.
HARRY: Serves her right for marooning
   A dashing spirit like you in the desert
   To dine on donkey giblets for a year.
YVONNE: Ah yes, it has been a cruel exile.
   So why did *you* ever come digging, Harry?

HARRY: In search of inspiration. Ancient passion.
   Magic of antiquity—en route to the lions.
YVONNE: And in the absence of adventure
   You invent it. As witness this face.
HARRY: That's how it is with poets.
   I create. Though I also shoot.
   Blood of death; blood of desire!
   Did you read those poems I sent you?
YVONNE: Oh yes. Très passionants.
HARRY: You know their true meaning, Yvonne,
   The meaning of the heart. If only
   Our lute-player could set music to them
   To serenade you.
YVONNE: If only.
HARRY: I still need keys, though.
   Unlike Raffles, I can't cut and file my own.
   Will you fetch the keys for me?
YVONNE: Oh yes. But the night's still young.
HARRY: True. I shouldn't make my move too soon.
   The guard needs a few hours to get sleepy.
   Ah les clefs! Les clefs de mon coeur!
YVONNE: The keys to your heart?
HARRY: To yours too,
   Yvonne?
(They embrace.)
YVONNE: Là là! I believe, ami,
   We are really speaking about another organ
   A little lower down the body than the heart.
   Let's touch on that, in the next hour or so.
*(They sink down together out of sight behind a dune.
Enter ALI BEY, clutching a rifle.)*
ALI BEY: First Muhammed quit. Today, Towfik.
   Let's hope the new man proves to be

A less cowardly, superstitious peasant!
Let's hope he just snores the night away
And doesn't complain of hearing faint music
Or spying tiny movements from the corner
Of his eye—scurryings out of sight
Which all turn out to be nothing.
Sheer imagination! Or at most
A scuttling spider or a scorpion
Which a rifle butt could crush in a trice.
(*Exit ALI BEY. From behind the dune mild sounds of ecstasy are heard.*)

CURTAIN

We were taken from our world and transported to a new one. What terrors and bewilderments we endured on the way. How hideous our existence once we arrived.

The new world was twice the size of the old, but its walls weren't of solid sheltering wood; they were of clear glass. Every now and then a giant demon would come to gape at us. That was during the bright time, time of the Sun. At first, stunned by such light and deafened by demon voices, we couldn't see or hear sensibly. But we adjusted. Somewhat. There was also a dark time of equal length, when we dared move around and discuss our predicament. The bright time and the dark time were *day* and *night*. Though even at night the demons could flood us with light, if they chose.

Could we continue to endure such an existence? Opinion was divided. Some of us said yes, others no. Otem's head parts insisted that we must tolerate our fate; his heart and viscera argued otherwise.

We were in a mockery of a world. Formerly God's bones had sheltered us; now box-houses made of card and straw stood here and there meaninglessly. Oh the loss of God's bones! Sand shifted treacherously underfoot. Our boat was locked upright immovably in a false river of glass. Only a trace of aether remained. A thin thread was still attached to the prow; this snaked away through the glass wall. And oh the loss of our treasure. We were robbed and ruined. Lucky that we had little appetite! There were only sand-mites to sustain us.

One night a dozen of us conferred.

"Are the demons really evil?" queried Carpenter Hote. "They didn't break us or crush us."

"Just as well," retorted Ep the Nurse, "since they stole all the honey that heals."

"Perhaps they are Gods like Hotemtep," said O the Soldier. "In which case maybe it is our duty to serve them by standing still wherever they put us."

"So *many* different Gods?" whispered Otem's loin. "I can comprehend a dozen Gods, or twenty. But these seem innumerable."

"Maybe they too live in a box," said Hote. "With the lamp of the Sun crossing the roof by day; the stars and Moon by night."

"No," said Otem's foot. "The land of life stretches forever."

"He's right about that," agreed Surveyor Oëp, "so far as I can see through that window over there."

"Could we appease the demons?" said Maidservant Emep. "Could we speak to them?"

Otem's mouth-part cackled. "Their words are not our words. And would you have sex with a demon's little finger?"

"We could attract them by moving about," she said. "By dancing and clashing our tools. Emtep could climb up and down the rigging. Em could play her lute by day, as she does by night."

"If they knew we could move they would destroy us," said Otem's mouth.

"How does our Priest know that? He even argues with himself."

"How does our Maidservant know that they *wouldn't* destroy us? Alternatively they might hamstring us, or bind us with iron stays."

"Iron!" Emt the Smith spat out. "The demons have so much of it. The little which we have is as nothing. So I am no one. Tep has no treasure left, so he is no one. Ep has no honey. Emtep's boat can never sail. We are all no one."

"No," I said fiercely. "Once we were nothing, with no existence. Now we possess existence. Our existence is equal to any other existence."

"Is it? Is it?" cried Emt. "Ask the parts of Otem their opinion on that score! Our existence is equal to that of a mite."

At that moment the giant distant door swung open. A sudden shaft of light swept across the white cliffs of the outer walls, towards us. We knew this searching light well. It sprang from an iron tube held in a demon's hand.

Immediately we scurried back to our given positions. I reached my own not a moment before the searching light turned night into day inside our world.

The light jerked and vanished. The giant door slammed shut again. The demon had withdrawn in haste. Demons, it seemed, were frightened by darkness.

Another night, a demon with a light tube came. It unlocked the glass lid of our world. This demon smelled of sex. It picked up the paralysed Musician Em, lifted her out, and bore her down along with the light to the hidden floor below. The sky stayed open.

Mason Te's position was close by me. Rashly he shuffled closer.

"Ho and Emtep are nimble climbers—"

"Fool! Get back!"

"If many of us go to the glass well and form a pyramid of bodies, Emtep might be able to—"

"To fall? To shatter on the floor far below?"

"He could take ropes from the rigging, to lower himself."

"He'd have to use *all* the rigging. And what if he did reach the floor? Where the demon is grunting! What then? Get back! Quickly."

Presently the demon rose up—too soon for Te's crazy scheme to have worked. Its hand descended. It put Em back into our world. Then away it went, having closed the lid on us. Within another turn our world was dark again; darkly visible.

We rushed to Em—and she faced us. Yes, faced us. For now she had a face!

It was a face quite unlike our own: with large eyes set well apart, with smoothly rounded cheeks. A nose more like a plump thumb than a thin crooked finger. Delicate lips. A firm little jaw. How strange, how alien. She explored her new face with her fingers—in particular feeling her eyeballs.

"I can see," she told us. Those were her first words, spoken in a lilting voice. "I'm still different from you all. So very different."

I caught hold of her hand. "Em, we're all of us different. We're all unique."

Nurse Ep asked to examine Em. She ran dextrous fingers around the edges of the Musician's face. "Perfect," said Ep. "Strange but perfect."

"Do you call that a face?" exclaimed Timekeeper Ote. "It's the mask of a demon! Whose face will the demons ruin next? We must flee this terrible place!"

In wrath I hit Ote. He fell, dropping the sands of time. Immediately I felt remorse and helped him to stand. "This place *is* terrible," I said to him, "and you're right that we must escape. But Em's new face is a delight—do you understand? It's a treasure."

"If you say so."

Mason Te handed Ote back his sand-glass. Ote stared at it numbly.

"I've lost count . . . I've forgotten the number of turns! Even during the days while I couldn't move my hands I counted inside myself. I was still in touch with the sands. And now I've forgotten. You knocked the total out of my head. We've lost our history." He brandished the sands at me in blame.

I might well have deserved his blame, but I wasn't prepared to accept it. "We already lost our history!" I shouted. "We lost it when the demons took us from our home. Our real history starts now—with Em's new face, and with the resolve to escape. Is that clear? Turn your glass again, Ote. Count again, from *one*."

Ote hesitated; for a short while he looked about to oppose me.

"Ote has lost count," observed Smith Emt. "So now he is nobody, either."

Far from encouraging Ote in rebellion, Emt's sneer had the opposite effect. Ote glared at Emt. "I am Ote," he said. "I count time, that's what." And he did as I bid.

"If we *could* escape from here," said Surveyor Oëp briskly, "I believe we could follow the thread of aether all the way back to the God . . ."

ACT 3. SCENE ONE.

(*Dusk, inside the Theodore Peck Gallery of the museum. White-washed walls, a chair, a stool; one window showing a desert of sand and stones. Waist-high on cast-iron supports stands the glass case containing the Ushabti tableau. Enter ALI BEY furtively, carrying a large matchbox in his hand.*)

ALI BEY: Maybe I'm not thinking straight.
  But oh the insult to my dignity as overseer!
  There'll be no more funny tricks;

Once a scorpion shares the display case.
And just supposing there's a grain of truth
In what those credulous cowards
Towfik and Muhammed said on quitting,
From now on nothing will dare move.
(*He unlocks the lid, raises it. From the matchbox he tips a live scorpion into the case, closes the lid and hurries off. Presently YVONNE enters. Musing, she lingers by the door.*)
YVONNE: I'm drawn irresistibly; can't help myself.
Oh I'm not drawn to the Earl of Dundalk
Particularly. Maman's wrong on that score.
Harry's amusing, but it's clear to me now
That his seductive rigmarole was mostly
An excuse to delay the moment of truth,
To avoid erotic action; at which, frankly,
He isn't too expert. To begin with
He spilled his seed prematurely on the sand.
His second attempt was adequate.
Third time round, he couldn't perform
At all; lay limp. I'd rate him somewhere
On a scale between semi-competence
And impotence. If I married him
I'd certainly need to take a lover!
Though that doesn't mean he isn't amusing.
No, it's here that I'm irresistibly drawn
(Though I try to resist): to that glass case,
To the doll within who wears my face
And whose pictures will soon be in all the journals
Though not on the society pages.
Whilst I, as Maman suggested in pique,
Ought to wear a black veil
Like a Moslem woman, to avoid
Revelation of the scandal.

Oh but I can't resist another peep . . .
(She tiptoes silently. She peers into the case—and gasps, wide-eyed with shock.)

CURTAIN

Emergency! Dire emergency! The armoured beast raced through our midst, scattering sand. The cruel claws of its arms snickered and snackered. Its tail writhed in twitching tension; a ball of poison flicked from its sting.

We stood paralysed; but this was no protection. The beast sensed what we were. It rushed at lame Hoë, seized her by her crippled foot, threw her this way and that way. It dashed at Manservant Temte and bowled him over. Its sting descended overhead. The sharp glistening tip stabbed Temte in the chest.

Poor Temte screamed and writhed. Then he convulsed and lay still. The beast's poison had destroyed him!

Now no one dared stay inert in its path. People blundered to hide in flimsy houses. Others skidded across the glass river, in haste to board the *Hotemtep*; which they did. From up the rigging Ho bellowed that they mustn't climb any higher. Unfortunately his voice attracted the monster, which rushed towards the river. Those on board cried out in fear and began to scramble up the rigging. The mast groaned alarmingly. However, as soon as the monster set foot on the river, its walking claws slid from under it. The beast drew back enraged, and charged elsewhere.

"Silence!" shouted O the Soldier. "Shut your mouths. Run soft-foot. Will any volunteers help me fight our enemy with tools?" That O needed help was a mighty admission; but it was realistic.

Emtep promptly shinned down from on high. He freed the steering oar, dropped it clattering on to the river, disembarked. He and Ho were soon advancing shoreward, struggling to hold the great oar out ahead of them.

Hottep the Butcher brandished a long knife, though the blade had been blunted by tunnelling. Pto the Brewer-woman armed herself with lame Hoë's spade. O held our only real hope: his spear with the iron tip.

Soon, skirmish began. Pto and the boatmen tried to herd the monster while O jabbed and stabbed. But his spear only bounced off the armoured shell. Several times O danced aside from claws and sting, not a moment too soon.

From the fringes of the combat I called out, "I have an idea!" The monster leapt round to face me. "I'll lure it to the river. We'll try to make it lose its footing. O can spear it in the underbelly."

Hastily I fled riverwards—and the beast lumbered after me. On the deck of the *Hotemtep* I heard Em's lute-strings strumming. Her voice sang:

"Oh who will help us . . . ?"

Just then a great shadow loomed across our glass sky.

ACT 3. SCENE TWO.

(*Inside the gallery a powerful paraffin lamp burns, attracting insects in from the night. The door stands wide open; as does the lid of the Ushabti case. The stool lies broken to pieces. ALI BEY, THEODORE, HARRY, TOM KEEVES, YVONNE and MARIANNE BIZOT are arguing.*)

ALI BEY: Maybe I did put a scorpion in the case.
    But that was to stop any more mischief.
HARRY: By stinging my hand? By killing me,
    Whom the lions of the Sudan couldn't touch?
    Hotter than fire, sharper than needles
    Is the sting of the scorpion!
    If you're stung you die in mindless agony.

> You're sacked, Ali Bey.
MARIANNE: He isn't your man.
> You don't employ him.
ALI BEY: The other reason
> Why I put a scorpion in there
> Was to keep the Ushabti in their places.
> May Allah have mercy on us all now,
> Even infidels. The Jinn are loose.
MARIANNE: Are you in your right mind, Ali Bey?
ALI BEY: Is your daughter in hers? Or is she
> Possessed?
MARIANNE: Insanity, insanity.
> This is another of your jokes, Dundalk.
> You heard how those wretched fellahin quit
> So you wanted to stir up some wild superstition
> Resembling the Curse of the Pharaoh.
> You corrupted my daughter, made her a thief.
> Where have you hidden the Ushabti?
> Return them promptly, and we'll say no more.
HARRY: *I* corrupted Yvonne? I assure you, Madame,
> She knows a lot more than me!
THEODORE: You ain't much of a gentleman.
HARRY: More about this incident, I mean.
YVONNE: I already *told* you all about it!
TOM: Why didn't you show us the dolls
> Busy dancing?
YVONNE: They were fighting so bravely.
> The scorpion was slaughtering them.
> I had to squash it with the stool leg.
THEODORE: Fine, fine; I can appreciate that.
> But did you have to pick them all up
> Afterwards and show them the exit?
> There are a damn sight more scorpions

Outdoors than indoors, any day.
YVONNE: It was her voice, her eyes . . .
HARRY: Her eyes.
   Enchanting eyes. I'm so in love
   With what I made. I made her.
THEODORE: You oughtn't to talk about making
   Young ladies. That's vulgar.
HARRY: One face is in my heart, one face alone.
YVONNE: Not mine; but mine in miniature—on her.
   That's safer, isn't it, Harry?
   You can love her because she's so small;
   Too small to make real love to, ever.
HARRY: Now I've lost her. She's gone.
YVONNE: Perhaps a lost love is preferable?
   A poet's kind of love! Needing fantasy
   To magnify it. If that's the size of the muse
   These days, poetry has sunk somewhat low.
HARRY: It doesn't matter what size . . .
   But oh her voice, and her eyes!
   At least there's something we agree on.
   Which way do you suppose they'll head?
YVONNE: I've no idea. Why do you ask?
   Do you want to give chase to your new love
   The way you pursue lions? In that case
   You'd best proceed humbly on hands and knees
   Otherwise you might destroy her
   In the moment of finding her.
   I beg you, leave them alone!
ALI BEY: In God's name, I agree!
   Once the Jinn are out of the bottle
   It's hard to cork the neck again.
HARRY: To the tomb's too far for tiny legs:
   Twelve miles as the crow flies

    Even if they could find the way.
    Besides, there's nothing left there;
    Not even a bone.
TOM: Speaking of bones,
    The boat you took from the coffin—
    The one in this case here—is carved
    Out of bone, now isn't it? Right,
    Mrs. Bizot? I'm the first to admit
    I'm no archeologist; but a bone boat
    Always struck me as queer . . .
MARIANNE: Another enigma; I quite agree.
    What's the point of this, Mr. Keeves?
TOM: The boat's the missing shoulder-blade
    Of old What's-his-name.
MARIANNE: Perhaps.
TOM: So when was it carved into a boat?
    And who carved it? Did that happen
    After Hottentot was in his coffin,
    All buried and sealed? Maybe it's true
    About these Ushabti people, hmm?
THEODORE: Gee, you're right, Keeves. Oh wow,
    I do believe you are. Here's me groaning
    About a slap in the face to my generosity,
    About fame suddenly becoming farce—
    And all along I'm missing the main chance.
    These Ushabti would be a million times better
    At pulling the crowds in, than any flea circus.
MARIANNE: The Ushabti aren't your private property,
    Mr. Peck. They don't belong to you.
THEODORE: If they've run off, they surely
    Aren't antiquities. They ain't your province,
    Madame. Finders, keepers. Ali Bey:
    Do you have men who know the desert?

Men who can track like bloodhounds?
ALI BEY: It's in my very blood. My own father—
May Allah smile upon his memory—
Escorted black gold from Cameroon to Arabia.
YVONNE: This is obscene. You're speaking
Of slavery—of the slave trade!
THEODORE: The Ushabti ain't human, honey,
Any more than a troupe of monkeys.
They're a freak of nature, that's what.
TOM: If you catch them, what makes you think
They'll dance and sing? Till the scorpion
Tickled them, they stood like statues.
THEODORE: I'm sure I could ginger them into action.
YVONNE: Using scorpions? Or cattle prods?
THEODORE: No, that's plainly unacceptable.
I'd find a kinder, more efficient way,
Such as mutual advantage. I offer protection;
They perform.
YVONNE: Freedom's what they want.
Sacred liberty.
THEODORE: Is a steer free on the range?
Yes, but in the long run, no.
Are people free in a score of countries
I could name? Such as France's colonies?
Or Britain's? The blacks are protected—
For their own sake. And in return
They deliver the goods. That's the way
The world goes round; and always has.
Maybe the Ushabti will think I'm a sort
Of God.
YVONNE: You? A God? What an ego!
THEODORE: I'll be magnanimous—great-souled—
Towards them. And who says *they* have egos?

How can they, when they're all the same?
HARRY: Save for the lute-player. She at least
   Has gained a soul.
THEODORE: Yvonne's soul?
YVONNE:
(*She rubs her brow.*)
   I think I have a migraine.
HARRY: I *created*
   A soul for the little musician
   When I created a face for her.
TOM: A black face, to be sure.
HARRY: A white face on a black body
   Would have looked rather silly.
THEODORE: Incidentally, Ali Bey, the Ushabti
   Don't know the tomb's empty, robbed utterly
   For the second time in history, by archeology.
ALI BEY: In the desert the little Jinn will face—
THEODORE: A long walk. An Odyssey.
ALI BEY: *Enemies.*
   Such as other scorpions. And wild dogs.
   Black-tailed vipers and horned adders.
   Overhead, ready to pounce, there'll be
   Sparrow-hawks, owls, kites, buzzards,
   And falcons—not to mention small eagles.
THEODORE: So we'll be doing the Ushabti a favour
   By finding them, ultra-fast.

CURTAIN

It was black night, with stars spilt all across the sky. The ground creaked and groaned, releasing the day's heat. Lumps of rock got in our way, ranging from little chunks the size of a body to boulders like hills. Yet threading our way through the stony regions was easier than wading across tracts of sand.

Easier as regards our footing. But in sandy areas we could almost pull ourselves along the aether thread as though it was a rope. When tumbles of rock forced us off course we had to cast around afterwards to regain the line where it snaked over the terrain; and who was to say for sure that it was the same aether cord which we latched on to? Thrice already other aether lines had cut our path crosswise.

"This way," squeaked Otem's neck.

"That way," insisted his foot.

"Left," said one hand.

"Right," said the other.

Fortunately for us Surveyor Oëp was navigating—with help from Ho, who had found he had skill in following stars.

We'd halted to count our numbers and gather in any stragglers. It was the three hundredth turn of the sands since the demon with Em's face had set us free on the wild barren land.

"Why did she do it, Em?" I asked.

Em thought a while then answered, "She did it out of love. But demon-love is like madness. The demons search for lost parts of themselves which they imagine are hidden in the hearts or bodies of others; thus they can never find what they seek. This drives them to wild excess and fantasies—unlike us, who are all one at heart."

"So they are sick, and we are sane? Then why did the scarab come out of you?"

"The aether-energy was roused, and had to create something. It wasn't the right time or place."

"How do you know these things, Em?"

"As to the aether, maybe my lute could play the answer... As to the motives of demons, the lips of my new face shape my reply for me. Hear me, Tep: we have all forgotten something of great importance. Its name is ever on our lips, but we don't hear."

"Hmm," I said. I tallied our numbers on my abacus. Ho had finally joined us, helping twice-lamed Hoë along. Only Temte the Manservant was missing. He would always be missing . . .

"Hmm, that doesn't help us discover our way."

Otem's head-part spoke up: "Find a pool where many aether streams meet. Join me together there; then we'll remember what we need to know."

"Join you *how?*" asked Ep the Nurse. "We have no honey."

Different pieces of Otem answered:

"Use mud."

"Use dung."

"Use the blood of a hot beast. Use its belly juices and its spittle, and its anal slime and the drooling of its eyes."

"Kill a beast the size of a mountain?" asked O sarcastically.

"We're all here," I announced. "Let's continue. We'll march till the Sun rises, then we must hide under stones."

"Why?" asked Emt the Smith. "I favour heat."

"So you might, but the Sun's heat could crack us the way it cracks these rocks into sand; and as Ep said, we have no honey. Besides, we'll need shadows to hide us from hungry, hunting beasts. And by day the demons might hunt us. They might quarrel about our liberation."

"You are wise," said O.

We proceeded through boulders, then over shifting sand, and then across a plain of pebbles. When we were mid-way across that plain, the Moon rose. That night, however, the Moon was only a thin silver sickle. The moonlight did not search us out. One time, a monstrous long snake with horns and a flickering forked tongue reared at our approach. But it was sluggish, so we all escaped.

Towards dawn, the brightening horizon silhouetted two masses swaying ever so slightly against the fading stars. One was a square, the other a pyramid. From their direction wafted the memory of fire-embers, and a rank stench of beasts. But we had cover. Dry spears of grass rose around us, and bushes of wire sprawled higher and higher. Ahead, grass and bush became an arid forest, with the roofs of those shapes looming above. Our view wasn't wholly blocked by the forest, though.

Surveyor Oëp called a halt. "I name those two soft buildings *tents*," he said. "The tents of demons. We must avoid them. We'll have to circle right round and pick up the aether-thread on the far side."

Emt objected. "That's an enormous detour you're proposing! It's as long as our whole journey already."

"And Hoë can only hobble," said Pto, who was currently supporting our gardener.

"We have to hide soon," said O. "Tomorrow night perhaps we could slip stealthily between the tents? I could scout ahead."

"March right on!" urged part of Otem's head (with nose). "I smell an aether pool beyond those tents. Powerful aether streams converge. My nostrils twitch like a hare's. That's why so many plants grow hereabouts."

"Yes, we'll stop here all day," I said. "We'll scoop holes under stones and hide ourselves; and we'll spy on that, that . . ."

"That *camp*," said O.

"Then this evening we'll decide whether to detour."

Everyone agreed. So we burrowed in under boulders, scooped sand over ourselves, and lay still.

Swiftly a golden gong of fire heaved itself up over the forested horizon, hurling light everywhere but also casting deep shadows. I say 'gong' because the Sun did indeed sound the day. Soon bleats of hunger rose from the camp, nasal but strident: beast voices crying the emotions of their churning tyrant bellies. Four beasts, perhaps five.

"I name those animals, *goats*," muttered Otep the Herdsmen

who had crowded in with me. "Goats'll gobble anything: rags, sandals, knobs of dung. You hobble 'em by night, loose 'em by day. By night they'll have stripped everything. Demons'll up their tents and shift away. Our way'll be clear, come the dark. You'll see."

By the evening, however, our path was still blocked. Maybe the secret presence of the aether pool caused the demons to linger, unawares of why. Maybe there was a more sinister reason.

I'd chosen a hiding place from which I could keep watch. Depending on my line of sight through the bushes, from time to time I saw the hairy monstrous goats wander about, cropping, ripping, chewing. A raggy boy with a big stick supervised them; but he never herded them in our direction, where the vegetation must have looked paltry to his eyes.

Before long, two male demons approached the tents. Both were familiar to me. One was white-faced. The other, with a swarthy face, was the demon who had put the monster in our world with us! This time the swarthy monster held a box big enough to fit us all in. He shouted at the boy; and a demon in dirty robes emerged from the square tent. Demon words were spoken. Circles of metal were held up, which I recognized as coins though they weren't of gold or silver; and thin rectangles of papyrus. A few pieces of metal were presented; most were put away together with the papyrus. And the visiting demons departed.

Morning wore on; then afternoon. Frequently the boy ignored his goats and ranged far and wide poking the ground with his staff, jabbing down holes, flipping boulders over. He came close, but never discovered any of us.

The Sun descended the far side of the sky and slipped redly out of sight. Dusk swiftly darkened; stars revived. We crawled out of hiding and formed up in a double line.

"We'll detour," I said, "however long it takes."

"Go straight to the aether pool!" squeaked Otem.

"Shut up, you."

Herdsman Otep had been right about one thing: the goats had indeed stripped much of the ground we were to cross. Oëp took the lead, with Ho sighting the stars. I brought up the rear, just in case anyone listened to their Otem amulet and was tempted to take a short cut.

We had only been marching for twenty turns when thunder drummed; when boulders flew from under the hooves of a hairy mountain—when a great goat loomed over us, horned and bearded! Its swollen sides sagged. Its eyes stared squarely down at us. A broken chain hung from its neck.

The first to be seized and gobbled was Oëp. Ho, a moment later.

Some of us were shocked into immediate paralysis where we stood. Others—me among them—first threw themselves flat, then froze. Perhaps a dozen fled; but the goat pranced after the fugitives and easily snatched them. Then it picked up those who were standing stock-still, and gulped them. Finally, it ate those who lay—one by one. Within a turn or two I, who had been at the rear of the column, was the only person left.

The goat's lips and tongue reached down for me, and

The goat isn't sated. It wanders past the two tents, out in the direction of the little secret aether pool, which even it hardly knows is there. Arriving, it browses around—till it begins to feel unwell. Kicking up its heels, it races away in the dark and the starlight to escape the sensations inside it. A goat possessed, it flees along the strongest stream of aether far far out into the desert till eventually, exhausted, it plunges into a deep invisible aether pool down in a rocky depression near where some ancient inscribed stones rise, worn by time and sandy winds.

Here the goat lies down thumpingly upon its side, flanks quaking, breathing heavily. Soon it slumps unconscious.

During the remainder of the night the goat's whole body writhes as though it is a sack of maggots, a big bag of worms. Although it's hard to see what's going on down there in the dark, the goat seems to be steadily losing its original goat shape.

When dawn comes

I am alive again. Alive!

I name myself. I am Hotemtep.

The Priest didn't lie. Old Hatshep-Siptah told me the truth. The aether has borne me down the stream of years and washed me ashore at last. Hatshep-Siptah alone in the double kingdom had honed his senses to know the aether; no one else. In his youth Hatshep-Siptah sailed to Ind and Chin. He met sages, secret lords of power. He brought back the abacus, too, in which he instructed Henet-Taa my treasurer.

Yet Hatshep-Siptah made no special preparations for his own death. Did he not fully believe in the method? Did he feel fulfilled in life, content with one existence? Or couldn't he afford the cost of secure burial, till the Ushabti could begin their work? Aye yes, the cost! But I paid Hatshep-Siptah handsomely. Surely he had enough money.

I never asked him. Or if I did ask, I've forgotten.

Why am I thinking about Hatshep-Siptah? He isn't here. The Sun is rising, showing me the stony dent in the desert where I have awoken. Hereabouts must be a powerful aether pool, though I can't sense it with these wits of mine. Hatshep-Siptah alone . . .

What did he advise me to do on waking?

Check yourself, Lord Hotemtep. Contemplate yourself. Consolidate yourself.

Let me rise and behold myself in the morning sun. Let me stamp my legs and hold up my arms.

Ach, part of my left hand is missing. The hand is narrow—thumb and two fingers only—as though it has been chopped in half down the center. Ach!

I'm wearing ill-cured goatskin. Hastily I lift and search beneath. Penis, yes. Scrotal sacks, aye. Shall I urinate or jerk seed to celebrate this new life of mine?

A goatskin.... Suddenly the memory of all my shattered age-long dreams assails me. And I know that many things went wrong.

I was robbed; the golden wealth in my antechamber was all stolen.

My Ushabti didn't scale the air-shaft. Instead, they were stolen away, as well.

The lute-player's music could bewitch. Her face was left blank so that it could grow the face of the host chosen for me. But my Ushabti didn't enchant a human being, then climb down the throat into belly and lungs. They entered the body of a goat!

Things have gone badly wrong. Yet how bad is badly?—compared with the fact that I am alive? The goat's body has become human.

Its body... How about my head? Let me feel it carefully. A goatee beard sprouts from the nub of my chin; perhaps that's just as well, since my jaw recedes.... Above my mouth: a huge nose. My ears are high and pointy. Two cranial bumps stud the sides of my skull like the buds of a kid's horns.... Yet undoubtedly it is a human face; so my fingers tell me.

Does it matter if there is some goat in me? Did not Anubis wear the head of jackal? Did not Khnum bear the head of a ram?

Afar off down the desert I spy a couple of tents. Beyond, are buildings of some sort. My eyes are keen. I feel strong and nimble.

And a young woman's face—exotic, foreign—is painted in my heart.

ACT 4. SCENE ONE.

(*The desert. Enter MARIANNE and YVONNE with parasols, TOM KEEVES carrying a cardboard box, and HARRY in a Panama hat with a hunting rifle.*)

MARIANNE: Fool's errand. Madness. Absurd. A jape.
    I've come for one reason alone:
    So that you can show me where you hid them!
    Ah no, *two* reasons . . . also to chaperone
    My rash daughter, since she insists
    On accompanying you—which you may say
    Is definitely a case of locking the door
    After the burglars have broken in.
    But I'm not prudish, understand!
    I sympathize with all true lovers.
    If only that's what you were!
    I hope to forestall some even greater folly.
YVONNE: You needn't worry about Harry and me.
    Maman. That's over and done with. . . .
TOM: Now that Lord Harry's in love with a real doll;
    As Mr. Peck might phrase it. But Mam'selle
    Wants Lord Harry to leave that doll alone—
    Can she be jealous?
YVONNE: Harry's pursuit
    Is the lesser of two evils; that's all.
    If *he* finds the Ushabti (second day lucky)
    At least he won't force them to become
    A side show at a circus. Will you, Harry?
TOM: Orfully vulgar idea.
HARRY: Never! I shall . . .

    I shall apotheosize her in verse.
TOM: So she'll be seated there on your desk
    Playing her lute to inspire you—
    Like that Frenchie, Colette, with her cat?
    Sure, we'll transport the whole bunch
    Back to the old ancestral sod in Ulster.
    Plenty of the little people there already!
    Sure, they'll skip like fairy folk
    Across his pages, won't they now?
    Though these'll be the first nigger leprechauns.
MARIANNE: Hotemtep may have had negro blood.
    There was nothing odd about being black
    In ancient Egypt, nothing disreputable.
    No more than in France's African colonies
    Where at least *our* negroes learn to speak
    Parisian French—not the English of pigeons.
    But that isn't why the Ushabti are black,
    Tom Keeves. It's normal and traditional.
TOM: Is pigeon English what's spoken in Trafalgar Square
    Where Nelson's Column stands; who sunk
    The French fleet, even though he was blind?
HARRY: Shut up, Tom.
TOM: Or you'll horsewhip me?
    Sure, let the blood flow, as at school
    On the whipping block.
HARRY: I have *no* interest . . . !
YVONNE: Why do you tolerate this person, Harry?
MARIANNE: Dear child, you have a lot to learn
    About the English. Their public schools,
    So called, where only rich boys go
    Mark a man for life, as surely as if
    His buttocks had been thrashed till scarred.
HARRY: I was *never once* . . .

MARIANNE: Sensitive poets
   Are specially marked by such experiences.
   Which is why they become such poor ones.
   Their imagery, suspect. Their view of woman,
   False: a mixture of ignorant fear and lust
   And soulful idealisation. Their performance
   In bed, less than perfect. Do you know
   That their slang word for a young schoolboy
   Who serves the older boys, is a 'fag'?
   The very same word is used for a catamite!
   Of course, they need to make love to women
   Since property has to be inherited properly.
   Their king seems to have the right approach,
   To his Mrs. Simpson; but mark my word,
   Hypocrites will soon chase him from the throne.
   And oh the educational standards, là là!
   The English only stumble in a foreign tongue,
   Just as they stumble in love. Moi-même,
   As well as French I speak fluent English
   And German and Italian and Old Egyptian—
   Though there's no one to speak Egyptian to.
   In sum, my dear, our Lord Harry *needs*
   The roughness of his man Tom, as his foil.
   And Tom Keeves plays up to the part.
TOM: Do I just? In my humble opinion
   Most French poets were perverts,
   Like that chap Rimbaud who grew lice
   In his hair. Or Bawdy Liar, poxed
   And wallowing in Filth. Disgusting.
MARIANNE: Actually they were alchemists
   Making golden music out of dirt.
   I do mistrust the English respect—
TOM: I'm Irish; all be it from the north!

MARIANNE: The English respect for hygiene,
 Particularly when they don't know
 What a bidet's used for.
TOM: A what?
MARIANNE: This comes from having to defecate fast
 In public school toilets deprived of doors
 So the boys can be caught if they play
 With themselves, or with each other.
 Hurrying to get your pants back on
 Becomes a habit. Perverted hygiene
 Finds a Freudian sublimation in English cookery.
 Thou shall not eat the slimy snail
 Or the thighs of frogs, or such.
 Thou shall boil all vegetables
 Until they're safely dead. Thy beef
 Shall wear no disguises. Thy sauces—
 If any—shall consist of boiled white milk
 And flour.
YVONNE: Maman! All of you, stop it!
(*Enter* HOTEMTEP. *Barefoot, and dressed in an off-the-shoulder goat skin which just covers his upper thighs, he resembles one of those anchorites or pole-squatters who infested the Egyptian desert in early Christian days, starving and scourging themselves, consequently seeing angelic visions and suffering devilish temptations. He is of middle height and swarthy skinned. Short dun-coloured hair coats his skull. Goatee beard, receding chin, big muzzle of a nose. His resemblance to a shabby madman is, however, superficial. His eyes gleam with vital energy. He holds himself proudly, with great self-possession.*)
HOTEMTEP: (*To Yvonne.*) It is thou, without a doubt,
 Whose face is painted on my heart!
YVONNE: Qu'est-ce-qu'il dit, Maman?
MARIANNE: Whatever did I say? That no one

Speaks Old Egyptian? But this man does!
(*In somewhat broken ancient Egyptian.*)
How is it you speak language?
HOTEMTEP: With my lips; and tongue. Which are also
The organs of love's preliminaries.
MARIANNE: True. But I mean: how do you talk
That language?
HOTEMTEP: Why, I drank it with milk
From my nursemaid's nipples. It is—it *was*—
The language of the double kingdom here.
I suppose words have changed since last I lived.
Hatshep-Siptah warned me of such a possibility.
You shall be my interpreter, strange woman.
I once had need of an interpreter
To converse with the Babylonians.
MARIANNE: Since you last lived, did you say?
TOM: Madame Bizot never told us she talks Arabic
Amongst her many other foreign talents.
HARRY: I've never seen anyone remotely as queer
As this chap, in the Sudan or anywhere else!
Why does he stare at Yvonne like that?
Has he stumbled upon the Ushabti?
Has he come across the lute-player?
YVONNE: I'm strangely drawn to this person,
God knows why. He's hardly personable.
Yet there's a vigour about him, a clarity
(Despite his smelly goat skin),
A new kind of fire—as though
He's a freshly discovered element of nature,
Radioactive, whose rays strip me naked
To the bone. Admittedly he's a bit
Disgusting. . . . Pity about his hand,
More like a crab's claw. Yet I fancy

It could grip firmly and caress softly.
Monsieur! Effendi! How do I address him?
HOTEMTEP: She speaks to me. She knows me.
(*HOTEMTEP's virile member lifts the goat skin somewhat.*)
It must be an age since last I knew
A woman, except in my shattered dreams.
My body cries out; it points.
HARRY:
(*He grips the rifle at the ready.*)
Good Lord! Upon my word! I say!
TOM: Positively indecent! Next thing we know,
This weird wallah will expose himself.
I bet he isn't wearing underpants,
No more than those Masai warriors
We met outside Nairobi three seasons back,
Who laughed at us for bottling our farts up
In our breeches.
YVONNE: He's a force of nature;
Yet also he is a man. So maybe we have met
Some desert nature-deity, a Pan of the sands?
His garments are certainly loose enough;
And he bears a resemblance to a capricorn.
I pray Harry doesn't go *pan! pan!* with his gun
In defence of modesty and repression.
MARIANNE: Tell me! What did you mean by saying
'Since you were last alive'?
HOTEMTEP: I was dead.
The sands have turned twenty million times
Since then; and now I am alive. I, Hotemtep.
MARIANNE: Do I have a fever, or sunstroke?
Am I hallucinating? How on earth
Can a dead man come back to life?
He wasn't even a whole corpse.

>   Just a ravaged, gutted mummy!
> HARRY:
> (*He lowers his gun.*)
>   I heard him say Hotemtep. Why?
> MARIANNE: That's who he says he is: the pharaoh,
>   Resurrected and reborn.
> HOTEMTEP: My Ushabti
>   Served me well; they found me a new body.
> HARRY: What's that about the Ushabti, eh?
> MARIANNE: Where *are* the Ushabti, Hotemtep?
> HOTEMTEP:
> (*He strikes his chest.*)
>   Within the new me; their duty done.
> MARIANNE:
> (*She wipes her brow.*)
>   But how? I don't understand.
> HOTEMTEP: Truly, it is the greatest of secrets.
>   I shall share it on receipt of a great sum
>   In gold—of which I have been robbed—
>   To provide for me adequately in my new life.
> (*He plucks disdainfully at his goat skin; while Marianne proceeds at some length to explain the situation to the others....*)
>
>   CURTAIN

How amazed we were still to exist! Admittedly we were all lodged in different parts of Hotemtep's new body: Musician Em in his windpipe, Ote in his heart beating time, Stonemason Te in one of his kidneys, myself in the purse of his scrotum; and so forth. We had no way to walk around and meet each other face to face. Nevertheless we could still call out and hear each other. Hotemtep's nerves carried our voices along their subtle wires. The assorted bodily clamours—the pumping of the blood, the gurgling of the stomach, the gassy oozing of the guts—didn't drown out reception.

To Gardener Hoë, lodged in the intestines, our present circumstances were a fulfillment, a blissful return to an innocent paradise of which the dead God, lying in his boxes of wood, then stone, inside the tomb had only been a shell, a husk. Now the living flesh of God was encysting us.

To Maidservant Emep, within God's stomach, we were all serving at a noble banquet, all of us contributing to a grand communal task: sustaining the new life of Hotemtep.

Others—the majority—weren't so satisfied.

From the brain-stem an angry rebel cry came down from Soldier O:

"Does Hotemtep know or care that we exist? He does not! Like mindless tools we rebuilt this body for him. And now we give up all our freedom to sustain him. By our presence we power his heart and lungs and loins. We are uttermost slaves! I can say this now that Manservant Temte is no longer with us. He was the soul of servility."

"No, he was not!" cried Emep, from the belly. "He knew his place—and now we all know ours. The God was with us all along. Each of us was always part of him; and now we have simply restored him to himself. Where were we going, I ask you, but back to the tomb of boxes? What other desire or ambition did we have? But we had forgotten how to accomplish it. You should be guarding against any mutiny or desertion of God's parts; not saying such things, O."

Surveyor Oëp kept watch behind Hotemtep's eyes. From that high eminence he could see what was happening outside.

"Friend O is right," he said. "We need to look out for ourselves. This bondage is worse than the glass world, worse than the wooden world. What future is there for us? I should have sought us a place for us to dwell on our own—in the empty burrow of some desert beast, perhaps."

My part of Otem spoke to me. "What future, he asks. Well, I'm the Priest. And I'm the Oracle. I'm the part of God who can guide, not through deserts but through destinies. If I'm put back together I can answer Oëp's question."

It transpired that all around God's body other Otem-parts were telling the same story.

"Was I not right about the star and the Sun?" Otem went on. "What a mess you made of things on your own, without my guidance. True, I forgot much. I made mistakes. But if I'm put back together here inside Hotemtep all my skill will be restored."

"Aye," said I, "and maybe our independence of thought will be at an end."

"I'm one of you. Believe me!"

Nurse Ep spoke out, from the cleansing liver. "How do we put our Priest together, when we can't meet each other? Not even O can travel. He can only jab nerves with his spear if he wants to discipline us. Isn't that so?"

O confirmed that it was so.

"Release me from your necks," pleaded Otem. "Loose me all at once. My parts will enter the blood and lodge in the heart, where they'll clot together."

We discussed this proposal for a long time, some assenting, some dissenting. In the end it was Musician Em's vocal support for the plan to reconstruct Otem which swayed the doubters. She had talked at length to Surveyor Oëp about what he saw outside. She, who wore a face and eyes which were not Hotemtep's, was willing to trust to Otem's superior vision.

ACT 4. SCENE TWO.

(*The same.*)

HARRY: What, the Ushabti are inside him?
 Including my beauty, with Yvonne's face?

HOTEMTEP: Failing gold, then diamonds will do.
  Diamonds are lighter to carry around.
HARRY: What did he say?
MARIANNE: That he'll settle for
  A fortune in diamonds to stake his new life;
  In exchange for which: the secret
  Of Resurrection. But what kind of life
  Can a pharaoh ever lead in Nineteen Thirty-Six?
TOM: Maybe the new king Farouk has a rival?
MARIANNE: There are already enough pharaohs
  In the world, with Hitler and Mussolini
  And that Franco creature clawing his way
  Through Spain!
TOM: What's wrong with old Adolf
  And Benito? Apart from them being foreign?
  You just said you speak German and Italian.
MARIANNE: I speak the German of Goethe and Schiller
  Not of these new uniformed barbarians
  And book burners; who don't much like Jews
  And Gypsies.
TOM: Oh, so *that's* it!
  You and your daughter are French Jews
  Out in Egypt to dig up the pharaohs
  Who enslaved you? Well, well, well.
HARRY:
(*To Yvonne.*)
  Are you Jewish?
YVONNE: Yes. What of it?
HARRY: Oh nothing. Good heavens.
TOM: And your Pharaoh here's a gypsy.
HARRY: What?
TOM: 'The Dukes of Egypt' is what
  The travelling people call themselves.

And their boss man is the 'Pharaoh' of the band.
You don't know much about words, for a poet.
The name 'gypsy' comes from 'Egyptian'.
MARIANNE: What to do? He has to survive.
YVONNE: I shall teach him French, Maman.
We must take him home secretly to Paris.
His education should begin at once.
TOM: What kind of education would that be?
A sentimental one, I'm thinking. . . .
Let's hark back for a moment
From matters of morality
To the business of immortality!
The golden path to living again.
I'd say we're on to a winner, wouldn't you?
HARRY: Oh but my lovely lost lute-playing muse!
YVONNE: Forget her. She's gone. Digested.
Swallowed up, incorporated, fused.
MARIANNE: The Ushabti bundled all together
Don't add up to a single kilogram.
They must have *stolen* a body; invaded it.
HARRY: Odd sort of body to find wandering round.
YVONNE: Remarkable! Full of animal magnetism!
MARIANNE: Hotemtep, whose body did your Ushabti
Take? Who did they kidnap for you?
HOTEMTEP: *That* is part of the great secret.
MARIANNE: He won't say.
TOM: I'm wondering if Jesus
Had Ushabti disciples—or angels—
With him in his tomb? After all, his Dad
Did visit Egypt not long after the Magi
Brought three boxes of rare gifts.
YVONNE: We'll find out the truth in Paris.
We can hide him in our apartment

Till he's fit to stroll the boulevards.
TOM: Unless your concierge gossips!
YVONNE: Madame Laval?
Maman and her are two peas in a pod.
TOM: Laval, indeed? And might she be
Any relation to Prime Minister Laval?
YVONNE: No fear! Maman despises that man.
MARIANNE: So should any Jew with sense.
Laval encouraged fascists and Nazis.
Oh the rumours that are leaking out of Germany!
It's no world for Jews, I fear. Or gypsies.
HOTEMTEP:
(To MARIANNE)
I'm waiting;
(To YVONNE)
                face of my heart.

CURTAIN

I cast loose my part of Otem's head. Throughout Hotemtep's body everyone did likewise with their amulets. These were quickly swept away by the processes of the body. Timekeeper Ote, who was stationed at the heart, counted the pieces as they arrived there and began to congregate.

Within a dozen or so turns Otem was complete again, save for the part which scorpion-slain Temte had worn: half of the priest's left hand.

Soon Otem spoke.

"Brothers and Sisters," he called out, "I foresee terrible things for Hotemtep, even worse than any *we* have known! I see him travelling to a city which is a hundred times the size of Thebes or Memphis. I see him hidden in the top story of a huge house, while he learns to speak a new language. Then for a time there is happiness. Exploration of the city, love, drunkenness on wines the like of which he never imagined, meals such as he never dreamed could exist; though not too much wealth. I see him becoming a local character, consorting in cafés with painters, poets, philosophers and clowns. I see a painting by one Pic-As-So called *Man with Goat's Head*. I see a book written later by one Jon-Pol-Sart called *Monsieur Hotemtep, Pharaoh and Faker*.

"Then I see *war*. I see iron birds dropping eggs of death from the sky. I see iron bulls goring fields and cities. I see armies of men with iron helmets riding narrow iron chariots which bound forth tirelessly like hunting dogs.

"I see Hotemtep hiding again at the top of that house, hiding from the iron men wearing the sign of the crooked cross and from the men in long leather coats, who smash on doors. I see his mistress and his mistress's mother hiding with him.

"I see the iron and leather men find them and drag them away, and crush them into a great closed wooden chariot packed with people wearing yellow stars. A dozen such chariots are chained together in a line, and pulled by a long iron chariot belching smoke; tugged by the wheels along iron tracks away from the city, through fields and towns for day after day while the people starve and cry for water. Then the chariots enter iron fences with high towers surrounding a hundred barracks of wood that stink of living death and of greasy smoke from high chimneys.

"I see worse! I see Hotemtep cry to a cruel commander dressed in black that he hides in him a great golden secret which the two women also share: the secret of resurrection.

"The black commander is mad with faith in wizardry. He has heard rumours of the streams and pools of aether. He and his brethren of the crooked cross have sent spies to Ind and Chin to hunt the source of this knowledge; in vain. He tries to discover the golden secret of Hatshep-Siptah through harsh experiments and tortures.

"But Hotemtep does not know the whole of the secret. When

the scorpion destroyed Temte the keystone was lost.

"Finally the torn body of Hotemtep is tossed into an oven; and burnt. We are all burnt with him, utterly consumed. That is what I see, Brothers and Sisters. And beyond that, *nothing*, forever."

So saying, Otem fell silent.

"What can we do?" Hoë called from the intestines. Many other voices took up this refrain.

"Hotemtep does not know us," said Otem, "so he cannot hear my guidance. We could perhaps warn him in dreams, which Em could sing to him; but he would ignore his dreams, as unbelievable, until they came true. Thus we must stop him. We must stop him in the only way he can be stopped, and pray that later when the world has changed we can start again. We are the Ushabti! What we have done, we can undo!"

"We are the Ushabti!" we all cried.

"Let me tell you how," said Otem, our true priest of wisdom once again.

ACT 5. SCENE ONE.

(*The lofty lounge of a suite in Shepheard's Hotel, Cairo. Bamboo furniture—the chairs with lace antimacassars; potted palms; an Empire sofa the size of a bed. A huge brown oil painting of shaggy Highland cattle amid rainy Scottish crags. Electric lightbulbs scintillate in a crystal chandelier. From the dark balcony, through veils of mosquito netting, step* HOTEMTEP, MARIANNE, *and* YVONNE. HOTEMTEP *is now wearing an off-the-peg creamy tropical suit, white shirt, brown tie, and patent leather shoes.*)
HOTEMTEP:
(*He discards his jacket and unknots his tie.*)
    Why do all men of importance
    Wear nooses round their necks?
    Is it a symbol of humility?
    A sign that anyone can strangle them?

MARIANNE: How can I explain that a necktie
  Is de rigeur in good society
  Such as one meets at Shepheard's?
  Ah, what bourgeois hypocrisy!
  He's perfectly right. A necktie is really
  A symbol of strangulation, by convention.
YVONNE: How refreshing he is! How natural.
  Who cares about the Bourgeoisie? Not I.
MARIANNE: We all disguise ourselves, my dear.
  We hide our feelings and our origins.
  A Jew wears the guise of a citizen of France
  Till something like the Dreyfus case occurs.
YVONNE: I shall not hide my feelings much longer.
  Maman, it is time for his next lesson.
MARIANNE: And I must find Harry, whose title
  Certainly oils the wheels of authority
  Notwithstanding the scandal of the 'robbery'
  Of the Theodore Peck Gallery.
  I hope we didn't rouse Ted Peck's suspicions
  By hastening off to Cairo. . . . Take care, Yvonne.
(She opens the door to a corridor which could probably accommodate a train; departs.)
YVONNE: Sit down, Monsieur Hotemtep. Stand up.
  Shut your eyes. Open them. Good.
  What is this called?
HOTEMTEP: Your nose.
YVONNE: And these?
HOTEMTEP: Your ears. And those, your lips.
  Below: your breast. Oh face of my heart,
  I must kiss you.
YVONNE: To kiss lips,
  Which haven't kissed a woman
  For the last three thousand years!

HOTEMTEP: My tongue will speak more smoothly
   After it touches yours.
YVONNE: Indeed? Why not?
(*They embrace. But after a few moments YVONNE pulls away in puzzlement. For HOTEMTEP stands paralysed. . . .*)
   What's wrong? Why don't you move?
   Stop pretending to be a statue!

CURTAIN

ACT 5. SCENE TWO.

(*The same, except that YVONNE is now apparently alone. On the carpet Hotemtep's shirt, trousers, and shoes lie mixed up in a pile of debris prominent among which are many bones. YVONNE bits her lip and digs her fingernails into her palms to ward off hysteria. Enter, from the corridor, MARIANNE and HARRY.*)

YVONNE: He kissed me, and he fell to pieces.
HARRY: *What?*
MARIANNE: My child!
YVONNE: It's true.
   As soon as we kissed, he stiffened.
   He froze. Not icily. More like stone
   Or marble. Suddenly cracks ran across him . . .
   And he crumbled—into this heap, my Hotemtep.
HARRY: Femme fatale, eh? That didn't happen
   When *we* kissed. . . ! You *are* joking,
   Of course.
YVONNE: No, no, no, no, no!
HARRY: Oh.
MARIANNE:
(*She kneels to sift the rubble.*)
   Here's one Ushabti. Here's another.
   Three, four, more.

HARRY: (*Helping.*) They're dead.
   Inanimate. Just figurines of clay.
(*As MARIANNE disinters still more, HARRY lays them out in a line on the carpet.*)
YVONNE: Maman... Harry... He was alive,
   And now he's dust.
HARRY: His golden secret
   Must have been fool's gold.
YVONNE: I'm shattered.
HARRY: (*Grimly.*) Nothing compared to him!
MARIANNE: But what do we do now?
HARRY: A bag:
   I'll fetch a bag, and we'll pop them in.
(*He dashes to the bedroom, to return with a leather travelling bag and a couple of newspapers.*)
MARIANNE:
(*She counts hastily as she sorts.*)
   ...Sixty-six, sixty-seven, sixty-eight,
   And here's the lute-player at long last.
   That's sixty-nine.
YVONNE: Show me her!
   Yes, it's me; still me... But look:
   She isn't wearing anything round her neck.
   Nor are any of them!
MARIANNE: You're right....
   Their amulets have all disappeared:
   Those broken chips stuck to gold thread.
HARRY: Sixty-*nine*, did you say? That's odd.
   There were sixty-nine to start with,
   Weren't there?
YVONNE: Oui, soizante-neuf.
HARRY: But one of them got left behind
   In the exodus: the one the scorpion stung,

Which disintegrated subsequently
In Ted Peck's beefy grasp.
MARIANNE: I must have counted one of them twice.
HARRY: You must have done.
(*Kneeling, he tears off squares of newspaper, wraps each Ushabti up individually in a paper twist, and lays them in the bag.*)
                                      Hmm, like boiled sweets.
But beware of swallowing. Who knows
What effect they might have on a fellow's
Constitution! I'll get Tom to dispose
Of the rags and bones and dust.
(*He reaches for the lute-player, which YVONNE has taken from her mother and still holds.*)
    Please?
YVONNE: You arid Anglo-Saxon pragmatist,
    You stiff upper lip. He just kissed me,
    A moment ago.
HARRY: I know. And *I* loved
    Her—impractically, after my fashion.
    Frankly, of a sudden I feel cured
    Of that particular intoxication.
(*YVONNE releases the tiny figure; HARRY wraps it.*)
MARIANNE: What do we do next? Take them
    Back to the museum?
YVONNE: No! Ted Peck would stop
    At nothing, to make them move again.
HARRY: And obviously they never will.
    I wonder. . . . I'm sure a psychoanalyst
    Would tell us that everything was caused
    By guilt and sex and infantile repressions. . . .
    I wonder, did we all hallucinate?
    Did we three together steal the Ushabti

    Unconsciously, and bring them here
    In a sack full of bones and stuff—
    Then suddenly become sane again?
MARIANNE: When a poet becomes sane, he's finished.
HARRY: Or else he matures.
YVONNE: To administer
    His estate? To take his rightful seat
    In that House of Nobles at Westminster?
    Why do you say with such certainty
    That they'll never move again?
HARRY: The secret was fool's gold. Dross.
    It fell apart. Thanks to a kiss,
    From reality. Just like the Sleeping Beauty,
    In reverse. And you are my reality, Yvonne;
    Reality is you. Will you be my wife?
    Will you be the Lady of Castle Dundalk?
    The Countess?
YVONNE: Me? But I'm a Jew.
HARRY: Who cares about Hitler's prejudices?
MARIANNE: You ought to!
HARRY: I should let Adolf Hitler
    Rule my life? Not likely. Listen, Yvonne,
    You *must* marry me. We have to be
    The custodians of the Ushabti, you and I.
(*He picks up the travelling bag for a moment, then sets it down.*)
    The guardians of Pandora's box.
MARIANNE: Also in reverse.
HARRY: How's that?
YVONNE: Yes, how?
MARIANNE: Hotemtep has fallen apart. The Ushabti
    Let him crack up—I'm sure of it.
    They have hidden away inside themselves,
    Unlike Pandora's imps. But why?

What prompted them? Surely not a kiss.
Maybe *I* should be lucky to hide away
For the next hundred years or so.
Maybe millions of people would be lucky.
HARRY: Don't worry, there'll never be another war
In Europe—not while the British Empire
Lasts. (*Gallantly*.) And the French Empire too.
MARIANNE: At least Yvonne will be safely
Out of it. Perhaps. For a while.
He's right, Yvonne, you ought to wed him,
And take the Ushabti with you.
Why shouldn't you build them a tomb
In Ireland, like the one they came from?
Milord the Duke of Hamilton did so
On his estate, in Eighteen-Fifty or about.
When he died he had himself embalmed
And placed in a genuine sarcophagus.
Have a copy of a sarcophagus made,
Harry. Lay them to rest in it.
HARRY: Along with a copy of a mummy?
Or should it be the corpse
Of a faithful Irish wolf-hound
To puzzle future archeologists?
Ah, there won't be any of those.
MARIANNE: There won't?
HARRY: Unless civilization ends!
And that can't happen nowadays.
MARIANNE: Egypt fell; Carthage fell; Rome fell.
HARRY: Yes, but those were isolated places.
There may be a few more wars to endure
Here and there, but believe me
From now on the whole world's continuous,
All one from Tasmania to Timbuctoo,

    From Madras to Marseilles to Mexico.
    As are you and I, Yvonne. Continuous.
YVONNE: Really?
HARRY: Yes. I'll get Tom to clear up.
YVONNE: No. *I* shall do it. With my own hands.
HARRY: There's enough to fill a suitcase or two.
YVONNE: Fetch two. We'll buy new ones.
    We'll take his remains and drop them
    Into the Nile. Together, shall we, Harry?
HARRY: Yes, but we'll sink them from a houseboat
    Off Gezira. I'll hire a houseboat
    For our engagement party. Fireworks
    And champagne and dancing—we'll waltz
    And lancer! There'll be photographers.
    We'll release a hundred white doves
    With streamers bearing good-will greetings.
MARIANNE: Won't guests be puzzled about the suitcases?
HARRY: We'll say. . . what shall we say? We'll say
    That we're throwing our old lives overboard.
YVONNE: Bravo! At last you're learning to be
    A poet—of life.
HARRY: Thanks, Yvonne.
    Incidentally, I think I'll never shoot
    A lion again. I've lost the need, I fancy.
    I'll never shoulder another gun—
    Not if I live to be as old as Hotemtep.
MARIANNE: Hitler and Mussolini . . .
HARRY: Champagne and fireworks!

FINAL CURTAIN